Victorian Taste

Jeannie Chapel

VICTORIAN TASTE

The complete catalogue of paintings at the Royal Holloway College

Foreword by Jeremy Maas

With 80 illustrations, 24 in colour

Royal Holloway College

THIS CATALOGUE IS DEDICATED TO

DR LIONEL H. BUTLER

PRINCIPAL 1973–81

© 1982 Royal Holloway College
First published 1982 by A. Zwemmer Ltd
Second impression 1993 by Zwemmer,
an imprint of Philip Wilson Publishers Ltd,
26 Litchfield Street, London WC2H 9NJ
All rights reserved.
No part of this publication may be reproduced,
stored in a retrieval system or transmitted in any
form or by any means without the prior
permission of the Publisher.
ISBN 0 902194 08 9
Printed and bound in Great Britain by
Balding + Mansell, Wisbech, Cambridgeshire

Contents

Foreword

The Royal Holloway College collection has at least two claims to uniquity both in its essential character and in the manner of its formation. If departure from the norm deserves our attention, so also does the extent to which the collection is typical of the kind formed during the Victorian period.

Thomas Holloway was cast in the very mould of the Victorian patron of modern art, fitting neatly into the class of immensely rich self-made men, the cotton kings, colliery owners, cutlers, iron masters and pharmacists, who cared little for the Old Masters, for which they lacked the necessary judgement, but liked the 'real thing', fresh paint from living artists with whom they knew exactly how they stood. At both ends of the Queen's reign lived two such men: firstly, Joseph Gillott, the penmaker, who from 1843 to 1871 bought (and often sold) thousands of modern pictures; and secondly, George McCulloch, whose fortune derived from an Australian tin-mine and who bought pictures from living artists for nearly 20 years (with a notorious want of discrimination) before dying in 1907. It was said of him that 'he purchased modern pictures with the same ease and catholicity with which a modern man buys gloves and ties'.

The same could be said of Holloway: he falls neatly between these two great patrons and contemporaneously with a host of others similar to himself. But here the resemblance ends: Holloway amassed his collection for the college, while nearly all his contemporaries bought solely for themselves; and he did so in the short space of two years, when he was already 81. This sets him apart from all other collectors of his time. Money was no object: he bought entirely from auctions at Christie's and was rarely outbid. We are told in the introductory essay that he bought nothing directly from the artists and that this caused resentment. But with unlimited funds, no heirs, and approaching the end of his life (he died within three months of his last purchase), it must then have seemed the most obvious method. It was as though he had lowered a net into the sea of High Victorian art and the collection was his catch from what was available for purchase at the time. It is an interesting exercise to study the auction catalogues of these two years and see which pictures he might have 'netted'. Among those that 'got away' were two famous early Pre-Raphaelite masterpieces by Millais, *Isabella* and *Mariana*, but this would certainly have been due to prejudice rather than discernment. The value of this collection lies – uniquely – in its original microcosmic character and its preservation thereafter in that state.

Happily, several famous pictures, such as Fildes' *Applicants for Admission to a Casual Ward*, Holl's *Newgate: Committed for Trial* (both apt subjects for a philanthropist), Landseer's *Man Proposes, God Disposes*, Frith's *Railway Station*, Long's *Babylonian Marriage Market* (somewhat inapt for a ladies' college), Millais' *Princes in the Tower* and Turner's *Van Tromp* – just these alone – are sufficient to sustain the collection to the level of national importance. This catalogue, so ably compiled by Jeannie Chapel, does full justice to Holloway's prodigious two-year spending spree.

JEREMY MAAS

The Collection and the Collector

The collection of 77 paintings belonging to the Royal Holloway College is in many ways unique. The founder of the College, Thomas Holloway, bought them for the edification of the students and the public in the short time between May 1881 and June 1883. He died six months later, and no further paintings were purchased. The collection, still intact, remains one of the few almost entirely Victorian ones, put together by one man.

Thomas Holloway was born on 22 September 1800 in Devonport (then called Plymouth Dock), the eldest of six children. His father was, successively, warrant officer in a militia regiment, then a baker in Devonport, then landlord of *The Turk's Head* in Penzance. He died in 1836 at 72, and was buried in Bermondsey; his portrait hangs in the picture gallery. Holloway's mother, Mary Chellew, eventually joined Thomas in his business when it was in the Strand, London, and she died there in 1843 at 67.

Thomas Holloway was educated at Camborne and at Penzance until 16; then he and his mother and brother Henry set up a grocery business in the Penzance market place. In about 1828 Thomas arrived in London, where, in 1836, he established himself at 13 Broad Street Buildings as a 'merchant and foreign commercial agent'. On 15 October 1837 he placed his first advertisement for Holloway's Ointment in three Sunday newspapers; two years later he produced Holloway's Pills. He had an unfortunate start to his business career and, owing to a misunderstanding over cash credit with newspaper proprietors, he spent a short time in Whitecross Street Debtors Prison.

In January 1863 Holloway published *A Sketch of the Commencement and Progress of Holloway's Pills and Ointment by the Proprietor*, in which he wrote: 'My beginning was in a small way – my task very difficult and disheartening. I may add, as proof of my early discouragements, that I had expended in one week the sum of £100 in advertising, and various other ways, for the purposes of my business, and all I sold in that time was two small pots of Ointment. In fact, no person would then have accepted the Medicines as a gift. I had to practise the most rigid economy and to work most assiduously. By four o'clock in the morning I had generally commenced my day, not to cease until ten at night, in order to do that myself for which I must else have paid others.'

In 1840 Thomas Holloway married Jane Driver, who joined him in the business. The year before, he had moved into new premises at 244 Strand. He continued to advertise his patent medicines and in his *Sketch* he described his advertising as being done 'not only with determination, but judiciously and carefully ... I used to go down to the Docks to see captains of ships and passengers sailing to all parts of the world, collecting from them such information as was necessary.' His advertising costs increased steadily, from £5,000 in 1842, to £20,000 in 1851, and £40,000 by 1863. He claimed that 'For the proper application of their use I have had most ample directions translated into almost every known tongue; such as Chinese, Turkish, Armenian, Arabic, Sanskrit, and most of the vernaculars of India, and all the languages spoken on the European Continent. Among my correspondents I number Kings and Princes, equally with other distinguished foreigners of all nations.'

His other advertising methods included pamphlets in 15 languages, testimonials, posters, ballad song sheets, illustrated general knowledge cards, and such publications as *Holloway's Almanac and Family Friend* devoted to blood sports, kangaroo hunting, moose hunting, fox hunting and bull fighting, and *Holloway's Abridged Medical Guide for the Use of Missionaries*. He distributed his pills through a widespread network of agents, as did many of his business rivals.

Holloway was much criticised by the medical journals and was often lampooned in the national press, particularly when, for a time, he styled himself Professor. The exact ingredients of his pills and ointment were never revealed during his lifetime. However, analysis has now shown that the pills consisted mostly of aloes, powdered ginger, powdered jalap, cambogia and hard soap, with a coating of sugar; the ointment was more complicated and contained mostly lanoline, liquid paraffin and yellow beeswax. All the ingredients were harmless and non-addictive. Both products sold rapidly and at high prices, from 1s 1½d to £1 13s a pot or box.

Holloway suffered continually from his name being used by unscrupulous imitators. He brought an action, in 1850, against his brother, Henry, who had set up a business in the Strand using the name Holloway; and another in 1862 against a Swedish physician, Dr Sillon or Sillen, who had patented Holloway's ointment in France as 'Pommade dite Holloway'. His greatest rival at the beginning of his career was a Scot, James Morison (1770–1840), whose 'Hygeian Vegetable Universal Medicine' first appeared on the market in 1825 and was mentioned by Thomas Carlyle in *Past and Present*. Latterly Thomas Beecham (1820–1907) was Holloway's main competitor, and it was Beecham's who finally bought up Holloway's in 1938, by acquiring Eno's Fruit Salts, who had taken over Holloway's in 1930.

In 1867 Holloway's premises in the Strand were requisitioned by the Crown for the building of the new Law Courts, and he moved to 533 Oxford Street (later 78 New Oxford Street), which he called Holloway House. He now employed about a hundred people. It was at about this time that he bought Tittenhurst Lodge at Sunninghill, Berkshire, an early 18th-century house, refaced in the 1830s. He and Jane lived there with her sister Sarah Ann and her husband, George Martin. They had no children. Jane died in 1875 and Thomas in 1883: he was buried at St. Michael and All Angels, Sunninghill, where, in 1887, his relations commissioned Holloway's architect, W. H. Crossland, to build a memorial chapel and chancel which were completed the following year.

Thomas Holloway lived modestly at Tittenhurst, despite the fortune he had made by patent medicines and careful investment in the stock market. He was described after his death as 'having become rich still remained humble-minded, never sought any advancement in public life, never attempted to enter into what is called "society", and died as he had lived, a hard-working single-minded individual.' The later part of his life was concerned almost exclusively with the establishment of the two institutions which bear his name, Holloway Sanatorium, built between 1873 and 1884, and the Royal Holloway College, founded in 1879 and opened by Queen Victoria on 30 June 1886.

According to Edwin Hodder (*The Life and Work of the Seventh Earl of Shaftesbury*, 1886), Holloway was greatly influenced by Lord Shaftesbury's proposals for hospital care for insane persons of the middle and lower classes. The two met and plans went ahead for a Sanatorium on St. Ann's Hill at Virginia Water, Surrey, a site chosen and bought by Holloway.

In 1872, Holloway launched a limited competition to find an architect. Ten entries were received and, with the advice of George Godwin (editor of the *Builder*, who had himself designed a lunatic asylum in 1847), T. L. Donaldson (Professor of Architecture at University College, London, and past President of the RIBA), and Thomas Henry Wyatt (consulting architect to the lunacy commissioners), Holloway chose a Yorkshire architect, William Henry Crossland, who had submitted designs in collaboration with John Philpott Jones (who died shortly afterwards). Holloway wanted 'the grand old Flemish style' mostly because the red bricks which he thought necessary were easily obtainable locally.

The first brick for the Sanatorium was laid by Jane Holloway in 1873. Holloway took immense care over the building, personally supervising every detail, both internally and externally. In 1882 the *Builder* commented on the interior of the great hall: 'such a combination of rich colouring and gilding is not to be found in any modern building in this country, except in the House of Lords.' The Sanatorium was opened by Edward, Prince of Wales, on 15 June 1885 and has been in constant use until 1981.

Holloway's architect for both his buildings, William Henry Crossland, a pupil of Sir George Gilbert Scott, was first in practice in Huddersfield, and in about 1860 moved to work in Halifax. From 1863 onwards he established a reputation as a church architect, both building and restoring a number of churches, particularly in South Lancashire and the West Riding of Yorkshire. He was responsible for Akroyden, outside Halifax, one of the earliest planned industrial estates, begun in 1861; and he won the competition for Rochdale Town Hall (1866–71). In 1867 he was elected FRIBA and about three years later moved to London.

Following his work at the Sanatorium, Crossland was re-employed to design the College. He gave a full account of his work there which was published in the *Transactions of the R.I.B.A.* in 1887, and in which he described Holloway as 'a client who sent me to school, a man who "always worked with his head, never with his heart", to use his own words.' Crossland's plans were bound in three large volumes but they were later destroyed by him.

Holloway's decision to build a ladies college followed some discussion in the *Builder*. He had written to the editor, George Godwin, in 1871: 'I desire in some way or the other to devote for public and useful purposes a sum equivalent to that given by the late Mr Peabody – but I find much difficulty in discovering the best means and purposes to which such a sum could be devoted, so as to do the greatest public good, and to avoid pauperising classes who might not be eligible in public opinion for such a gift.' He asked that the printed notice requesting ideas should be anonymous. The *Builder* published it under the title 'How best to spend a quarter of a million or more'. This sum was doubled five weeks later. About 700 proposals were sent in but the *Builder* claimed the majority were 'utterly worthless'.

Eventually, it was on the advice of his wife that Holloway decided to build a college, which was, according to the Deed of Foundation of 8 May 1876, 'to be called "Holloway College", to afford the best education suitable for Women of the Middle and Upper Middle Classes and is intended to be mainly self-supporting'; sadly, Jane Holloway was to die of bronchitis on 25 September 1875, before the building had been begun.

Holloway took advice from Dr William Hague of Vassar College in Poughkeepsie, Massachusetts, and from the Principal of Girton College, Cambridge, the first women's college to be established in England in 1869. Holloway, Crossland and the latter's assistant, Taylor, visited the Loire Valley in the autumn of 1873, and for nearly three weeks Crossland and Taylor made plans and drawings of the Château de Chambord where, according to Holloway, 'my work consisted in referring to what they had done and to determine how much of the château I wanted for my purpose'.

In 1874 Holloway bought the site for his college on Egham Hill in Surrey, an area of 93 acres. Work began there only after a period of indecision as Holloway, in the meantime, had had plans drawn up by Crossland of various parts of some Cambridge colleges, Trinity and St. John's in particular, which were combined into one design.

On 30 July 1879, a contract was agreed with the builder, Messrs Thompson of Peterborough, for £257,000, of which Crossland was to be paid five per cent; building went ahead, but by this time Holloway had changed his mind about the style of the building. In a letter of 29 May 1876 he wrote that the College 'has all its basement plans ready but the plan of the superstructure is being changed from the Gothic style to the Renaissance'. Consequently Crossland's earlier drawings of Chambord were put into use and the first brick was laid by George Martin on 12 September 1879.

It was Crossland who appointed the sculptor for the decorative work on the buildings: the Italian Ceccardo Fucigna, who had also worked with George Gilbert Scott and at Castell Coch, outside Cardiff, for William Burges. In 1875 he had taken over John Birnie Philip's studio. Fucigna died shortly before completing his work at the College.

Holloway died on 26 December 1883, two and a half years before the formal opening of the College by Queen Victoria. The two large sculptural groups in the quadrangles were not at that stage completed. In September 1883 Holloway had advertised in *The Times* for 'Sculptors of Eminence' and had commissioned Count Gleichen, Prince Victor of Hohenlohe-Langenburg (1833–91), to execute the two works: *Queen Victoria* in the north quadrangle, and *Thomas and Jane Holloway* in the south quadrangle. Count

Gleichen's mother was Queen Victoria's half-sister. Though born in Würtemberg and educated in Dresden, he had been in the British Royal Navy from 1848 to 1866; on his retirement he had taken up sculpture and was given a studio at St. James's Palace. He completed the College statues in 1887 and remained a great friend of the Holloway family. The statues were unveiled in December 1887: Queen Victoria's by Princess Christian, and the Holloways' by Lord Thring, a Governor of the College.

The cost of the land, the building and the furnishings came to nearly £600,000 and Holloway left a further £200,000 as an endowment. After his death, at his request, his two brothers-in-law, Henry Driver and George Martin, added the name of Holloway to their surnames by deed poll. Henry Driver-Holloway carried on Holloway's patent medicine business, and George Martin-Holloway supervised the completion of Holloway's building schemes. He was knighted by the Queen at Osborne in 1887.

William Henry Crossland was retained by the College as architectural adviser on an annual basis until 1900. He designed the College swimming bath in 1893, and periodically reported on the fabric of the building. Very little is known of his career after 1890, and he died in obscurity in 1909, leaving only £29 2s 9d.

On 30 June 1886 Queen Victoria formally opened the College and commanded that it should be styled Royal. Its academic life began in October 1887, with the arrival of the first women undergraduates and their tutors; Ellen Bishop was Principal. During the closing years of the 19th century attendance built up, and the range of studies in arts, music and science widened. The College formed part of no University, but was an independent institution for the higher education of women. Its pupils divided about equally among those who took the examinations of London University (success in which entitled them to London degrees), those who took the Oxford examinations (which entitled them only to a published result, for Oxford did not confer degrees on women until 1920), and those who preferred one or two years' College experience to a full course. Three possibilities were open to the College: to stay as it was; to realise the bold vision of a British University for Women, for which

Holloway had at least laid strong foundations; or to become part of the federal University of London as reconstructed by the University of London Act of 1898. The views of a brilliant new Principal, Emily Penrose, probably turned the scales in favour of London. The College joined the University as a constituent School in 1900, and has remained so, as an independent foundation governed by the Royal Holloway College Act of Parliament, taking its share in the management of the University, and accepting University academic and financial control, with all its students taking the London degrees. The founders' great benefaction, one of the most munificent in the history of modern Universities, developed by 1980 into a College of 1,500 undergraduates and postgraduates in Arts, Music, Drama and Science, its community life still centred upon Crossland's double quadrangle and the picture gallery.

Holloway was 81 when he began to purchase pictures, mostly at Christie's. Four works were bought from either the Fine Art Society or Graves & Company, and one of the Morlands from a private owner, the Earl of Dunmore. Holloway was too frail to travel to London from Sunninghill, and his brother-in-law, George Martin, acted as his bidder for the paintings. It is assumed that Holloway chose the paintings in advance from Christie's catalogues.

Charles W. Carey, Curator of the collection from 1887, stated that it was with his brother-in-law's advice that Holloway selected the paintings. However, there is no other evidence that this was so. The *Builder* announced in October 1881 that 'Mr Holloway . . . contemplates the formation of a picture gallery in the college and the paintings he has already purchased for the purpose show that it will be a collection of no common kind.'

The name of Holloway as a buyer and seller in the salerooms is to be found repeatedly from 1829 to 1876; but this may have been the Mr Holloway who opened a commercial art gallery in Bedford Street, Covent Garden, in 1873, selling paintings and engravings. His gallery was taken over by Goupil two years later. Thomas Holloway certainly owned a large collection of pictures at Tittenhurst. They were mostly Old Masters (Dutch, Flemish, French and Italian). Some of them came from the collection of the King of the

Netherlands and had been shown in the Manchester Art Treasures exhibition in 1857. Amongst the paintings he owned were Giovanni Bellini's *St. Francis in Ecstasy* and Gerard David's *Deposition*. Both were exhibited at the Winter Exhibition of Old Masters at the Royal Academy in 1912 and are now in the Frick Collection in New York. Sixty-five pictures were sold at Christie's in 1912 after the death of Holloway's sister-in-law. The majority fetched very low prices. Those which were not sold then were retained by the family and most appeared in later sales.

Of the paintings which hung at Tittenhurst, 78 originated from another Sunningdale house called Broomfield Hall, which Holloway had purchased with its contents in 1869 for £25,000 from Captain Joseph Dingwall. Holloway had the house demolished except for two large rooms in which he temporarily stored the contents: paintings, wooden statues, bronzes, china and furniture, valued at about £10,000.

When Holloway began to buy pictures for the College in May 1881, at the sale of Edward John Coleman of Stoke Court, he bid under the name of Thomas. The first five pictures he bought, for £18,847, included two by Clarkson Stanfield, the *View of the Pic du Midi d'Ossau* and *The Battle of Roveredo*, Landseer's *Man Proposes, God Disposes*, Millais's *The Princes in the Tower* and Creswick's *Trentside*. This caused considerable excitement in the press and *The Times* devoted a leading article to what it described as 'Saturday's splendid extravagance . . . this Titanic battle of rival biddings . . . Some mystery seems to envelop the destination of the more conspicuous objects of Saturday's sale. They are allotted by one report to an English banker, and by another to an American millionaire.'

The *Art Journal* stated that 'the prices were the result of a *carte blanche* having been given to the auctioneers to buy them for a well known philanthropist at any price'. Thereafter Holloway used his brother-in-law's name Martin for bidding. The provenance details in this catalogue, therefore, give the names of Thomas and Martin as the final buyers, together with that of Mason, which Holloway occasionally used in 1881.

By July of this year, however, the exact identity of the collector began to transpire, and in May 1882 *The Times'* report of Edward Hermon's Wyfold Court Gallery sale stated that 'It was not improbable that that gentleman [Mr Holloway] was the real purchaser, and has acquired these fine pictures for the splendid gallery, which, it is understood, is to be attached to a benevolent institution founded by him.'

Both before and after Holloway's death, the daily press and the art journals criticised him for paying record prices, thus falsely inflating the art market. He had purchased Edwin Long's *Babylonian Marriage Market* for 6,300 guineas, a saleroom record for the work of a living British painter; and the outstanding price of 6,500 guineas for Landseer's *Man Proposes, God Disposes* remained unsurpassed until 1892 when the distillers John Dewar & Sons paid over £7,000 for Landseer's *Monarch of the Glen* for use as an advertisement on their whisky bottles.

The Times commented at some length on the prices paid by Holloway in its report of the William Lee sale in May 1883. 'The presence of late of an amateur buyer with apparently unlimited means at command, has created no small excitement on the great Fine Art Exchange in King Street [Christie's], and quite a flutter among the artists, who never could have dreamt of such prices for their pictures. Such an impetus has been given to the commercial value of good pictures as has not been seen since the memorable Gillott sale ten years ago, but the artists must observe that it is only pictures of first-rate merit that command these high prices. The indifferent good, the "pot-boilers" and the "poor things" remain where they were, for Mr. Martin does not contend for them.' It was in this sale report that the only recorded instance of Holloway's standing down on a bid is noted. This was for 'Muller's beautiful little picture of "Gillingham Church", in which Mr Vokins won with his spirited bid of £1,018 10s.'

Holloway's pattern of buying appears to be somewhat random. The earliest painting in the collection is Gainsborough's *Peasants going to Market: Early Morning* from the Stourhead Heirlooms sale; it is Holloway's last purchase. It would seem that he was not interested in collecting either Pre-Raphaelite paintings or religious works. Two of his most remarkable purchases were the two famous 'social realism' paintings, Luke Fildes's *Applicants for Admission to a Casual Ward* and Frank Holl's *Newgate: Committed for Trial*.

Holloway's obituary in the *Art Journal* began: 'The Death of Mr Thomas Holloway, on the 26th of December, removes from the world of Art a collector who, had he commenced at an earlier stage in his career, would probably have amassed a gallery of modern pictures unequalled in its cost and size.' Thus stated, it continued with a series of bitter criticisms of his collecting methods, concentrating mostly on the fact that he had not benefited the artists themselves in paying such extortionate prices for their works. 'We believe [he] never purchased a picture direct from the artist. Those who were fortunate enough to send to auction pictures he fancied benefited no doubt largely from his princely mode of procedure, but into the artists' coffers no portion of his money found its way, and those whose productions he acquired may possibly have to regret the inflated prices which for the moment their works assumed.' Holloway himself explained his reluctance to buy pictures directly from private sources in a letter of May 1876: '[pictures] are frequently offered to me but I invariably decline to purchase for the reason that in private hands proof cannot be given, or rarely so, of their identity.'

The original plans of Royal Holloway College made no provision for a picture gallery. While the College was being built the paintings were hung nearby at the Holloway Sanatorium in Virginia Water. When, in 1886, the College was officially opened by Queen Victoria, the paintings had been removed to the room intended as a students' Recreation Hall, where they have remained. Queen Victoria commented on a few of the paintings in her diary for 30 June 1886; mistakenly in some cases: 'We were taken to the Picture Gallery, where there are fine specimens of modern art and many well known pictures, such as "the 2 Princes in the Tower" by Millais, Landseer's "Palace Bears", Frith's "Derby Day", Long's "Marriage Market", &c.'

The Recreation Hall, however, was not considered by the *Art Journal* to be an ideal space for hanging Holloway's collection, mainly because of the lack of top lighting and the pilasters along the walls which interfered with the hanging of the larger paintings. The writer suggested that a completely new gallery should be built, and cited Dulwich as a good precedent. However, less drastic measures were taken: the lower level of pilasters was removed in 1903 on the advice of Briton Riviere, who is represented by two paintings in the collection.

Holloway seems to have had little contact with other collectors or dealers, except for the instances already mentioned. Henry Tate, later to found the Tate Gallery, gave a scholarship to the College in 1887, but does not appear to have been a friend of Holloway's. Ernest Gustave Girardot (fl. 1860–93) carried out most of Holloway's personal painting commissions. There is a record of a portrait of Jane Holloway by the miniature painter Sir William Charles Ross (1794–1860) but this has not been traced. Two portraits of Thomas and Jane Holloway, dating from the 1840s, are by William Scott (1811–90), about whom very little is known. It seems to have been characteristic of the self-made men of that period to commission unknown painters to portray them.

Charles W. Carey, a young man who had just completed his training at the Royal Academy Schools, visited the collection when it was hanging at the Sanatorium and met there one of Holloway's brothers-in-law. As a result he was appointed Curator of the paintings in 1887 and he remained at the College until his death in 1943. His tasks were many, the most important being to write a catalogue of the paintings which ran into three editions published in 1888, 1890 and 1896. This is the work referred to as 'Carey' in this catalogue. Carey instructed the students in painting and drawing and looked after the private collections of pictures belonging to Holloway's brothers-in-law, for whom he made copies of many of the Royal Holloway College paintings, some of which are still in the possession of the family.

A few paintings were given to the College after Holloway's death. Those by Charles Leslie and David Murray have been listed with the original collection, together with the portraits of Thomas and

Jane Holloway. The painting of the *Tomb in the Water, Telmessus, Lycia* by Muller was part of the original collection, and was moved to the dining hall in 1903. This room also houses portraits of former Principals.

References to the paintings in the collection appearing in the following bibliography are not included in the catalogue entries.

Bibliography

Some Small Memories as to the Origin of Holloway College for Women (being Mr. Holloway's address on meeting some friends, to explain his views, and some correspondence with Mr. James Beal, as to its initiation), n.d., Printer, G. Stahl.

Walter Armstrong, 'A Women's University', *Art Journal*, 1885, pp. 24–8, 64.

W. H. Crossland, FRIBA, 'The Royal Holloway College', *Transactions of the R.I.B.A.*, Vol. III, New Series, 1887, pp. 141–8, summary published in *Builder*, 2 April 1887, pp. 496–7.

C. W. Carey, *Royal Holloway College, Egham. Catalogue of Pictures*, three editions, 1888, 1890, 1896.

Walter Shaw Sparrow, 'The Royal Holloway College Picture-Gallery', *Magazine of Art*, 1891, pp. 234–41, 269–75.

C. W. Carey, 'The Royal Holloway College Collection', *Art Journal*, 1897, pp. 129–33, 202–06, 306–10, 334–40.

Charles Ray, 'A Model Women's College', *Good Words*, 1902, Vol. XlVIII, pp. 636–44.

Sir Lindsey Smith, J.P., *Thomas Holloway and The Erection of Holloway Sanatorium*, privately printed, 1932.

The Story of Thomas Holloway (1800–1883), printed for private circulation by the Governors of Holloway Sanatorium, Glasgow University Press, ? 1933.

Derryan Paul, *Royal Holloway College Archives, A Guide*, privately printed, 1973.

Acknowledgements

It is a profound sadness that the late Principal of the College, Dr Lionel H. Butler, died suddenly in November 1981 before the publication of this catalogue. He had a sincere interest in, and affection for, the collection and from the beginning of the project he gave me support and encouragement, advised at all stages and edited the complete typescript. It is to him that I owe my greatest debt of gratitude and I would like to dedicate this work to his memory.

Other members of the staff of the College to whom I owe grateful thanks are: Dr Francis Robinson, of the Department of History, who was initially responsible for the idea of a catalogue and whose continual assistance and concern I have much appreciated. Professor Peter Brown, formerly Head of the Department of History, welcomed me into the Department and gave me much valuable help. I am also sincerely grateful to Miss Janet Christie, Mrs Pat New, Mrs Rita Townsend, Mr Douglas Barge, Mr Kevin Livesey and Mr David Ward.

I would also like to record my gratitude to Mr Jeremy Maas, who not only gave specific guidance on the Frith entry and very kindly wrote the foreword, but, as did Ms Rosemary Treble, answered endless questions and unfailingly gave sound counsel. For assistance on individual catalogue entries I would particularly like to thank Mr Frank Bicknell, Miss Margaret Christian, Mr David Cordingly, Dr Catherine Gordon, Miss Helen Guiterman, Mrs Joan Linnell Burton, Dr Pieter van der Merwe, Mr John Munday, Mr Richard Ormond, Mr Gavin Ross, Miss Rosamund Strode, Mr Malcolm Warner, Mr Giles Waterfield, Mr Christopher Wright, Messrs Thomas Agnew & Sons Ltd and the staff of the Witt Library and the London Library. I am grateful to H.M. The Queen for gracious permission to quote from Queen Victoria's diary.

For their hospitality and access to family papers I would like to thank Mrs Pamela Munford, Miss Betty Driver-Holloway, Mr and Mrs Gerald Oliver and Mrs C. Held. For financial assistance towards the catalogue I would like to acknowledge The Paul Mellon Centre for Studies in British Art and the Jubilee Fellowship Fund of the Royal Holloway College.

Photographic acknowledgements are due to the Royal Holloway College; the Frith drawing (pl. 4) is reproduced by kind permission of The Ironbridge Gorge Museum, Telford, Shropshire.

List of Plates

1   Frank Holl RA, *Newgate : Committed for Trial* (cat 29)

2 William Scott, *Thomas Holloway* (cat 67)

3 William Scott, *Jane Holloway* (cat 68)

4   William P. Frith RA, *Sketch for 'The Railway Station'* (Cat 23 see pl. 6)

5   Luke Fildes RA, *Applicants for Admission to a Casual Ward* (cat 22)

6   William P. Frith RA, *The Railway Station* (cat 23)

8 Benjamin W. Leader RA, *The Rocky Bed of a Welsh River* (cat 35)

7 James B. Pyne, *Haweswater, from Waller Gill Force* (cat 62)

9 Ludwig Munthe, *Snow scene* (cat 54)

10   William J. Muller, *Tomb in the Water, Telmessus, Lycia* (cat 53)

11   Benjamin W. Leader RA, *Unterseen, Interlaken ;*
Autumn in Switzerland (cat 36)

12   Clarkson Stanfield RA, *View of the Pic du Midi d'Ossau, in the Pyrenees, with Brigands* (cat 72)

13   Clarkson Stanfield RA, *The battle of Roveredo* (cat 71)

14   Jules Achille Noël, *The Quay,
Hennebont, with Boats and Figures* (cat 58)

15   Jules Achille Noël, *Abbeville, with
Peasants and Horses in the foreground* (cat 57)

16   James Holland, *Piazza dei Signori, Verona ; with the Market Place* (cat 30)

17   James Holland, *Venice, Piazza di San Marco* (cat 31)

18   James Webb, *Carthagena, Spain* (cat 78)

19   Erskine Nicol ARA, *The Missing Boat* (cat 56)

20   Abraham Solomon, *Departure of the Diligence, Biarritz* (cat 69)

21   John E. Hodgson RA, *Relatives in Bond* (cat 28)

22   David Roberts, *A Street in Cairo* (cat 66)

23   William J. Muller, *The Opium Stall* (cat 52)

24   David Roberts, *Pilgrims approaching Jerusalem* (cat 65)

25   Henry Dawson, *Sheerness, Guardship saluting* (cat 16)

26   J. M. W. Turner RA, *Van Tromp going about to please his Masters, Ships at Sea, getting a good wetting* (cat 76)

27   Edwin Ellis, *The Harbour Bar* (cat 18)

28   Edward W. Cooke RA, *Scheveningen Beach* (cat 9)

29   Clarkson Stanfield RA, *After a Storm* (cat 70)

30   Edward W. Cooke RA, *A Dutch Beurtman aground on the Terschelling Sands. In the North Sea after a Snow Storm* (cat 10)

31   James C. Hook RA, *Leaving at low Water, Scilly Isles* (cat 32)

32 John Brett RA, *Carthillon Cliffs* (cat 2)

33 Theodor A. Weber, *Dover Pilot and Fishing Boats* (cat 79)

34 James Webb, *Dordrecht* (cat 77)

35   George Morland, *The Pressgang* (cat 49)

36   Frederick D. Hardy, *Expectation : Interior of a Cottage with a Mother and Children* (cat 26)

37   George Morland, *The Cottage Door* (cat 48)

38   George Morland, *The Carrier preparing to set out* (cat 50)

39   William J. Muller, *Interior of a Cottage in Wales, with a Woman at a spinning wheel and a Child feeding chickens* (cat 51)

40   Henry Lejeune ARA, *Early Sorrow* (cat 38)

41   Paul F. Poole RA, *The Gleaner* (cat 61)   42   Paul F. Poole RA, *Crossing the Stream* (cat 60)

43   Thomas Faed RA, *Taking Rest* (cat 20)

44   Sir John Everett Millais RA, *The Princes in the Tower* (cat 46)

46 John B. Burgess RA, *Licensing the Beggars in Spain* (cat 3)

45 Sir John Everett Millais RA, *Princess Elizabeth in prison at St James's* (cat 47)

47 Alfred Elmore, *The Emperor Charles V at the Convent of Yuste* (cat 19)

48   Edwin L. Long RA, *The Suppliants. Expulsion of the Gypsies from Spain* (cat 40)

49   Daniel Maclise RA, *Peter the Great at Deptford Dockyard* (cat 42)

50   Edwin L. Long RA, *The Babylonian Marriage Market* (cat 41)

51 Briton Riviere RA, *Sympathy* (cat 63)

52 Edmund B. Leighton, *A Flaw in the Title* (cat 37)

53 Tito Conti, *Good-Bye* (cat 8)

54 Tito Conti, *Approved* (cat 7)

55 Tito Conti, *Playing her respects to His High Mightyness* (cat 6)

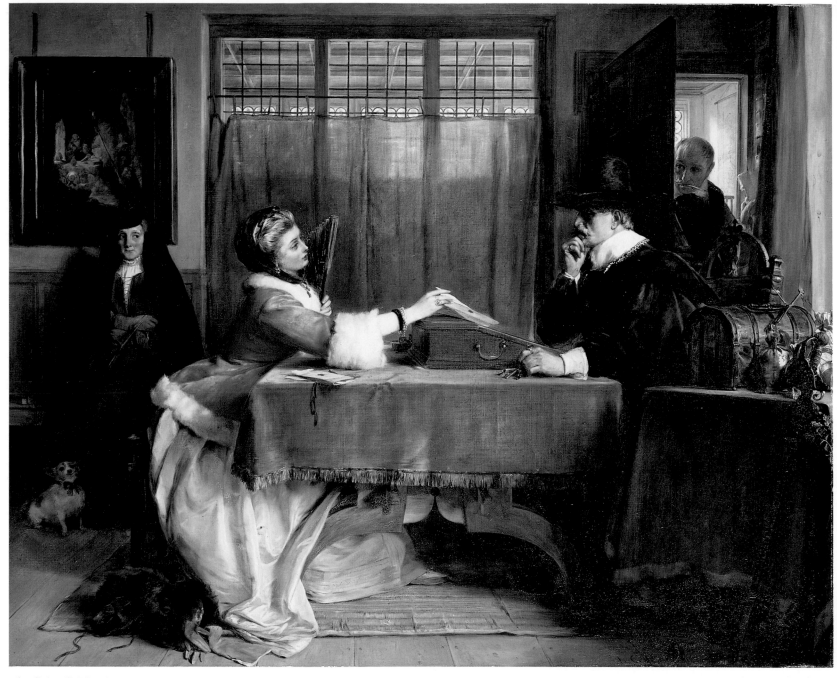

56   John C. Horsley RA, *The Banker's Private Room ; Negotiating a Loan* (cat 33)

57   John Pettie RA, *A State Secret* (cat 59)

58   Henry Thomas Dawson, *Salacómbe Estuary, South Devon* (cat 17)

59   Thomas S. Cooper RA,
Landscape with Sheep and Goats (cat 12)

60   John Linnell, *Wayfarers* (cat 39)

61   John MacWhirter RA, *Night* (cat 43)

62   Thomas Gainsborough RA, *Peasants going to Market : Early Morning* (cat 24).

63   Follower of Crome, *A Woodland Scene* (cat 15)

64   Thomas Creswick RA, *The First Glimpse of the Sea* (cat 13)

65   William Collins RA, *Borrowdale, Cumberland, with Children playing by the Banks of a Brook* (cat 4)

66   A. V. Copley Fielding, *Travellers in a Storm. Approach to Winchester* (cat 21)

67   Thomas Creswick RA, *Trentside* (cat 14)

68   John Constable RA, *A Sketch for View on the Stour, nr Dedham* (cat 5)

69   John Syer, *Welsh Drovers* (cat 74)

70 John MacWhirter RA, *Spindrift* (cat 44)

71 John Syer, *The Windmill* (cat 73)

72 Patrick Nasmyth, *Landscape, with Trees and Figures in the foreground, a Church in the distance* (cat 55)

73 Constant Troyon, *Evening, driving Cattle* (cat 75)

74   Thomas S. Cooper RA, *Landscape, with Cows and Sheep* (cat 11)

75　Peter Graham RA, *A Highland Croft* (cat 25)

76 Richard Ansdel RA, *The Drover's Halt, Island of Mull in the Distance* (cat 1)

77 James H. Hardy, *A young Gillie, with setters and dead game* (cat 27)

78 Joshua H. S. Mann, *The Cauld Blast* (cat 45)

79   Briton Riviere RA, *An Anxious Moment* (cat 64)

80 Sir Edwin H. Landseer RA, *Man proposes – God disposes* (cat 34)

Catalogue

Abbreviations

Agnew's 1981   Catalogue of the exhibition 'Thomas Holloway. The Benevolent Millionaire', Nov–Dec, 1981.

A.J.   *The Art Journal.*

ARA   Associate of the Royal Academy

ARSA   Associate of the Royal Scottish Academy.

ARWS   Associate of the Royal Watercolour Society.

Binyon, 1898–1907   Laurence Binyon, *Catalogue of Drawings by British Artists and Artists of foreign origin working in Great Britain, Preserved in the Department of Prints and Drawings in the British Museum*, 4 vols., 1898–1907.

Blackburn, *R.A. Notes*   Henry Blackburn, *Academy Notes*, with Illustrations of the Principal Pictures at Burlington House.

Blackwood's   *Blackwood's Edinburgh Magazine.*

B.I.   British Institution.

Caw, 1908   James L. Caw, *Scottish Painting Past and Present 1620–1908*, Edinburgh, 1908.

Chesneau, 1885   Ernest Chesneau, *The English School of Painting*, translated L. N. Etherington, 2nd edition, 1885.

Clement and Hutton, 1879   Clara Erskine Clement and Laurence Hutton, *Artists of the Nineteenth Century and their works*, 2 vols., 1879.

Cook and Wedderburn, 1903–12   E. T. Cook and Alexander Wedderburn, *The Works of John Ruskin*, (Library Edition), 39 vols., 1903–12.

Cunningham, 1880   Allan Cunningham, *The Lives of the Most Eminent British Painters*, revised edition, 1880 by Mrs Charles Heaton.

FRSA   Fellow of the Royal Scottish Academy.

Forbes, 1975   Catalogue of the Forbes Magazine Collection, *The Royal Academy (1837–1901) Revisited*, 1975.

Fraser's   *Fraser's Magazine for Town and Country.*

Gaunt, 1972   William Gaunt, *The Restless Century, Painting in Britain 1800–1900*, 1972.

Hardie, 1966–68   Martin Hardie, *Water-Colour Painting in Britain*, 3 vols., 1966–68.

Hardie, 1976   William Hardie, *Scottish Painting 1837–1939*, 1976.

Hodgson, 1887   John Evan Hodgson RA, *Fifty Years of British Art*, 1887.

HFRPE   Honorary Fellow of the Royal Society of Painters and Etchers.

HRBA   Honorary Member of the Royal Society of British Artists, Suffolk Street.

HRSA   Honorary Member of the Royal Scottish Academy.

I.L.N.   *The Illustrated London News.*

Int. Ex.   International Exhibition.

Irwins, 1975   David and Francina Irwin, *Scottish Painters at Home and Abroad 1700–1900*, 1975.

Maas, 1969   Jeremy Maas, *Victorian Painters*, 1969.

Mag. of Art   *The Magazine of Art.*

ed. Meynell, 1883   Wilfrid Meynell, *Some Modern Artists and their work*, 1883, mostly reprinted from *The Magazine of Art.*

ed. Meynell, 1886–88   Wilfrid Meynell, *The Modern School of Art*, 4 vols., 1886–88.

N.W.S.   New Watercolour Society.

Ottley, 1886   Henry Ottley, *A Biographical and Critical Dictionary of recent and living Painters and Engravers*, 1886.

O.W.S.   Old Watercolour Society.

PRWS   President of the Royal Watercolour Society.

Quilter, 1892   Harry Quilter, *Preferences in Art, Life and Literature*, 1892.

R.A.   Royal Academy.

RBA   Member of the Royal Society of British Artists, Suffolk Street.

RI   Member of the Royal Institute of Painters in Watercolours.

ROI   Member of the Royal Institute of Painters in Oil colours.

RP   Member of the Royal Society of Portrait Painters.

RSA   Member of the Royal Scottish Academy.

Abbreviations

RWS — Member of the Royal Watercolour Society.

Redford, 1888 — George Redford, *Art Sales*, 2 vols., 1888.

Redgrave, 1947 — Richard and Samuel Redgrave, *A Century of British Painters*, first published 1866, republished 1947.

Reynolds, 1953 — Graham Reynolds, *Painters of the Victorian Scene*, 1953.

Ruskin, 1902 — John Ruskin, *Academy Notes*, ed. 1902.

Stephens, 1884 — Frederic George Stephens, *Artists at Home*, 1884.

Temple, 1897 — A. G. Temple, *The Art of Painting in the Queen's Reign*, 1897.

Wood, *Dictionary*, 1971 — Christopher Wood, *A Dictionary of Victorian Painters*, 1971.

Wood, *Panorama*, 1976 — Christopher Wood, *Victorian Panorama – Paintings of Victorian Life*, 1976.

All the publications listed above were published in London unless otherwise stated.

Catalogue

1. Richard Ansdell

1815–85, ARA 1861, RA 1870

The Drover's Halt, Island of Mull in the Distance 1845
(*pl. 76*)

oil on canvas, 38 × 71½ in (96 × 181.5 cm)

INSCR: Richd Ansdell 1845

PROV: Bought from the artist by James Eden of Fairlawn, Lytham; his sale, Christie's 30 May 1874 (64) bt Col. White £609; Hon. Charles White; his sale 13 May 1876 (109) bt in (400 gns); his sale 18 May 1878 (95) bt in again (290 gns); his sale 29 April 1882 (124) bt Martin £262 10s.

EXH: 1846? B.I. (217); 1981 Agnew's (1)

LIT: (for 1846 B.I. ex.) *Art Union* 1846 p. 77; *Athenaeum* 21 February 1846 p. 203; *Literary Gazette* 1846 p. 132; *Spectator* 1846 p. 188; *Times* 9 February 1846 p. 6; *A.J.* 1860 p. 234; ex. catalogue Atkinson Art Gallery Southport, *A Selection of Victorian Oil Paintings 1878–1978*, 1978 p. 8.

VERSION: *The Drover's Halt*
38 × 72 in (96 × 182.8 cm)
Prov. George Audley 1921; Atkinson Art Gallery, Southport.

Richard Ansdell exhibited a painting of this title at the B.I. in 1846 and was greatly applauded by the reviewing journals. However, it is not certain whether the painting exhibited in 1846 was this one or *The Drover's Halt* signed and dated 1846 and now in the Atkinson Art Gallery, Southport.[1]

The two paintings have not only many of the same features, but also the same dimensions. The reviews for 1846 could refer to either, for they all concentrated on details which are included in both. It could be that this painting of 1845 was exhibited in the 1846 B.I. exhibition, since the exhibition opened at the beginning of February; and that following its success, Ansdell was commissioned to paint another picture of a similar subject, which was executed later that year, dated 1846 and is the version now in Southport.

On the back of the frame of this painting is Ansdell's address in Liverpool, from where he moved in 1847, and the inscription 'No. 1'.

The 1846 exhibit was his first at the B.I. and the address may have been added for the painting's return after the exhibition. This may be further evidence that this was the picture actually exhibited. Of the 1846 B.I. painting James Dafforne wrote in his 1860 article in the *A.J.* on Ansdell that 'in 1846 Mr. Ansdell contributed for the first time to the British Institution; it was by far the best work he had hitherto exhibited, and different in subject from his previous productions. *The Drover's Halt, Isle of Mull in the Distance*, is a large picture, showing a numerous group of figures and cattle halting at a roadside bothie in the Highlands; much study was evidently given to the composition, and great care bestowed on its execution: every object is painted with exceeding delicacy, combined with freedom of handling and force of expression.'

More paintings of the same title followed. There is one illustrated in *A Book of Sporting Painters* which bears no resemblance to either of the two paintings mentioned so far.[2] Another was exhibited in 1852 at the B.I. (146) and again at the International Exhibition of 1873 in London (1338); on this Creswick (q.v.) had collaborated by painting the animals. Painting joint works was quite usual with Ansdell, who also painted with Frith (q.v.) and John Phillip (1817–67). From the description in contemporary reviews, this painting (not traced) was similar to those at Southport and in the collection here.[3]

Highland drovers were a popular theme of Ansdell's. They first occur as early as 1839, when he was still living in Liverpool and exhibited at the Academy there *Scotch Drovers, with the Island of Mull in the Distance.*

Richard Ansdell was born in Liverpool, where he became a member of the Academy in 1837 and its President in 1845. In 1847 he moved from Liverpool to London, having established a reputation as an animal painter with subjects taken from farming and sporting life. His first major work executed in London was *The Battle of the Standard* (Royal Hospital, Chelsea) of 1848, which was a great success at the R.A. The painting, depicting the Battle of Waterloo, became famous through engravings. Ansdell also painted pictures of Spanish subjects inspired by two visits to Spain in 1856 (when he travelled with Phillip) and 1857.

In 1861 Ansdell had a house built at Lytham, North Lancashire (the home town of James Eden JP, who bought this painting from him), which he called Starr Hills. Ansdell's popularity was such that, according to Arthur Todd, a road, then a railway and finally an entire district of Lytham became known as Ansdell. He sold this house about three years later and bought a property on Loch Laggan in Invernesshire, where he lived in the summer months. He was particularly fond of the Highlands of Scotland, as his contemporary Landseer (q.v.), and the district provided him with much raw material. He continued to exhibit at the R.A. until his death in 1885.

[1] See their catalogue, *A Selection of Victorian Oil Paintings 1878–1978*, 1978, p. 8, by Andrew W. Moore. I am grateful to Mr Moore for his help in trying to sort out these pictures.
[2] Walter Shaw Sparrow, *A Book of Sporting Painters*, London and New York, 1931, repr. between pp. 176–7.
[3] In particular, *A.J.*, 1852, p. 71 and *I.L.N.*, 1852, p. 147.

BIBLIOGRAPHY
'British Artists: Their Style and Character, No. L, Richard Ansdell', *Art Journal*, 1860, pp. 233–5.
W. W. Fenn, 'An Open-Air Painter', *Magazine of Art*, 1882, pp. 450–3. reprinted in: ed. Wilfrid Meynell, *Some Modern Artists and their Work*, 1883, pp. 218–23.
Art Journal, 1904, p. 217.

H. C. Marillier, *The Liverpool School of Painters*, 1904, pp. 51–4.
Arthur Todd, *The Life of Richard Ansdell, R.A.*, Manchester, 1919.

2. John Brett

1831–1902, ARA 1881, retired 1901

Carthillon Cliffs 1878 (*pl. 32*)

oil on canvas, 18 × 36 in (45.7 × 91.4 cm)

INSCR: John Brett 1878

EXH: 1981 Agnew's (2)

PROV: Painted for William Lee; his sale Christie's 26 May 1883 (45) bt Martin £273.

Unfortunately Brett did not re-start his *Record Book* until the year after this picture was painted, and, as far as is known, there is no contemporary record of it made by him. Brett himself, in an 'Introductory Note' to the *Record Book* begun in 1879, stated under 10 December: 'Many years ago I kept a record of this kind, and as sales were then rare it was filled in pretty regularly, and it exists still at my studio in the form of a copybook. I forget for how many years this record has been neglected, but certainly the particulars of a great many pictures are thus lost.' He continued: 'it has been my invariable practice to sign all my finished pictures', as indeed he did with this one.[1]

A small amount of information can be pieced together about Brett's career during this period, but it is difficult to trace full details, probably because of his absorbing interest in astronomy. Brett was in Paignton in the summer of 1878 and began his summer journals in the following year, together with his *Record Book*. He used to take long summer holidays with his family, either in South Wales or the West of Scotland, or in Cornwall, where it seems likely that this picture was painted, or a 'sketch' for it was.

It was recorded by Beatrix Potter in her diary that Brett used a sailing yacht in the summer months in order to make oil sketches of coastal scenery which he would use as raw material for paintings in the winter months.[2] Much of his time, after his marriage in 1870, was spent aboard his yacht sailing around the British Isles. It was also during this period that he developed his interest in astronomy. He was made a Fellow of the Royal Astronomical Society in 1871, published his findings on solar observations in the Society's *Notices* and had an observatory built at his home in Putney.[3]

John Brett was born in Bletchingley in Surrey, the son of an Army officer. He entered the R.A. Schools in 1854 and two years later he had his first exhibit at the Academy. In that year he visited Switzerland, which brought him in contact with the Pre-Raphaelite landscape painter John William Inchbold (1830–88). Brett made a most forceful impact at the Academy with his famous *The Stonebreaker* (Walker Art Gallery, Liverpool) of 1858. This painting attracted Ruskin's interest and Brett became to Ruskin 'one of my keenest-minded friends' and 'a fine fellow as well as a good painter'. Ruskin prompted Brett's Pre-Raphaelite style further and in 1859 Brett exhibited the *Val d'Aosta* (Private Collection) which was painted as a result of a visit to Northern Italy. However, Ruskin's approval did not last and by 1865 their friendship was over, mostly because of a scientific argument and Brett's insistence on increasing the scale of his work beyond the limits of Ruskin's satisfaction. In 1875, Ruskin was writing in his *Academy Notes* that since the year of *The Stonebreaker* Brett 'has gained nothing – rather, I fear, lost, in subtlety of execution, and necessitates the decline of his future power by persistently covering too large canvas'.

After his promising beginning as a Pre-Raphaelite landscape painter and Ruskin's disappointment in him as such, Brett turned his energies to painting mostly coastal scenes, which he exhibited continually from about 1870 until his retirement from the Academy in 1901. They proved extremely popular, and were particularly praised for their use of brilliant colour and high degree of draughtsmanship. His chief rival in marine painting was Henry Moore (1831–95) who was elected a Royal Academician, which Brett was not.

[1] I am indebted to Mrs A. Wales and Mr Peter Brett for information from family papers in their possession.
[2] Quoted by Jeremy Maas, *Victorian Painters*, 1969, p. 193.
[3] See his obituary in *Monthly Notices of the Royal Astronomical Society*, Vol. LXII, 1902, pp. 238–41.

BIBLIOGRAPHY
John Brett: Three Months on the Scottish Coast: A Series of Sketches and Pictures painted during the summer of the Present Year etc., 1886, exhibition catalogue, Fine Art Society.
John Brett, 'Landscape at the National Gallery', *Fortnightly Review*, Vol. LVLL, 1 April 1895, pp. 623–39.
P. H. Bate, *The English Pre-Raphaelite Painters*, 1899.
Art Journal, 1902, p. 87 (Obit.).
Monthly Notices of the Royal Astronomical Society, Vol. LXII, 1902, pp. 238–41 (Obit.). (Herbert Hall Turner).
F. Maclean, *Henry Moore R.A.*, 1905, pp. 167–73.
R. Ironside and J. A. Gere, *Pre-Raphaelite Painters*, 1948.
William Even Fredeman, *Pre-Raphaelitism: A Bibliocritical Study*, Harvard Press Cambridge, 1965.
Allen Staley, *The Pre-Raphaelite Landscape*, 1973, pp. 124–37.

3. John Bagnold Burgess

1830–97, ARA 1877, RA 1888

Licensing the Beggars in Spain 1877 (*pl. 46*)

oil on canvas, 48 × 76 in (121.8 × 192.9 cm)

PROV: Purchased from the artist by Thomas Taylor of Aston Rowant Gallery, Oxfordshire; his sale Christie's 28 April 1883 (43) bt Martin £1,165 10s.

EXH: 1877 R.A. (1377); 1981 Agnew's (3).

LIT: *Academy* 2 June 1877 p. 496; *Annual Register* 1877 p. 361; *A.J.* 1877 p. 271; *Athenaeum* 26 May 1877 p. 677; Blackburn, *R.A. Notes* 1877 p. 71 and repr. same page; *Saturday Review* 16 June 1877 p. 737; *The Times* 22 May 1877 p. 11; Clement & Hutton, 1879 p. 107; *A.J.* 1880 p. 300; *Mag. of Art* 1882 p. 311 and repr. p. 309; Temple, 1897 p. 293; *A.J.* 1898 p. 31 (Obit.); Meynell, 1886–88 p. 61 and repr, p. 57; Arts Council, *Great Victorian Pictures*, 1978 p. 94.

Licensing the Beggars in Spain was exhibited at the Academy of 1877, the year Burgess was elected an ARA. It was well received by the critics. The *A.J.* described it as 'his most life-like picture', the *Academy* as 'his amusing subject, rather outré in its inevitable suggestions . . . here is a great deal of character, and plenty of well-varied grouping and minor incident', and the *Saturday Review* called it 'a happy and dramatic example of the painter's work'. The *Athenaeum* was less enthusiastic: '[it] has a good deal of "common" character, even some grotesqueness in the petitioning mendicants and the officers who award the licences to beg, but it is rather dirty in colour, and heavy in execution.' The painting gained in stature as time went by: the *A.J.* remarked on it in 1880 as 'a remarkably original work' and later still, in Burgess's obituary, in 1898, as 'his most famous picture'.

A lengthy description of the painting, written by Charlotte J. Weeks appeared in *The Magazine of Art* of 1882, when the painting was still in the possession of Thomas Taylor of the Aston Rowant Gallery, who had bought it from Burgess. The Gallery was well known to critics and the public, who were able to visit it at Aston Rowant, near Thame, Oxfordshire, every Wednesday by purchasing entrance tickets in the adjoining villages. His collection was mostly of British pictures, including works painted at different periods of the artists' careers. Some of Taylor's paintings were bought by Holloway, the most famous being Luke Fildes's *Applicants for Admission to a Casual Ward* (no. 22).

In an undated letter, written from St. John's Wood, possibly in 1887, Burgess commented: 'I fear I cannot give a very graphic account of my picture. The custom of licensing the beggars I believe extends up to the present time in Seville where my picture was studied. I made a lot of sketches of beggars there and the room may be any sort of public room used for the purpose. A man to gain the licence is supposed to be unable to work very often and they thus practise all sorts of deceits, for instance in the foreground of my picture a beggar is looking with one eye on the gains of the day. There is a famous story of these beggars in Cervantes stories published in English in London. The Magistrate or the Priest is questioning the first beggar, whom they seem to suspect.'[1]

The sketches for the beggars have not been traced.

John Bagnold Burgess came from a family of painters. His great grandfather was Thomas Burgess (fl. 1766–86) who had studied at St. Martin's Lane Academy and afterwards had his own academy in Maiden Lane. His grandfather was the portrait painter William Burgess (1749–1812) and his father, H. W. Burgess (fl. 1809–44) was landscape painter to William IV.

John Burgess went to J. M. Leigh's school in Newman Street, London, in 1848 and in 1851 began to study at the R.A. Schools where he won a first-class medal for life drawing. The year before, 1850, Burgess had first exhibited at the R.A. and he continued to do so until 1896, the year before his death.

He began his painting career with genre scenes and portraits, encouraged by the miniature painter, Sir William Ross. However, as the result of a visit to Spain, he turned from portraiture to painting almost exclusively 'Spanish' pictures. According to *The Magazine of Art*, Burgess was chiefly attracted to 'rough, ragged, dirty, sheepskin-clad, parched-up peasantry, gipsies and *contrabandistas* of the Sierra Morena, with the surroundings of the low *venta* and *posada*'.[2] He travelled frequently to Spain with Edwin Long (q.v.) to search for subjects of the type already popularised by John 'Spanish' Phillip (1817–67). Burgess made his reputation at the R.A. with his "*Bravo, Toro!*" of 1865, which shows a Spanish bull-fight crowd.[3]

[1] Royal Holloway College Archives. This letter was partially published by Carey.
[2] *Magazine of Art*, 1882, p. 134.
[3] See Arts Council, *Great Victorian Pictures*, 1978, p. 94.

BIBLIOGRAPHY
'Works of John Bagnold Burgess, A.R.A.', Art Journal, 1880, pp. 297–300.
'John Bagnold Burgess, A.R.A.', *Magazine of Art*, 1882, pp. 133–7.

4. William Collins

1788–1847, ARA 1841, RA 1820

Borrowdale, Cumberland, with Children playing by the Banks of a Brook 1823 (*pl. 65*)

oil on canvas, 34 × 44 in (86.3 × 111.7 cm)

PROV: Painted for Frederick Ripley Esq. for £157 10s; William Sharp of Endwood Court, Handsworth, Nr Birmingham; his sale Christie's 9 July 1881 (71) bt Mason £2,625.

EXH: 1823 R.A. (88) entitled *Scene in Borrowdale, Cumberland*; 1951–2 R.A. (315) *The First Hundred Years of the R.A. 1769–1868*.

LIT: *Athenaeum* 1847 p. 200; Collins, 1848 Vol. I pp. 215, 216, Vol. II p. 345.

REPR: Gaunt, 1972, pl. 34.

VERSION: *Borrowdale* 1821
oil on canvas, 30 × 25 in (76.1 × 63.4 cm)
Inscr: W. Collins 1821
Prov. Painted for William Marshall of Patterdale Hall, Ullswater for £105 as *Scene in Borrowdale, Cumberland*; bequeathed to the Guildhall by Charles Gassiot 1902.
Exh. 1821 R.A. (87)
Lit. Collins, 1848, Vol. I p. 170, Vol. II p. 345; Gustav Friedrich Waagen, *Treasures of Art in Great Britain.* 1857 Vol. IV p. 184; Temple, 1897 p. 19.
Repr. ed. G. M. Young, *Early Victorian England, 1830–1865*, 1934, Vol. II p. 150.

Collins was primarily a painter of landscape, rustic genre and coastal scenes. William Sandby described him as an artist whose attention was chiefly attracted by 'groups of children engaged in their sports . . . he studied the simple habits of country children, observed the characteristics of rural and coast scenery, and combined them together so artistically, that a purpose is evident in every group, and an individuality in every scene he painted.'[1]

The writer Wilkie Collins was William Collins's son and in 1848, the year after his father's death, he published *Memoirs of the Life of William Collins* in two volumes. He recorded some extracts from his father's diary in his biography and quoted Collins's interest and ambition as having been 'to study in the country for future figures and groupings, with the accompanying backgrounds, and to make the most accurate painting and drawing studies of any thing *in itself* a subject.'[2] Wilkie Collins described this painting somewhat lyrically as 'an inland view, with fertile wood and mountain scenery, rising high in the canvas, and a group of Cumberland children playing by the banks of a brook, that ripples into the foreground of the picture – the tone of which is bright, lively and transparent; the character of the figures being remarkably attractive, in their aspect of simplicity and truth.'[3]

William Collins kept a record of his paintings and

their buyers in *Sale Books* and this painting is recorded in his 'List of Pictures and Patrons' as finished in 1823 and painted for F. Ripley, Esq., who bought it for £157 10s.[4] The rise in the market value of Collins's works was to be notable: in 1881 Holloway was prepared to pay £2,625 for this painting.

Collins had painted a smaller version of this work two years earlier, in 1821, for William Marshall of Patterdale Hall, Ullswater.[5] It was exhibited at the R.A. of that year (87). Entitled *Scene in Borrowdale, Cumberland*, it is now in the Guildhall collection and came there from the Charles Gassiot Bequest of 1902. It has no figures in the centre middle distance and there are other minor differences. It was hanging in Marshall's London residence, 85 Eaton Square, in 1854 when Dr Gustave Waagen visited and reported in Volume IV of his *Treasures of Art* that it was in the front drawing room there. He called it 'Three Children by Some Water' and said it was 'very naive in feeling and of good keeping'. This reference to its condition may have been included because some of Collins's paintings did suffer from his using pigments which caused discolouring. His works, with their sense of peace and rustic charm, were very popular, as witnessed by the rise of prices over a moderately short period of time.

William Collins was born in London. His father was a painter and picture-restorer as well as one of George Morland's (q.v.) biographers, and it was from Morland that Collins received his first lessons. In 1807 Collins started to attend the R.A. Schools and in the same year he first exhibited at the Academy: two small landscape scenes of Millbank. In 1822 Collins married the daughter of the Scottish painter Andrew Geddes (1783–1844), and it was about this time that he painted several portraits.

Collins made a number of visits to the Continent where he painted landscapes and street scenes and it was after a stay in Italy between 1836 and 1838 that he temporarily diverted his interest to paint religious subjects and scenes from Italian life. He held the official post of Librarian to the Academy from 1840 to 1842.

[1] William Sandby, *The History of the Royal Academy of Arts*, 1862, Vol. I, pp. 366, 368.

[2] W. Wilkie Collins, *Memoirs of the Life of William Collins Esq. R.A.*, 1848, Vol. I, p. 71.

[3] op. cit. pp. 215, 216.

[4] In the first volume, dated 1818–27, MSS in Victoria and Albert Museum Library.

[5] Confusion could arise over William Marshall, see *Collected Correspondence of J. M. W. Turner*, ed. John Gage, 1980, pp. 268–9.

BIBLIOGRAPHY
Art Union, 1847, p. 137 (Obit.).
W. Wilkie Collins, *Memoirs of the Life of William Collins Esq. R.A.*, 2 vols., London, 1848, reprinted in one vol. Wakefield, 1978.
John Eagles, 'Memoir of W. Collins, R.A.', *Blackwood's Edinburgh Magazine*, February 1850, pp. 192–207.
'British Artists: Their Style and Character, No. V, William Collins R.A.', *Art Journal*, 1855, pp. 141–4.
M. A. Salvesen, *William Collins and William Mulready, the increase of child genre*, Courtauld Institute of Art, University of London, Unpublished M.A. Report, 1968.

5. John Constable

1776–1837, ARA 1819, RA 1829

Sketch for 'View on the Stour, near Dedham' c. 1821–22 (pl. 68)

oil on canvas, 51 × 73 in (129.4 × 185.3 cm)

PROV: ? 1838, 16 May Foster's sale Constable's Executors Sale (36) 'Sketch for the picture, View on the Stour' bt Morris £12 12s (for 'A Landscape' also); ? 1875, 12 June Christie's sale Thomas Woolner RA (134) *On the Stour* bt Denison £56 14s; 1883, 5 May Christie's sale J. M. Dunlop, late of Holehird, Windermere (61) bt Martin £1,249 10s.

EXH: 1937 Tate Gallery *Centenary Exhibition of Paintings and Watercolours by John Constable R.A.* (46); 1949 Lisbon and Madrid *A Century of British Painting 1730–1830* (5); 1949–50 Hamburg, Oslo, Stockholm, Copenhagen *British Painting from Hogarth to Turner* (15); 150 Venice, The Biennale, *Exhibition of Works by John Constable, Matthew Smith, Barbara Hepworth* (20); 1951–52 R.A. *The First Hundred Years of the R.A. 1769–1868* (209); 1953 Paris *Le Paysage Anglais* (12); 1956–57 New York, St Louis, San Francisco *Masters of British Painting 1800–1950*; 1960 Moscow, Leningrad *British Painting 1700–1960* (58); 1967 Montreal *Man and His World* (84); 1968–69 R.A. *Bi-Centenary Exhibition* (89); 1969 Vienna, Prague *Two Centuries of British Painting*; 1972 Paris *La Peinture Romantique Anglaise et les Pre-Raphaelites* (52); 1975 Milan *British Paintings* (142); 1976 Tate Gallery *Constable* (201).

LIT: Windsor, 1903, p. 40 and Appendix I, p. 199 and Appendix II, pp. 208–9 and Appendix III, p. 214 *Burlington Magazine*, Vol. LXIII, 1933, pp. 286–9 and repr. pl. IIA; C. R. Leslie, 1937, p. lxix, pp. 127, 137 and repr. pl. 78a; Beckett, 1952, p. 80, reprinted; Beckett, vol. VI, 1968, p. 75; Reynolds, 1960, p. 27; Reynolds, 1965, pp. 69, 148.

REPR: William Gaunt, *The Restless Century, Painting in Britain 1800–1900*, 1972, pl. 24; Taylor, 1973, pl. 79.

STUDIES: In Sketchbooks, V & A Print Room. 1831 Reynolds Cat. no. 121, p. 11 *Barges*. 1841 Reynolds Cat. no. 132, p. 52 *View on the Stour* taken from the bank below Bridge Cottage and Flatford old bridge.
Lit. Reynolds, 1960, p. 16.

ENGR: David Lucas, mezzotint, 7 × 9 in (17.7 × 25.3 cm) *The River Stour Suffolk*, 1831.
Repr. C. R. Leslie, 1937, pl. 78.
Lit. Shirley, 1930, pp. 6, 7, 155, 178, cat. no. 19 and repr. pl. XIX.

This painting is the full-size sketch for the *View on the Stour, near Dedham*, exhibited at the R.A. of 1822 (183) and at the B.I. (35) the following year, and now in the Huntington Library and Art Gallery, San Marino, California. The finished painting, together with *The Hay Wain* (ex. R.A. 1821 [339] entitled *Landscape: Noon*, National Gallery) and *Hampstead Heath* (not identified), was shown at the Paris Salon of 1824 where all three paintings had been submitted for exhibition by the Paris art dealer John Arrowsmith. *View on the Stour, near Dedham* was no. 359, as *Un Canal en Angleterre; paysage*. The success of these paintings at the Salon gained a gold medal for Constable, which was awarded to him by the King of France, Charles X. The King also presented gold medals to Copley Fielding (q.v.) and Richard Parkes Bonington (1801–28). The name of Constable 'became the battle-ground of the French critics' but the paintings were not purchased by the French nation, possibly because Arrowsmith wanted to sell *The Hay Wain* and *View on the Stour, near Dedham* together.[1]

View on the Stour, near Dedham was the fourth of six 6-ft large canvases based on scenes of daily life on the canalised river Stour. This painting depicts a part of the river upstream from Flatford Mill, between that and Flatford Lock, with Dedham Church in the distance. The first 'six-footer' was *The White Horse* (ex. R.A. [251] as *A Scene on the River Stour*, now Frick Collection, New York) exhibited at the Academy in 1819. The second large painting was *Stratford Mill* (ex. R.A. [17] as *Landscape*, Private Collection) which Constable exhibited the following year. This was followed by *The Hay Wain* (*Landscape: Noon*) in 1821. The other two canal scenes of this scale were *A Boat passing a Lock* (ex. R.A. 1824 [180], Trustees of the Walter Morrison Pictures Settlement) and *The Leaping Horse* (ex. R.A. 1825 [224] as *Landscape*, R.A. Collection, London).

Constable's working process in the *View on the Stour, near Dedham* is described in his letters to his clergyman friend, Archdeacon John Fisher, who bought Constable's first two 'six-footers', *The White Horse* and *Stratford Mill*. These letters are printed in R. B. Beckett's *John Constable and The Fishers, The Record of a Friendship*.[2] Constable referred to the sketch for *View on the Stour, near Dedham* as 'The Bridge' which is the wooden foot-bridge in the painting. His first mention to Fisher of the work is in a letter written from Hampstead, dated 20 September 1821. Constable wrote: '. . . I am so much behind hand with the Bridge, which I have great hindrances in. I cannot do it here – & I must leave my family & work in London'.[3]

Constable found that painting landscapes on this large scale was physically exhausting. In another letter to Fisher he wrote: 'Believe, my dear Fisher, I should almost faint by the way when I am standing before my large canvasses, was I not cheered and encouraged by your friendship and approbation.'[4] Again, on 23 October 1821: 'I am most anxious to get into my London painting-room, for I do not consider myself at work without I am before a six-foot canvas.'[5]

Constable was pleased with the *View on the Stour, near Dedham*, for he wrote to Fisher on 13 April 1822: 'I have sent my large picture to the Academy. I never worked so hard before & now time was so short for me – it wanted much – but still I hope the work in it is better than any I have got done – but hardly any body saw it.'[6] He wrote that William Collins (q.v.) had praised it saying 'that the sky was very beautiful and there were parts in it that could not be better'. He also mentioned that he was short of money and it was therefore vital for him to have a successful Academy picture. However, he felt that 'I hope, indeed I really believe, I have never yet done anything so good as the one now sent [to the Academy] – at least it has fewer objections than can be made to it. It is difficult to distinguish superiority in these things. Opie says of Titian – "if not the best painter he certainly has produced the best pictures in the world . . ." My conscience acquits me of any neglect of [my] last picture. I have dismissed [it] with great calmness and ease of mind.'

Constable also mentioned to Fisher the changes that took place from the sketch stage to the finished oil, since Fisher had obviously seen the sketch while on a visit in January 1822. Constable outlined these compositional differences: 'I have taken away the sail, and added another barge in the middle of the picture, with a principal figure, altered the group of trees, and made the bridge entire. The picture has now a rich centre, and the right-hand side becomes only an accessory.'

Indeed, the sketch for *View on the Stour, near Dedham* differs in composition from the finished painting in many ways. The major differences are the addition in the finished painting of a second barge alongside the one shown in the sketch and the exclusion of the two small children fishing on the bottom right in the sketch who have been replaced by a girl heading towards Bridge Cottage.

These large-scale paintings were, however, difficult to sell. It infuriated Constable that collectors still preferred to buy landscapes by Old Masters. Again he wrote to Fisher, this time in great disappointment: 'I have no patron but yourself and you are not the Duke of Devonshire – or any other great ass. You are only a Gentleman and a Scholar, and a real lover of the art, whose only wish is to see it advance.'[7]

The beginnings of Constable's ideas for the final *View on the Stour, near Dedham* can be traced to drawings in his sketchbooks of 1813 and 1814.[8] Graham Reynolds has pointed out that Constable would work out compositional problems on a small scale which he could transfer later into large-scale works, as with this painting.[9] These drawings are of two barges one of which Reynolds considers to be a possible study for the finished painting.[10] It shows a man and a boy pushing on poles both of which point down towards the bridge.

The second drawing listed by Reynolds in relation to the finished picture is in Constable's 1814 sketchbook.[11] Entitled by Reynolds *View on the Stour near Dedham*, it shows Flatford old bridge and Bridge Cottage placed as in the oil sketch here.

The catalogue of the 1951–52 exhibition held at the R.A. to celebrate its first 100 years of existence incorrectly states that the Huntington Library and Art Gallery also owns another study for the painting.[12] It is now thought that that sketch of the *View on the Stour near Dedham* is a later copy based on the David Lucas mezzotint.[13]

The sketch, and not the finished picture, was engraved by David Lucas (1802–81);[14] the engraving, entitled simply *River Stour Suffolk*, was one of a series after Constable's works published as *English Landscape* in 1831; it was finally published by Henry G. Bohn of Covent Garden in *English Landscape Scenery* (no. 14) in 1855.[15] Lucas worked for Constable from 1829 to 1837, the year of Constable's death, producing mezzotints mostly from small rough sketches (the large painting here must have been an exception) which were not painted specially for the engraver. This sketch was apparently sent to Lucas in August 1830 and returned to him later the following year after continual minor changes had been made to the plate.[16]

Following this, the painting appears to have remained in Constable's studio until the sale at Foster's carried out by order of Constable's executors in 1838. It is presumed that lot 36 'Sketch for the picture View on the Stour' is the same painting as this sketch. It was almost certainly the painting entitled *On the Stour* which appeared in the sale of the sculptor Thomas Woolner at Christie's in 1875. This painting was catalogued as 'A study for the large work in the Miller Collection at Preston'; this refers to Thomas Horrocks-Miller who was known to have owned the finished picture. Its history after this remains uncertain until Holloway purchased it in 1883.

John Constable was born in 1776 in East Bergholt, Suffolk, the son of a mill-owner whose property included the tenancy of Flatford Mill on the River Stour. In 1799 he arrived in London with an invaluable letter of introduction to the painter and diarist, Joseph Farington (1747–1821) who helped him quite considerably. Constable became a probationer in the R.A. Schools and in 1800 was enrolled as a student. His first exhibit at the Academy was in 1802, an unidentified *Landscape*[19] and it was in this year that Constable resolved (in a letter to his friend, John Dunthorne) to become 'a natural painter'. He quoted Sir Joshua Reynolds's phrase that 'there is no *easy* way of becoming a good painter' and went on to write: 'For these two years past I have been running after pictures and seeking the truth at second hand . . . I shall shortly return to Bergholt where I shall make some laborious studies from nature.' This he did: he returned to Suffolk, bought a studio in East Bergholt and began what was to become a lifetime of 'laborious studies from nature'.

In the autumn of 1806 Constable visited the Lake District where he drew his first recordings of weather conditions. He found, however, according to his biographer Leslie, that 'the solitude of mountains oppressed his spirits' and he felt more sympathetic to landscape which involved human activity.

He spent most of his time painting in Suffolk, making occasional journeys around the country to visit friends. In 1815 he exhibited *Boat building* at the R.A. (215), a canvas of 20 × 24 inches (50.8 × 60.9 cm) of which Leslie claimed: 'I have heard him say he painted entirely in the open air'. Before this, Constable had already begun his series of five large canal scenes the first of which, *The White Horse*, was exhibited in 1819. It was in 1821, the year *The Hay Wain* was exhibited, that Constable seriously started to make cloud studies whilst at Hampstead. He did them as oil sketches and called the process 'skying'.

1824 was an important year: his landscape paintings met with great success at the French Salon and were admired by Delacroix. It was also the year of his first visit to Brighton, which became one of his favourite places to work.

In 1829 he began to formulate his ideas for a series of mezzotints after his paintings by David Lucas. This became a constant enterprise and resulted in the published *English Landscape Scenery*.

The painting on which he was working in the year of his death, *Arundel Mill and Castle*, was exhibited posthumously at the R.A. (193) in their new premises in Trafalgar Square.

[1] See the Introduction, C. R. Leslie, *Memoirs of the Life of John Constable, R.A.*, 1937, p. xxxiv.
[2] R. B. Beckett, *John Constable and the Fishers, The Record of a Friendship*, 1952, and reprinted in *John Constable's Correspondence*, Vol. IV, ed. R. B. Beckett, 1968, Suffolk Records Society.
[3] Op. cit. R. B. Beckett, 1952, p. 78.
[4] C. R. Leslie, 1937, p. 108.
[5] Op. cit. p. 117.
[6] R. B. Beckett, 1952, pp. 91–4.
[7] Sydney J. Key, *John Constable; His Life and Work*, 1948, p. 61.
[8] In the Victoria and Albert Museum Print Room.
[9] Graham Reynolds, *Catalogue of the Constable Collection*, 1960, p. 16.
[10] Op. cit. no. 121, p. 11.
[11] Op. cit. no. 132, p. 52.
[12] As does H. Isherwood Kay in his *Burlington Magazine* article, 'The Hay Wain', Vol. LXII, 1933, p. 286.
[13] I owe this information to Dr Robert Wark of the Henry E. Huntington Library and Art Gallery.
[14] The finished picture was engraved slightly later as *View on the River Stour, near Dedham* by W. R. Smith for E. and W. Finden in 1840 for their *Finden's Gallery of British Art*, since the finished version was still in France, see the exhibition catalogue, *Constable*, Tate Gallery, 1976, p. 124.
[15] See Hon. Andrew Shirley, *The Published Mezzotints of David Lucas after John Constable, R.A.*, 1930, no. 19.
[16] Op. cit. H. Isherwood Kay, p. 286.

BIBLIOGRAPHY
Sir Charles J. Holmes, *Constable*, 1901.
Sir Charles J. Holmes, *Constable and his Influence on Landscape Painting*, 1902.
Lord Windsor, *John Constable R.A.*, 1903.
Hon. Andrew Shirley, *The Published Mezzotints of David Lucas after John Constable, R.A.*, 1930.
ed. Peter Leslie, *Letters from John Constable R.A. to C. R. Leslie R.A.*, 1931.
H. Isherwood Kay, 'The Hay Wain', *Burlington Magazine*, Vol. LXII, 1933, pp. 281–9.
C. R. Leslie, *Memoirs of the Life of John Constable, R.A.*, ed. and enlarged by Hon. Andrew Shirley, 1937, reprinted with Introduction by Jonathan Mayne, 1951.
S. J. Key, *John Constable, His Life and Work*, 1948.
R. B. Beckett, *John Constable and the Fishers. The Record of a Friendship*, 1952.
Michael Kitson, 'John Constable, 1810–1816: a Chronological Study', *Journal of the Warburg and Courtauld Institutes*, Vol. XX, 1957, pp. 338–57.
G. Reynolds, *Catalogue of the Constable Collection*, 1960.
ed. R. B. Beckett, *John Constable's Correspondence*, Suffolk Records Society, Vol. I, 1962, Vol. II 1964, Vol. VI, 1968.
G. Reynolds, *Constable, The Natural Painter*, 1965.
B. Taylor, *Constable, paintings, drawings and watercolours*, 1973.
R. Gadney, *Constable and his world*, 1976.
Exhibition catalogue, *Constable*, Tate Gallery, 1976.
Ian R. Fleming-Williams, *Constable: landscape watercolours and drawings*, 1976.
Robert Hoozee, *L'opera completa di Constable*, 1979.
John Sunderland, *Constable* (rev. ed.), 1981.

6. Tito Conti
1842–1924

Paying her respects to His High Mightiness (*pl. 55*)

panel, $17\frac{1}{2} \times 12\frac{1}{2}$ in (44.4×31.7 cm)

INSCR: Tito Conti

PROV: Thomas Frederick Walker of Birmingham; his sale, Christie's 21 April 1883 (85) bt Martin £157 10s.

This painting fits the description of Conti's work in the *A.J.* of 1880 more than the other two in the collection.[1] The *A.J.* commented that Conti and some of his fellow Italian painters were 'prone to 16th- and 17th-century scenes and personage; partial to roystering blades in leather doublets, with feathered hats, lace cuffs and ruffles, long stockings, trailing rapiers, and a general rakish make-up: renaissant lords and ladies, courtiers and servants, with palatial or feudal backgrounds and high life of the old aristocratic stamp, sportive maids, guzzling card-playing monks, or whatever else that serves to make up a picture that has no other *raison d'être* than the artist's fancy, backed by an ample stock of studio *bric-à-brac* properties to select from, with good male and female models at command'.

In this elaborate small-scale painting Conti depicted a lady gathering the skirt of her fine dress to curtsey to the figure of a mandarin sitting on a neo-classical pedestal and wearing a superior expression in contrast to her smiling face. Conti has included a wide range of details and has given great attention to the texture of the different paint surfaces.

[1] *Art Journal*, 1880, p. 261.

7. Tito Conti
1842–1924

Approved (pl. 54)

panel, 15 × 11 in (38 × 27.9 cm)

INSCR: Tito Conti

PROV: Thomas Frederick Walker of Birmingham; his sale Christie's 21 April 1883 (87) bt Martin £162 15s.

ENGR: Arthur L. Cox, 1936.

Conti sometimes used the same figures and the same accessories for different paintings of similar subjects. An example is found in *The Last Drop*, 1874, where he painted a similar single drinker.[1] *The Last Drop*, of almost the same proportions as *Approved*, is also on panel.

Conti has once more reduced the detailed background of the painting to concentrate on the connoisseur's approach of the contented-looking wine-taster to the glass in his hand. The painting is much more robust than the other two in this collection.

[1] This was sold at Sotheby's, 24 November 1976 (42).

8. Tito Conti
1842–1924

Good-Bye 1877 (*pl. 53*)

oil on canvas, 25 × 18 in (63.4 × 45.7 cm)

INSCR: Tito Conti 1877

PROV: Thomas Frederick Walker of Birmingham; his sale, Christie's 21 April 1883 (88) bt Martin £294.

EXH: R.A. 1878 (322).

LIT: *A.J.* 1878 p. 167; *Saturday Review* 22 June 1878 p. 791.

Of the three paintings by Conti in this collection, only *Good-Bye* was exhibited at the R.A. (where his work appeared from 1874 to 1884), and it was reviewed well by the *A.J.* of 1878. They described it as 'full of Art intelligence and sound work'. The *Saturday Review* likewise praised it for having 'all the charm of grace and of clever painting with which Continental painters are apt to invest somewhat commonplace subjects.'

The painting represents a cavalier who is leaving the weeping lady (whose dress at the waistline resembles that in *Paying her respects to His High Mightiness*), possibly for a chivalrous errand. Conti has emphasised the simplicity of her gown by contrasting it against the more complex man's costume and partially framing them both in the patterned border of the stair carpet. By contrast with *Paying her respects* Conti omitted a mass of objects for a background of a tapestry hanging and a sturdy staircase and column.

Tito Conti was born in Florence in 1842, studied painting there and later became Professor at the Florentine Academy. He exhibited in many European countries, particularly Germany and Britain, and had great success with his genre painting, particularly historical, as well as his portraits.

These three small-scale paintings came from the same collection, that of Thomas Frederick Walker of Birmingham. They represent the interest of Victorian collectors in highly-finished, theatrical costume pieces in bright colours.

9. Edward William Cooke
1811–80, ARA 1851, RA 1863

Scheveningen Beach 1839 (*pl. 28*)

oil on canvas, 18 × 36 in (45.7 × 91.4 cm)

INSCR: E. W. Cooke Redleaf Dec 1839

EXH: Agnew's 1981 (4).

PROV: Painted for William Walls of Redleaf for 500 gns; ?Foster's sale 15 February 1855 (no owner given) (48) bt Leggatt £76; G. Radford; his sale Christie's 29 April 1882 (173) bt Martin £152 5s.

STUDY: Oil on board, 12 × 18 in (35.5 × 45.5 cm) dated 1838; anon. sale Sotheby's Belgravia 15 December 1981 (44) entitled *Dutch Fishermen Selling Thornback; Shrimp Boats pushing off.*

After the signature by Cooke on the lower left-hand corner of the painting there is the inscription 'Redleaf', the home of William Wells, who commissioned the painting; it is dated December 1839. It seems likely that Cooke composed this picture from sketches made in Holland.

The fact that Scheveling was used as another name for Scheveningen leads to difficulties in tracing the history of the many pictures bearing these two place-names in their titles. Cooke kept a ledger of his paintings from 1829 to 1878 which seems to be a fairly accurate record of which works were painted for whom, when, where they were exhibited, their prices and sizes.[1] Without doubt he painted a work exhibited at the B.I. in 1840 with the title *Scheveling Sands* (174). A painting of this title, lent by E. Atkinson, appeared in the Manchester Royal Jubilee Exhibition of 1887 (749), but there is no certainty that the two works are the same. There is also a drawing of this title in the British Museum.

In Cooke's ledger the only possible painting of this period which was painted for William Wells, and could be *Scheveningen Beach*, has the wrong dimensions (38 × 26 in, 96.5 × 66 cm) and is listed as being finished in May, not December. It was entitled *Sheveling Cart and Beach*. It seems that Cooke painted different versions of this picture in 1839, with different titles, as can be seen to some degree from his diary.[2]

William Wells (d. 1847) was a well-known and popular patron and friend of many painters. He came from a family of shipbuilders and settled in Kent on his retirement; there he entertained a number of painters including Frith, Landseer, Turner and Cooke himself, who called Wells's house 'a kind of sanctuary for art and a home for artists'.[3]

Cooke was staying at Wells's house, Redleaf, at Penshurst in Kent, at the beginning of 1839. He wrote in his diary on 25 February 1839: 'Finished small panel of Scheveling'. This 'panel' may well have been the painting for William Wells finished in May of that year. Cooke recorded in his diary his work on the picture until 1 May, when he 'painted on and finished picture of Scheveling'. However, he began two more pictures of Scheveling in May, seemingly one for Lord Northwick and one bought by Sir Thomas Baring. There is further reference to a Scheveling picture later that year which must be *Scheveningen Beach*.

Cooke was again staying at Redleaf when, on 27 November 1839, he 'Painted on Mr. Wells' picture of Scheveling and finished it'. He did not return there in December; so it does seem probable that the November reference was to the painting here. It appears not to have been exhibited, nor is there any record of its having passed out of Wells's ownership through the sale-room in the three sales of his paintings which took place before 1882, when it was bought by Holloway.[4]

[1] In the Library of the Royal Academy, and quoted from with their kind permission.
[2] Transcribed by Mr John Munday of the National Maritime Museum.
[3] See John Munday, *Mariner's Mirror*, Vol. LIII, 1967, pp. 99–113.
[4] William Wells' sales were all at Christie's, 12–13 May 1848, 21–22 January 1857 and 27 April 1860.

10. Edward William Cooke
1811–80, ARA 1851, RA 1863

A Dutch Beurtman aground on the Terschelling Sands. In the North Sea after a Snowstorm 1865 (*pl. 30*)

oil on canvas, 42 × 66 in (106.6 × 167.5 cm)

INSCR: (painted on the boat) KOOK

PROV: Painted for William Leaf of Park Hill, Streatham; his sale Christie's 7 May 1875 (509) bt Agnew £483; sold by them 10 May 1875 to Edward Hermon M.P. of Wyfold Court, Henley-on-Thames; his sale Christie's 13 May 1882 (50) bt Martin £535 10s.

EXH: 1865 R.A. (595); 1979 Brighton Art Gallery (87).

LIT: *A.J.* 1865 p. 171; *Athenaeum* 20 May 1865 pp. 688–9; *I.L.N.* 20 May 1865 p. 490; *Reader* 24 June 1865 p. 719.

Formerly entitled *Dutch Ship Aground*, this picture is similar in composition to other marine works by Cooke of the mid-1860s. Two examples are *Scheveling Pincks running to anchor off Yarmouth* (ex. R.A. 1864, now in the R.A. collection) and *The Van Kook and other Dutch Fishing Smacks Trawling off Shore* of 1863.[1] *The Van Kook* relates to the painting here which has the inscription 'KOOK' on the bows of the boat – the Dutch for Cooke's own name.

The picture was painted for William Leaf, whose name appears in Cooke's ledger for 1865. Unfortunately no title is listed, but only 'Royal Academy 1865'. Cooke exhibited three other marine subjects at the B.I. of that year: *Dutch Fishing Craft off Dordrecht* (133), *Pilot Boats off the North Forland* (139) and *French Fishing Craft, mouth of the Seine* (150).

In his diary for 1865, the one reference to William Leaf is on 27 March: 'My Birthday ... Mr Leaf came in aft. and his son Leaf and Wife, they bought my large picture and 3 of the Venetian subjects!!!' The painting was later in the collection of Edward Hermon, M.P. for Preston, from whose collection Holloway bought eight works, including Edwin Long's *The Babylonian Marriage Market* and *The Suppliants*.

The reviews of the Royal Academy exhibition of 1865 varied. Cooke had been elected an R.A. two years before and the *A.J.*, in an unfair reference to this, stated that the picture was executed 'with firmer hand [than before], yet in colours we miss the tempered harmony of grey, green, and blue, which the elder Academician transfuses into sea and sky.' The *I.L.N.*, having praised the 'drawing of the labouring craft' as 'admirable', went on to say: 'On the whole, however, it is not quite so favourable an example as some of its predecessors ... we should say that his method of painting the sea in motion requires revision: for example, convexity in waves, even breakers, is, we suspect, more rarely seen.'

In contrast to the *Athenaeum* ('it requires a great deal more than this to make a good picture'), the *Reader* praised the painting as 'one of the few pictures of which

we may be proud as the work of an English artist'.

Edward William Cooke was born in London, the son of George Cooke (1781–1834), a well-known landscape engraver. From his own account, we know that he attended 'Mr. Stark's [Chelsea] and he gave me my first lesson in painting [a small coast scene]' and later commenced his career 'with the oil brush'.[2] He was a draughtsman for Pugin and is also said to have worked for Clarkson Stanfield (q.v.), making detailed studies of ships.[3] Cooke obviously enjoyed working on details, was a keen scientist with a special interest in botany, and was elected to the Linnaean Society in 1855. His father had taught him to engrave and he assisted him with illustrations for his *London and Its Vicinity* of 1820; he followed this with his own *Shipping and Craft* of 1827 with 65 etched plates. This was followed by his work for *Botanical Cabinet*, a publication which ran from 1817 to 1833. He was also a talented watercolourist.

In 1846–7 Cooke went to Italy for 15 months; on another visit to Venice in 1851, he made friends with Ruskin, who wrote to his own father that year that Cooke was 'the smallest clever man I ever knew ... full of affection, most unselfish ... full of accurate and valuable knowledge in natural history ... he is the most curious mixture of conceit and humility I ever met.'

In 1851 Cooke was also involved in the plans for the Great Exhibition and later became a director of the Crystal Palace Company. He was a regular exhibitor at the R.A. and became a Fellow of the Royal Society in 1863, a Fellow of the Zoological Society in 1865 and a Fellow of the Society of Antiquaries in 1876.

Cooke's preoccupation with the sea often led him to the coasts of Belgium and Holland which provided material for paintings such as the two here, which represent both the beginning and the end of his painting career. He also travelled to Spain in 1860–61, and to Egypt in 1873–74 for a sketching tour. Engravings from drawings made on his foreign tours were published as *Landscapes, British and Foreign* in 1874 and *Leaves from my Sketch-Book* in two volumes, 1876 and 1877.

The success of his work enabled Cooke to employ the architect, Richard Norman Shaw, who designed a house for him in Kent, Glen Andred at Groombridge, built in 1867–68, and a London house, at Hyde Park Gate, built in 1871.

[1] In Sotheby's sale of 9 April 1974 (37) and repr.
[2] Written on a note stuck in his ledger, in the Library of the Royal Academy.
[3] See Andrew Saint, *Richard Norman Shaw*, Yale University Press, 1976, p. 443.

BIBLIOGRAPHY
James Dafforne, 'British Artists: Their Style and Character, Edward William Cooke, RA, FRS', *Art Journal*, 1869, pp. 253–5.
E. W. Cooke, *Landscapes, British and Foreign*, 1874.
E. W. Cooke, *Leaves from my Sketch-Book*, 1876 and 1877.
Portfolio, 1880, p. 36 (Obit.)
John Munday, 'E. W. Cooke, marine painter', *Mariner's Mirror*, Vol. LIII, pp. 99–113.
Exhibition catalogue, 1970, Guildhall Art Gallery.

11. Thomas Sidney Cooper

1803–1902, ARA 1845, RA 1867, CVO 1901

Landscape with Cows and Sheep 1850 (*pl. 74*)

oil on canvas, 25 × 32 in (63.4 × 81.2 cm)

INSCR: T. Sid[y] Cooper ARA 1850

PROV: John Prescott Knight RA; his sale Christie's 2 July 1881 (100) bt Thomas £273.

EXH: ? Birmingham (n.d.); 1981 Agnew's (5).

LIT: Sartin, 1976 p. 62, Cat. no. 79.

12. Thomas Sidney Cooper

1803–1902, ARA 1845, RA 1867, CVO 1901

Landscape with Sheep and Goats 1856 (*pl. 59*)

oil on canvas, 35 × 50 in (96.4 × 126.9 cm)

INSCR: T. Sidney Cooper RA 1856

PROV: ? Purchased Daniel Lee at Royal Manchester Institution 1858; William Sharp of Endwood Court, Handsworth, nr. Birmingham; his sale Christie's 9 July 1881 (69) bt Mason £546.

EXH: 1858 Royal Manchester Institution (228).

LIT: Sartin, 1976 p. 64, Cat. no. 137.

These two paintings by T. S. Cooper are characteristic of much of his work. Animal painting was the only subject matter in which, it seems, Cooper had any interest.

Cooper was born in Canterbury and, at 11, began to study painting. He started his career by working for a coach-building firm and then by painting stage scenery, but by 1823 he was in London, initially spending his time copying in the British Museum and then, two years later, learning to paint at the R.A. Schools. He left there to return to his native Canterbury and become a drawing master. He then went to Brussels in 1827, where he was employed again as a teacher and befriended the contemporary Belgian animal painter Eugene Joseph Verboeckhoven (1799–1881), whose work greatly influenced him. His contact with the Dutch school, especially 17th-century animal painters (e.g. Paulus Potter), was also important for his work.

Cooper returned to settle in London in 1831 and began to exhibit at the R.A. two years later with a painting entitled *Landscape with Cattle* (319); he continued to exhibit his work there without interruption until his death in 1902, a total of 266 works. Cooper's concentration on painting animals, especially cows and sheep, led him to making his studies from life. In London, during the 1830s, he spent much time drawing in Regent's Park, where animals were grazed. He also studied animals at Smithfield Market. In 1848 he received a commission from Queen Victoria to paint the Victorian Jersey cows at Osborne.

Cooper painted very few figure subjects. Amongst these was his entry for the Palace of Westminster competition in 1847 when he submitted *Defeat of Kellerman's Cuirassiers by Somerset's Cavalry Brigade at Waterloo, June 18, 1815* (Williamson Art Gallery, Birkenhead), which was well received but failed to win a prize. From about this time until 1860 Cooper painted in the cattle for other painters, including Frederick Richard Lee (1798–1879) and Thomas Creswick (q.v.)

During the 1850s Cooper moved to the country to breed his own stock to paint from. In 1865 he established a drawing school at Canterbury and later, in 1872, gave the town a school and a gallery called the Sydney Cooper Gallery of Art.

The 1870s were one of the most successful decades for Cooper and he painted some of his best pictures in that period, among them his famous work *The Monarch of the Meadows* (ex. R.A. 1873 [680], now in a Private Collection). His work inevitably began to decline in his old age, but his tenacity to his subject and his regular contributions to the R.A. exhibitions, and their success, must be seen as a singular achievement.

BIBLIOGRAPHY
'Memoir of T. S. Cooper, ARA', *Art Journal*, 1849, pp. 336–7.
James Dafforne, 'British Artists: Their Style and Character, No. LV, Thomas Sidney Cooper ARA', *Art Journal*, 1861, pp. 133–5.
T. Sidney Cooper, *My Life*, 2 vols., 1890.
Art Journal, 1902, p. 125 (Obit.)
'Thomas Sidney Cooper, RA, 1803–1902', *Magazine of Art*, 1902, pp. 272–5.
E. Keble Chatterton, *T. Sidney Cooper RA, His Life and Art*, 1902.
Stephen Sartin, *Thomas Sidney Cooper, CVO, RA, 1803–1902*, Leigh-on-Sea, limited edition, 1976.

13. Thomas Creswick

1811–69, ARA 1842, RA 1851

The First Glimpse of the Sea 1850 (*pl. 64*)

oil on canvas, 40 × 60 in (101.5 × 152.3 cm)

INSCR: T. CRESWICK 1850

PROV: Sam Mendel of Manley Hall 1870; bt by Agnew 22 Sept. 1873; sold by them to Baron Albert Grant 8 Dec. 1873 for £2,750; his sale Christie's 28 April 1877 (157) bt Agnew £1,102 10s; sold by them to William Lee 15 May 1877; his sale Christie's 26 May 1883 (60) bt Martin £1,312 10s.

EXH: 1850 R.A. (258); 1873 London Int. Ex. (1320).

LIT: *Annual Register* 1850 p. 64; *A.J.* 1850 p. 169; *Athenaeum* 25 May 1850 p. 559; *Critic* 1 August 1850 p. 382; *Examiner* 11 May 1850 p. 294; *I.L.N.* 1 June 1850 p. 398; *Spectator* 4 May 1850 p. 427; *The Times* 4 May 1850 p. 5; *A.J.* 1870 p. 154; Chesneau, 1885, p. 129; Temple, 1897 p. 208; *A.J.* 1908 p. 106 and repr.

There was no mention in the exhibition catalogue for the 1850 R.A. exhibition that Creswick had been assisted with this work. However, *The Times* sale report in 1883,[1] when the painting was purchased by Holloway, stated that the figures had been painted by P. F. Poole (q.v.) and the sheep had been painted by Richard Ansdell (q.v.).[2] There is no further evidence to support this, and there was no mention at the time in contemporary reviews of any collaboration on the picture.

The reviews were encouraging; the *I.L.N.* reported that 'There is no painter who is making more rapid strides in his art than Mr. Creswick. He is engrafting his own beautiful style on certain excellences which Mr. Linnell renders with a grace and feeling till now peculiarly his own . . . [this picture] is our own, and, as we observe, the public favourite of the five [of the paintings exhibited that year by Creswick].' The *Athenaeum* commented: 'The passing gleam of light is here, however, rendered with closest observation and with a beauty of means that is the painter's exclusive possession.'

In 1897 A. G. Temple wrote of it that it 'instances perhaps more clearly than others the total absence of exaggeration from his works' and that although Creswick had 'an extremely difficult foreground to deal with . . . it is skilfully brought into harmony with the tenderly painted mountains in the distance and the brilliant glimpse of sun-touched sea'.

This painting was one of the three in the collection of Sam Mendel of Manley Hall, and it came to Holloway via the famous collections of Baron Albert Grant and William Lee.[3]

[1] *The Times*, 28 May 1883, p. 10.
[2] W. Roberts, *Memorials of Christie's*, 1897, Vol. II, p. 52, report of the sale stated that John Phillip had painted them.
[3] For Sam Mendel, see no. 71 Clarkson Stanfield's *The Battle of Roveredo*.

14. Thomas Creswick

1811–69, ARA 1842, RA 1851

Trentside 1861 (*pl. 67*)

oil on canvas, 45 × 72 in (114.2 × 182.8 cm)

INSCR: THOs CRESWICK

PROV: John W. Marshall of Great Barr, Staffs. in 1873; his sale Christie's 28 May 1881 (43) bt Thomas £2,100.

EXH: 1861 R.A. (305) as *Trentside: a recollection*; 1873 London Int. Ex. (1403) as *View on the Trent*; 1981 Agnew's (6).

LIT: *Athenaeum* 11 May 1861 p. 634; *Examiner* 25 May 1861 p. 329; *Saturday Review* 1 June 1861 p. 559; *Spectator* 18 May 1861 p. 530; *The Times* 13 May 1861 p. 6; Temple, 1897 p. 208; *A.J.* 1908 pp. 106–7.

? STUDY: 14 × 18 in (35.5 × 45.7 cm)
Prov. James; Agnew purchased *On the River Trent* from him for £210, 27 May 1871; Agnew sold to Charles P. Matthews of Mayfair and Havering-atte-Bower, Essex, 17 June 1871 £120; his sale Christie's 6 June 1891 (21) *A River Scene* with church and figures bt Smith £58 16s.

When this painting was exhibited in the Academy in 1861, it was entitled *Trentside: a recollection* and it was stated that the cattle in the picture were painted by J. W. Bottomley. The scene represented is possibly a view of Clifton Hall and St Mary's Church in Nottinghamshire.[1]

Among the three works which Creswick exhibited at the Academy that year was one entitled *In the "North Countrie"* (111) (untraced) and both it and *Trentside* were acclaimed by the critics. *The Times* described them as 'two of this favourite painter's largest and best works' and the *Spectator* commented that *Trentside*, although larger, 'is equally commendable for its freedom from meretricious trickery'.

The *Athenaeum* was particularly enthusiastic about *Trentside*: it 'holds a place upon the walls by its brightness and cheerful airiness, and may be taken as a valuable hint to our ordinary landscape painters on the advantages of introducing a far larger amount of sky than is commonly practised . . . Mr. Creswick's work shows a bright and gleaming river flowing through a champaign [sic] country . . . A certain icy clearness, which can hardly be styled coldness, pervades this work. There are objections somewhat technical in their nature, and not intended to depreciate the many delightful qualities of this artist's works, of which the picture before us is an admirable specimen.' Indeed

Trentside is considered one of Creswick's best works.

An article in *Blackwood's Magazine* in the same year commented that Creswick's landscapes 'are essentially English in subject and in sentiment. And then, moreover, in the best sense of the word, they are academic – free from all false pretence and affectation – free from clap-trap effects, and from those lower pictorial tricks by which inferior artists seek popular sensation. They are academic also in quiet, unobtrusive propriety of manner: nature comes before us with a modest bearing – no black thunder in the sky or tumultuous earthquake on the ground, but a landscape placid in deportment.'

Neither of these two paintings by Creswick lost their appeal. The article in the *A.J.* of 1908 praised them both very highly, especially *Trentside*, and mentioned in particular the accuracy of the detail and 'loving, conscientious care very different from the sloppy paintiness we nowadays affect'.

Thomas Creswick was born in Sheffield and studied under John Vincent Barber in Birmingham. He moved to London in 1828 and immediately began to exhibit at the B.I. and the R.A. His paintings were a great success during his lifetime and although Ruskin had reservations about Creswick's ability to paint trees (his chapter 'Of Truth of Vegetation' in *Modern Painters*), he respected him as 'a man who has sought earnestly for truth' and because 'he is one of the very few artists who *do* draw from nature, and try for nature'. He painted almost exclusively landscapes, either English or Welsh, and he particularly liked to paint water into them. He also did etchings and book illustrations.

Graham Reynolds wrote of Creswick in *Victorian Painting* that he was 'more a continuer of the traditions of Glover than of Constable . . .' and that his 'work stands out . . . by its integrity and power of construction. He diversifies the generally thin painting of his canvasses in a restrained yet homogeneous tone, with moss-like patches of impasto which, in the context, have the same quality as the relief on Samuel Palmer's early watercolours.'[2]

Creswick often incorporated into his pictures figures or animals painted by his friends. Amongst those who worked with him were Frith, Elmore, Cooper, Ansdell and Bottomley.

Creswick's popularity can be gauged by the fact that 109 of his works were exhibited with those by John Phillip in a separate section of the International Exhibition in London in 1873, with a catalogue written by T. O. Barlow RA.

[1] I owe this suggestion to Mrs J. Tate of Nottingham who kindly answered a letter, appealing for suggestions as to the whereabouts of this view, published in *Country Life* of 19 April 1980 Vol. CLXVII, p. 1203.
[2] Graham Reynolds, *Victorian Painting*, 1966, p. 152.

BIBLIOGRAPHY
'British Artists: Their Style and Character, No. XIV, Thomas Creswick R.A.', *Art Journal*, 1856, pp. 141–4.
Art Journal, 1870, p. 53 (Obit.)
C. Collins Baker, 'Thomas Creswick, R A., and Mid-Victorian Landscape Painters', *Art Journal*, 1908, pp. 104–7.

15. Follower of Crome
A Woodland Scene (*pl. 63*)

panel, 31 × 48 in (78.7 × 121.9 cm)

INSCR: J Crome 1813

PROV: W. Fuller Maitland of Stanstead Hall, Essex by 1875; his sale Christie's 10 May 1879 (79) bt Graves 340 gns entitled *Group of Oaks on a Sandy Bank with a white heifer in the foreground*; purchased from Graves 6 August 1881 for £550 by Thomas Holloway.

EXH: 1875 R.A. Winter Old Masters Exhibition (41).

This painting has been considered to be by John Crome (1769–1821; known as Old Crome) ever since it was in the Fuller Maitland collection where it was known to have been in 1875 when it appeared in the R.A. Winter Exhibition as owned by him. It was bought by Holloway from the dealer Graves of Pall Mall as by Crome but its authenticity is now in doubt. There is a notable lack of references to it in published work.

A similar painting appeared in an important sale of Crome's work at Christie's on 1 May 1858. According to Derek and Timothy Clifford, who made no mention of the Royal Holloway College painting, this was the collection of James Sherrington of Yarmouth,[1] who collected works by Crome between 1835 and 1863. The catalogue entry for number 24 in the Sherrington sale

was entitled 'A LANE SCENE' and reads: 'A thickly wooded landscape; to right hand, an outlet enlivened by a gleam of sunshine; in foreground, to left, a white cow browsing and a peasant on horseback. Rich and powerful in tone, and excellent in composition – on panel.' There was no mention of a signature and date on the painting and it would seem certain that they were added later. The picture was bought in at 120 guineas. The Cliffords described it as 'clearly one of the most important pictures in the sale [which] has not since been recognised'.

The Cliffords claim that the Sherrington sale contained pictures which belonged to Louis Huth, a dealer who had purchased a number of Cromes from Sherrington's widow; and that among the 23 paintings which Huth owned, there were some not by Crome, although they had in all possibility been originally acquired from Sherrington.[2] In the sales held by Huth at Christie's between 1862 and 1872, no paintings by Crome were included. The Cliffords suggested that Huth would have been responsible for the attribution of all these paintings to Crome: 'We are inclined to believe that what happened was that certain genuine Cromes in the Sherrington Collection, being in poor condition, were copied (with improvements) by John Berney Crome [Crome's eldest son], perhaps also by Robert Ladbrooke and Bristowe, and that these pictures were sold, probably in good faith as "versions by other hands" to such as Huth who were less scrupulous to make clear that the goods they passed on were not autograph.'

Writing of the works in the Fuller Maitland collection in 1921, Collins Baker stated: 'Another large picture, called "Oaks, Sandy Bank and White Heifer", which, though lost to sight, sounds equally dubious'.[3] He had not seen the painting, for, in an appendix, he listed it as a canvas, with the simple comment that it was 'doubtful'.[4]

Collins Baker, writing about the large number of so-called Crome paintings, stated that 'The date of this factory's chief industry [of Crome imitations] must have been about 1830–60. It has been alleged, with what base of truth we cannot now decide, that Joseph [sic] Sherrington, whose sale was in 1858, co-operated

with J. B. Crome in producing unauthentic Cromes . . . It is therefore clear that within forty years of Crome's death a steady business had been done in spurious works, which were craftily insinuated even into fine collections.'

After careful consideration, Dr Miklos Rajnai, formerly of the Castle Museum, Norwich, has suggested that this painting is definitely not by Crome but by either a pasticher or a copyist, although it does contain elements which demonstrate that the painter followed Crome's technique closely. Mr Andrew Hemingway has kindly put forward the theory that this painting could be a record of a lost Crome composition with additions.[5]

[1] Derek and Timothy Clifford, *John Crome*, 1968, p. 275.
[2] Op. cit. p. 277.
[3] Charles H. Collins Baker, *Crome*, 1921, p. 59.
[4] Op. cit. p. 155.
[5] I am particularly grateful to Dr Rajnai and Mr Hemingway for their advice and help with this painting.

16. Henry Dawson
1811–78

Sheerness, Guardship saluting 1875 (*pl. 25*)

oil on canvas, 32 × 50 in (81.2 × 126.9 cm)

INSCR: 18 Ɗawson 75; on verso: Sheerness The Flagship 'Duncan' Saluting HDawson 1875.

PROV: Henry Dawson; his sale of remaining works Christie's 25 March 1882 (512) bt Martin £577 10s.

EXH: 1978 Nottingham University Art Gallery (61); 1981 Agnew's (7).

LIT: Dawson, 1891 p. 107; Williams, 1978 p. 31.

Dawson had two sons who were marine painters. One of them, Alfred, wrote a biography of his father which was published in 1891. The inscription on the verso confirms that it is the work listed in Dawson's biography under 'Principal Pictures of 1875' as *The Duncan Saluting – Sheerness*. This painting was included in the sale of remaining works of Henry Dawson's studio held at Christie's four years after his death, having been painted only three years previously. The guardship is apparently saluting the Royal Yacht, seen billowing steam to the far right.[1]

Henry Dawson was born in Hull and was brought up in Nottingham. He worked firstly in a lace factory and then, about 1835, he took up painting. Although mostly self-taught, Dawson took some lessons from the landscape painter J. B. Pyne (q.v.). He went to Liverpool in 1844, where he began to attend the life class of the Academy in the following year; he became a member in 1847 until 1852, having moved to live in Croydon in 1850. It was in Liverpool that Dawson became chiefly interested in landscape and marine painting; many of his works were very large and therefore not popular with the Hanging Committee of the R.A., who 'skied' them or rejected them altogether. Dawson entered the Palace of Westminster competition in 1847 but his *Charles I raising the Standard at Nottingham* (Nottingham Castle Museum and Art Gallery) did not win a prize and was bought by a Liverpool art dealer.

In 1850 Dawson apparently appealed to Ruskin for advice as to whether he should continue with his painting career. Ruskin recommended him to continue and Dawson achieved more success. However, recognition did not come to him until much later and he was never elected an Associate or Member of the Royal Academy.

In 1853 Dawson moved to live in Thorpe, near Chertsey, Surrey, not far from the Royal Holloway College. Both the College and the Holloway Sanatorium were mentioned later by Alfred Dawson, who wrote of the area that 'It is little altered, but Mr. Holloway's big buildings, and certain new and not beautiful houses, interfere greatly with the old feeling of the place'.[2] By the mid-1850s, Dawson's work had gained new strength and greater acclaim, particularly his *The New Houses of Parliament, Westminster* (Private Collection) which was exhibited at the B.I. in 1858 (539). In 1862 Dawson moved again, this time to Chiswick, where he lived for the rest of his life.

In 1878, the year of Dawson's death, at the opening of the Castle Museum, Nottingham, an entire room was devoted to 57 of Dawson's paintings, which was considered a great success. By this time his works were commanding high prices and had become very popular.

[1] See Heather Williams, exhibition catalogue *Henry Dawson*, Nottingham University Art Gallery, 1978.
[2] Alfred Dawson, *The Life of Henry Dawson, Landscape Painter 1811–1878*, 1891, p. 66.

BIBLIOGRAPHY
Art Journal, 1879, p. 48 (Obit.)
Portfolio, 1879, p. 24 (Obit.)
Alfred Dawson, *The Life of Henry Dawson, Landscape Painter, 1811–1878*, 1891.
H. C. Marillier, *The Liverpool School of Painters*, 1904, pp. 114–18.
Henry Dawson Centenary Exhibition, 1978, Nottingham University Art Gallery.

17. Henry Thomas Dawson
Born *c.* 1842 *fl.* 1860–78

Salcombe Estuary, South Devon 1882 (*pl. 58*)

oil on canvas, 30 × 42 in (76.1 × 106.6 cm)

INSCR: *D*awson, 1882

PROV: Henry Dawson; his sale of remaining works Christie's 25 March 1882 (489) bt Martin £152 5s.

Henry Thomas Dawson was the eldest son of Henry Dawson (q.v.) and the older brother of Alfred, who was also a marine painter and wrote the biography of Henry Dawson. H. T. Dawson was taught painting by his father in Nottingham.

He exhibited mostly marine paintings between 1860 and 1873 at the R.A., the B.I. and the Society of British Artists.

This painting is one of the latest in date in the collection and came from the same sale of paintings at Christie's of the remaining works of the late Henry Dawson, as *Sheerness, Guardship saluting*.

18. Edwin Ellis
1841–95

The Harbour Bar (*pl.27*)

oil on canvas, 16 × 30 in (40.6 × 76.1 cm)

INSCR: E. ELLIS

PROV: John Burr R.W.S.; his sale Christie's 23 April 1883 (53) bt Martin £111 6s.

This painting is characteristic of the work of Ellis, a marine and landscape painter who worked mostly in London.

Edwin Ellis was born in Nottingham, the son of a lace manufacturer. At the age of 15, he went to work in a lace factory; after five years he turned to painting, studied with Henry Dawson (q.v.) and afterwards went to France.

He settled in London in the 1860s and regularly contributed to exhibitions of the Society of British Artists and sometimes at the R.A. The majority of his works were seascapes, painted mostly on the coasts of Yorkshire, Wales and Cornwall. He painted in watercolour as well as in oil.

In 1893 Nottingham Museum honoured Ellis with a large comprehensive exhibition of 84 of his paintings. His early death prompted the *A.J.* to write: 'his sudden death at the age of fifty-four has carried him off before he had even yet accomplished all that had been hoped of him'.[1]

[1] *Art Journal*, 1895, p. 191.

BIBLIOGRAPHY
Exhibition catalogue, 1893, Nottingham Art Gallery.
Art Journal, 1895, p. 191 (Obit.)

19. Alfred Elmore
1815–81, ARA 1845, RA 1857

The Emperor Charles V at the Convent of Yuste 1856 (*pl. 47*)

oil on canvas, 48 × 66 in (121.8 × 167.5 cm)

INSCR: Alfred Elmore 1856

PROV: T. Barker 1862; Sam Mendel of Manley Hall 1870; bt by Agnew 22 Sept. 1873; sold by them to Baron Albert Grant 8 Dec. 1873 for £2,750; his sale Christie's 28 April 1877 (171) bt Agnew £1,260; sold by them to William Lee 15 May 1877; his sale Christie's 26 May 1883 (62) bt Martin £1,417 10s.

EXH: 1856 R.A. (175); 1862 London Int. Ex. (683); 1951–52 R.A. *The First Hundred Years of the R.A. 1769–1868* (322); 1981 Agnew's (8).

LIT: *Annual Register* 1856 p. 111; *A.J.* 1856 p. 165;

Athenaeum 1856 p. 621; *Examiner* 3 May 1856 p. 278; *I.L.N.* 10 May 1856 p. 514; *Literary Gazette* 10 May 1856 p. 259; *Saturday Review* 24 May 1856 p. 79; *Spectator* 17 May 1856 p. 534; *The Times* 3 May 1856 p. 9 and 12 May 1856 p. 12; *A.J.* 1857 p. 115; *A.J.* 1870 p. 209; *Portfolio* 1881 p. 54; Ruskin, 1902 ed. pp. 49–50.

REPR: Cook & Wedderburn, 1903–12, Vol. XIV p. 56.

VERSION: oil on canvas, 46½ × 64 in (118 × 162.4 cm)

Inscr. A. Elmore 1856

Prov. Henry McConnel 1870; sold by Robert Taylor Heape to Rochdale Museum in 1911 for £100.

Exh. 1878 Manchester Royal Institution (100).

Lit. A.J. 1870 p. 287.

STUDY: 18 × 24¾ in (45.7 × 62.8 cm)

Prov. Henry McConnel; his sale Christie's 27 March 1886 (24) bt Vokins £267 15s; J. Vavasseur of Blackheath and Kilverstone Hall, Thetford; his sale Christie's 23 April 1910 (28) bt Lister.

When this painting was exhibited at the R.A. in 1856, it was accompanied by a long quotation, from Sir William Stirling-Maxwell's *The Cloister Life of the Emperor Charles the Fifth*, which explains the subject matter of the painting in detail.[1] It depicts the last days of the Emperor Charles V, who retired to the monastery at Yuste, near Placencia, Spain, in 1556, taking with him his favourite pictures. The painting shows the moment when the Emperor, sitting in an open loggia, is being shown two works by Titian: the portrait painted posthumously in 1548 of his beloved wife, the Empress Isabella, and the *Trinity* (Gloria) of *c.* 1551–54 (referred to by Charles V as *The Last Judgement*), both of which are now in the Prado. The two paintings appeared in the Yuste Inventory of 1558 following Charles V's death.

The subject had already been painted by William Maw Egley (1826–1916) three years earlier and exhibited at the R.A. (327),[2] with the same title as Elmore's but with the addition of the date (31 August, 1558) and with the same quotation from Stirling-Maxwell. According to the *A.J.* review of the 1853 R.A. exhibition[3] and Egley's own catalogue of his paintings, Charles V was depicted seated in a long black velvet robe in contemplation of the same pictures as in Elmore's painting. Egley stated that 'Mr. Stirling [he later became Stirling-Maxwell] gave me some valuable information to aid me in my researches.'[4]

While the R.A. reviews of the painting were enthusiastic about Elmore's work, Ruskin, in his *Academy Notes*, was more reserved. He described it as 'One of the works still belonging wholly to the old school. There is a good deal of fair painting in it, but an extraordinary missing of the main mark throughout . . . the walnut-tree is grey, not green; the air, judging by the look of it, cannot be perfumed by anything but paint; and there is no sunshine anywhere, while the whitish light, which is given for it, shines not over the tree into the gallery, but from the back of the spectator. The exhibited pictures, by Titian (!) are greyer than all the rest. Charles must have bought them from an exceedingly dishonest dealer.'

The comments in the 1856 journals were an interesting mixture. The *A.J.* remained consistently in favour of the painting: 'The work is however a composition of great power; the subject is the best the artist has ever entertained, and he has done it ample justice.' In the following year they were even more complimentary: 'For originality of treatment and powerful colouring, [it] must be considered as the artist's *chef-d'oeuvre*.' The description of the Mendel collection in the *A.J.* of 1870, although misquoting the date as 1865, commented that they had 'always regarded [it] as the most complete of Mr. Elmore's productions. The title scarcely indicates the subject, which, as an expression of sentiment, has a profound and touching interest.'

The *Athenaeum* called Elmore's paintings generally 'such as engravers revel in and the public purchase. There is nothing to dazzle and astonish, but everything to calmly delight.' They described the painting as one which was 'treated as a gentlemanly, scholarly, well-read, picturesque artist would treat so good a subject . . . In colour and composition, apart from greater depths of Art, this is a most excellent work.' Many of the reviews concentrated their remarks on the high quality of the representation of the dying emperor and the fact that Elmore had not attempted to sentimentalise the figure. The *I.L.N.* commented on this and on the textures of the fabric with: 'The Figure of the Emperor is a most happy creation. Never has senility with strength been better exhibited. You see what is passing through the old man's mind – observe, too, the action of his feet. You see the cushion on which they rest bending beneath their pressure . . . When was velvet – not new, but of various ages – painted more truly?'

The Emperor Charles V at the Convent of Yuste was considered one of the best historical paintings at the Academy that year.

Alfred Elmore painted mostly historical subjects and had a great sense of the romance of history. He was an Irishman, born in Clonakilty, Co. Cork, the son of a retired army surgeon of the 5th Dragoon Guards. He went to London aged about 12 and started his career by learning to draw from sculpture in the British Museum. In 1833 he entered the R.A. Schools and later went to live in Paris and then Munich, visiting Rome to study the Old Masters and returning home in the early 1840s.

Elmore took his subject matter from English, French and Italian history and from literary sources, including Shakespeare. He also painted episodes from contemporary life, which sometimes proved more popular than his history paintings. He was an excellent water-colourist and was compared by Martin Hardie to Bonington and Delacroix.[5]

William Sandby in *The History of the Royal Academy of Arts* wrote of Elmore that 'he groups his figures with ease and grace, draws with great correctness and force, and colours richly'.[6]

Elmore died in London having been thrown off his horse.

[1] Sir William Stirling-Maxwell, *The Cloister Life of the Emperor Charles the Fifth*, 1891 ed., p. 340 (first published 1852). This was quoted in full by Carey.

[2] The painting, 42 × 60 in (106.6 × 152.4 cm), was sold by Egley to Tooth's but has not been traced.

[3] *Art Journal*, 1853, p. 146.

[4] MSS in the Victoria and Albert Museum Library.

[5] Martin Hardie, *Water-Colour Painting in Britain, II: The Romantic Period*, 1967, p. 187.

[6] William Sandby, *The History of the Royal Academy of Arts*, Vol. II, 1862, p. 304.

BIBLIOGRAPHY

'British Artists: Their Style and Character, No. XXIII, Alfred Elmore R.A.', *Art Journal*, 1857, pp. 113–5.

Art Journal, 1881, p. 95 (Obit.)
Portfolio, 1881, p. 54 (Obit.)
Magazine of Art, 1881, p. xvii (Obit.) in 'Art Notes'.
W. G. Strickland, *Dictionary of Irish Artists*, Dublin and
London, Vol. I, 1913, pp. 322–33.

20. Thomas Faed

1826–1900, ARSA 1849, HRSA 1862, ARA 1861, RA 1864,
retired RA 1893

Taking Rest 1858 (*pl. 43*)

oil on canvas, 33 × 25 in (83.7 × 63.4 cm)

INSCR: Faed 1858

PROV: Bought by Gambart from Faed 1859 as *The
Sailors Beacon* for £250; sold by Agnew to John
Farnworth of Woolton, nr. Liverpool 27 Oct. 1860 as
The Sailor's Return; his sale Christie's 19 May 1874
(97) bt Agnew £945 as *Mother and Child: The Weary
Travellers*; sold by them to Edward Hermon M.P. of
Wyfold Court, Henley-on-Thames, Oxfordshire, 26
June 1874; his sale Christie's 13 May 1882 (57) bt
Martin £745 10s.

EXH: 1858 Gambart's French Gallery, 120 Pall Mall
Winter Ex. (44); 1981 Agnew's (9).

LIT: *A.J.* 1858 p. 354; *Athenaeum* 30 Oct. 1858 p. 559;
I.L.N. 27 Nov. 1858 p. 508; *Literary Gazette* 30 Oct.
1858 p. 567.

This painting was first exhibited as *The Fisherman's
Beacon* at Gambart's French Gallery in Pall Mall in
1858.[1] There is, indeed, a boat seen in the distance
across the water on the left-hand side of the painting.
Agnew's listed it as *The Sailor's Return* in their
Daybook of 1860 and when it was sold in 1874 by John
Farnworth, the title had been changed again to *Mother
and Child: The Weary Travellers*. Some time between
then and 1882, when Holloway bought it, the painting
had become *Taking Rest*. There are two letters in the
College Archives concerning this picture. The first
letter from Faed simply states: 'My pictures change
their names so often after they leave my studio that I
can't remember "Taking Rest". If you will describe it I
may remember.'[2] This sums up the difficulties caused
by the constantly changing nomenclature of paintings,
which occurred so frequently in the 19th century. In his
second letter Faed wrote that 'it was called "The
Fisherman's beacon"'.[3]

Faed often used his sister Susan as a model for his
paintings of young girls and consequently many of his
works of this type tend to be similar.[4] The critics of
Gambart's Winter Exhibition of 1858 were moderately
complimentary about the picture. The *I.L.N.* perhaps
summed up best, with the description of a 'buxom,
homely-looking woman with a chubby, healthy child,
sitting by a cottage near the shore. There is an air of
content and comfort about them which is pleasant to
contemplate, and the colouring, so clear and pure, is in
happy keeping with the sentiment.' The *Literary
Gazette* called it 'a good example of his bolder style' and
the *Athenaeum* described it as 'more than usually
conventional. This is a mere study of a full-faced
model, pleasantly coloured with drapery thrown into a
conventional balance of light and shade.'

Thomas Faed was the younger brother of the painter
John Faed (1820–1902), and of James Faed
(1821–1911) a mezzotint engraver. Thomas was born at
Barlae Mill, Kirkcudbrightshire, the son of a mill
wright and engineer. He studied painting in
Edinburgh, firstly with his brother John and then at the
Trustees' Academy with Sir William Allan and
Thomas Duncan. He was a member of the painters'
club founded in 1848, called The Smashers, which was
re-assembled in London 15 years later as the Auld Lang
Syne Club, by which time it included, among others,
Erskine Nicol (q.v.).

Faed achieved considerable success in his own time;
his painting of *The Mitherless Bairn* (National Gallery
of Victoria, Melbourne, Australia) was greeted with
enormous enthusiasm at the R.A. exhibition of 1855.[5]
He had settled in London in 1852 and until the early
1890s, when he retired because of failing eye-sight, he
was a regular exhibitor at the R.A. His subjects were
mostly medium scale, sentimental scenes of Scottish
rural life, many of which were regarded with great
admiration for being what Caw described as 'simple
and sincere . . . worthy of respect, if not of high
admiration'.[6]

W. M. Rossetti was in the minority when he wrote in
1867 that he was 'dextrous, and often with an intrusive
air, tending to the affected in sentiment, and the silly in
humour'.[7] A contrary view of his work was put forward
by the *A.J.* of 1872, whose praise read: 'With greater
ease and rapidity of touch than that of the Scottish
Hogarth [that is, Wilkie], he has also combined a more
artistic conception, and a happier rendering, of rustic
female beauty than it has fallen to the lot of many
painters to attain. Domestic poetry, expressed in
characteristic forms, and in harmonious colour; such is
the character of the scene depicted by Thomas Faed . . .
Faed's rustics are, indeed, the rustics of poetry. They
are but rarely to be met with in these days of economic
improvement. But the rarer they become, the more
cause have we of gratitude to the artist who has given a
painter's immortality to a goodly type of British rural
life.'[8]

Thomas Faed's *Scrapbook* notes that *Taking Rest*
was purchased from him by the dealer Ernest Gambart
for £250, and also mentions a sketch which was sold to
another dealer, Huth, for £30.[9] This sketch has not
been traced.

John Farnworth of Woolton, Liverpool, who owned
the painting from 1860 to 1874, was a worthy patron of
the arts and typical benefactor to his native town and
was described in glowing terms, especially for 'helping
artists when they needed help'.[10]

[1] I am grateful to Mr Jeremy Maas for drawing this to my
attention and for pointing out the references to it.
[2] Dated 27 October 1896.
[3] Dated 10 March 1897. These two letters were in response
to Carey's appeal for information about the painting.
[4] I am grateful to Mrs Mary McKerrow for sharing her
research on Faed.
[5] See Arts Council, *Great Victorian Pictures*, 1978, pp. 33–4.
[6] Sir J. L. Caw, *Scottish Painting, Past and Present
1620–1908*, 1908, p. 165.
[7] William Michael Rossetti, *Fine Art, Chiefly Contemporary*,
1867, p. 151.
[8] *Art Journal*, 1872, p. 220.
[9] In the Department of Prints and Drawings, National
Gallery of Scotland.
[10] *Art Journal*, 1874, p. 221.

BIBLIOGRAPHY
James Dafforne, 'Thomas Faed R.A., H.R.S.A.', *Art Journal*,
1871, pp. 1–3.

'The Engraved Works of Thomas Faed', *Art Journal*, 1872, p. 220

'Our Living Artists: Thomas Faed, R.A.', *Magazine of Art*, 1878, pp. 92–5.

R. Walker, 'Thomas Faed R.A.', *Good Words*, 1885, pp. 305–8.

ed. Wilfrid Meynell, *The Modern School of Art*, 4 vols., 1886–88, pp. 227–32.

Walter Armstrong, 'Scottish Painters X', *Portfolio*, 1887, pp. 227–34.

Marion Hepworth Dixon, 'Thomas Faed, R.A.', *Magazine of Art*, 1893, pp. 268–75.

Magazine of Art, 1900, pp. 564–70 (In Memoriam).

Sir James L. Caw, *Scottish Painting Past and Present, 1620–1908*, Edinburgh, 1908, pp. 164–6.

David Faed MacMillan, *The Artists Faed*, (five copies for private circulation), 1965.

David and Francina Irwin, *Scottish Painters at Home and Abroad, 1700–1900*, 1975, pp. 300–3.

Mary McKerrow, The Faeds, 1981.

21. Anthony Vandyke Copley Fielding

1787–1855

Travellers in a Storm. Approach to Winchester 1829 (*pl. 66*)

oil on canvas, 40 × 50 in (101.5 × 126.9 cm)

INSCR: Copley Fielding 1829

PROV: William Sharp of Endwood Court, Handsworth, nr. Birmingham 1862 (bought by his agent for £240); his sale Christie's 9 July 1881 (70) bt Mason £3,150.

EXH: 1829 R.A. (397); 1981 Agnew's (10).

LIT: *Literary Gazette* 1829 p. 378; *The Times* 12 July 1881 p. 4; *A.J.* 1906 p. 298.

The Times report of the sale at Christie's of William Sharp of Handsworth, Birmingham, stated: 'This is the highest price ever paid at auction for a work by this painter [the price was £3,150] and is attributable in great measure to the rarity of his pictures in oil colours, of which this was a large and singularly effective one.'[1] Indeed this painting, exhibited at the R.A. in 1829, was one of 17 which Copley Fielding exhibited there between 1811 and 1842. He worked mostly in water-colours and on them he built his reputation. The 17 oil paintings were all landscapes, seascapes or views of buildings. From 1810 onwards the bulk of his work, 40 or 50 watercolours a year, was shown at the (Old) Watercolour Society of which he became a member in 1813 and President from 1831 until his death in 1855.

His achievements in both media were pointed out in the *Literary Gazette* review of the 1829 R.A. exhibition, where this painting was shown as *Distant View of Winchester: a shower passing off*. 'It is seldom that we find an artist equally successful in two distinct branches of his profession. We have frequently expressed our high opinion of Mr. Fielding's talents in water-colours; and we have now the pleasure to speak as favourably of him in oil. The effect in this picture is singularly true, and nearly approaches to the sublime.'

Ruskin, in *Modern Painters* (1843), focused on Copley Fielding's qualities concisely. He believed he had enough potential to be one of the leading artists of his time. 'My own sympathies and enjoyments are so entirely directed in the channel which his art has taken . . . many who, like myself, have derived more intense and healthy pleasure from the works of this painter than of any other whatsoever; healthy, because always based on his faithful and simple rendering of nature, and that of very lovely and impressive nature, altogether freed from coarseness, violence, or vulgarity.' Ruskin particularly praised Copley Fielding's 'most perfect and faultless passages of mist and rain-cloud which art has ever seen. Wet, transparent, formless, full of motion, felt rather by their shadows on the hills than by their presence in the sky.' His skies 'will remain . . . among the most simple, unadulterated, and complete transcripts of a particular nature which art can point to.'

Copley Fielding was one of the best known and most popular of the drawing masters of his time. He had studied under his father Nathan Theodore Fielding and John Varley (1778–1842). He was awarded a medal for his work shown at the Paris Salon of 1824 with Constable and Bonington, but, like Constable, he never went abroad. Among Copley Fielding's best works are those set in the Sussex Downs, or depicting lakes and mountains in Scotland, the North of England or Wales.

Shortly after acquiring this painting in 1881, Holloway bought from dealers three watercolours by Copley Fielding: one English and two Scottish landscapes. There is a record of his selling the two Scottish landscapes the following year and the English one was sold later by his relations. There is no evidence whether Holloway wanted them for his private collection or for the College, but they are the only instance of his collecting watercolours.

[1] *The Times*, 12 July 1881, p. 4.

BIBLIOGRAPHY

Art Journal, 1855, p. 108 (Obit.)

John Ruskin, *Modern Painters*, 1897 ed., Vol. I, pp. 103–7, 264–6.

'Two Pictures by Copley Fielding', *Art Journal*, 1906, pp. 298–9.

S. C. Kaines Smith, 'Anthony Vandyke Copley Fielding', *Journal of Old Watercolour Society*, Vol. III, 1925 26, pp. 8–30.

22. Sir (Samuel) Luke Fildes

1844–1927, ARA 1879, RA 1887, KB 1906, KCVO 1918

Applicants for Admission to a Casual Ward 1874 (*pl. 5*)

oil on canvas, 54 × 96 in (137.1 × 243.7 cm)

INSCR: Luke Fildes 1874; on verso: '*Applicants for admission to a casual ward*' by Luke Fildes London.

PROV: Bought from the artist by Thomas Taylor of Aston Rowant Gallery, Oxfordshire for £1,250 (with copyright); his sale Christie's 28 April 1883 (71) bt Martin £2,100 (with copyright).

EXH: 1874 R.A. (504); ?1874 Liverpool Autumn Exhibition; 1876 Philadelphia Int. Ex. (45); 1878 Paris Expo. Univ. (73); 1892 Guildhall (8); 1928 R.A. Winter Ex. (280); 1939 London County Hall *Jubilee Exhibition*; 1965 Ottawa N. G. *Prints and Drawings by Victorian Artists in England* (38); 1968–69 R.A. *Bi-Centenary Exhibition* (311); 1970 V. & A. *Charles Dickens Exhibition* (1.67); 1981 Riverside Studios, Hammersmith, London *Victorian Paintings At Riverside* (23); 1981 Agnews (11).

LIT: *The Academy* 2 May 1874 p. 500 and 23 May 1874 p. 585; *A.J.* 1874 p. 201; *Athenaeum* 2 May 1874 p. 602 and 30 May 1874 p. 740; *Examiner* 25 July 1874 p. 802;

Graphic 9 May 1874 p. 455; *I.L.N.* 9 May 1874 p. 446; *Manchester Courier* 27 May 1874 p. 6; *Saturday Review* 2 May 1874 p. 562 and 23 May 1874 pp. 653–4; *Spectator* 9 May 1874 p. 597; *The Times* 26 May 1874 p. 6; *Portfolio* 1878 p. 65; *Blackwood's* Oct. 1878 p. 463; *Mag of Art* 1880 p. 51 and repr. p. 41 reprinted in Meynell, 1883 pp. 106–9 and repr. p. 107; *Mag. of Art* 1882 p. 310; Chesneau, 1885 p. 286; Quilter, 1892 pp. 314, 317 and repr. opp. p. 316; Croal Thompson, 1895 pp. 2–6, 26–7, 32 and repr. p. 5; Temple, 1897 p. 341; Frederic G. Kitton, *Dickens and His Illustrators*, 1899 pp. 207, 215–16; Reynolds, 1953 pp. 28–9, 94 and repr. pl. 84; Fildes, 1968 pp. 24–7 and repr. p. 51; Maas, 1969 pp. 235, 238 and repr. p. 239; Linda Nochlin, *Realism*, 1971 p. 154 and repr. pl. 89; *Connoisseur*, Vol. 185 1974 pp. 34–5 and repr. no. 3; Arts Council, *English Influences on Van Gogh*, 1974–5 pp. 33, 34 and repr. p. 24; Forbes, *R.A. Revisited*, 1975 p. 50; *Victorian Social Conscience* Ex. Catalogue, N. S. Wales, Sydney, 1976 pp. 11–12; John Sunderland, *Painting in Britain, 1525–1975*, 1976, pp. 39, 224 and repr. pl. 147; Wood, *Panorama*, 1976 pp. 52–3 and repr. pl. 45.

REPR: Wood, *Dictionary*, 1971 pl. 267; L. C. B. Seamen, *Life in Victorian London*, 1973 detail p. 43; Quentin Bell, *Victorian Artists*, 1967 pl. 97.

STUDY: Original sketch, 24 × 45½ in (60.9 × 115.5 cm) Retained by Luke Fildes; his sale Christie's 24 June 1927 (2) bt Sir Aston Webb £16 16s.

REPLICA: oil on canvas; 22½ × 37 in (57.1 × 93.9 cm) after 1908.

Prov. Retained by Luke Fildes; his sale Christie's 24 June 1927 (5) bt Gooden & Fox £57 15s; F. W. Wignall J.P. of The Rookery, Tattenhall, Cheshire; his sale by order of his executors following his widow's death 1958; by 1960 Sir Leonard Stone O.B.E.; his sale Christie's 10 July 1970 (152) bt Maas £1,680; Tate Gallery.

Exh. 1960 Manchester City Art Gallery *Works of Art from Private Collections in the North West and North Wales* (172).

Houseless and Hungry

LIT: Arts Council, *Vincent van Gogh*, 1968 no. 141, p. 96; ed. Margaret Cardwell, *The Mystery of Edwin Drood*, 1972 Intro. p. xxi–ii and Appendix E; Arts Council, *English Influences on Van Gogh*, 1974–75, pp. 39, 40, 44, 51 and repr. p. 58.

REPR: *The Graphic* 4 December 1869 No. I, Vol. I p. 9 repr. in *Graphic Portfolio* No. 2 1876.

The idea for this painting has a long and interesting history. The *Graphic*, a highly popular periodical founded by William Luson Thomas, used an illustration by Fildes in their first issue of December 1869. This was a woodcut engraving entitled *Houseless and Hungry*. According to a letter from Fildes 'the promoters of an illustrated newspaper eventually published as 'The Graphic' desired me to draw anything that in my opinion would suit the proposed Journal and in the June of that year I made a drawing of an incident I saw in the streets one winter's night when I first came to London in '63'.[1] *Houseless and Hungry* was published in the *Graphic* with a commentary, of which this extract is part: 'It is by virtue of that Act [the Houseless Poor Act] that the group before us will obtain food and shelter tonight . . . they present themselves at a police station and ask for a ticket for admission to the casual ward of a workhouse. This is always given them . . . The figures in the picture before us are portraits of real people who received the necessary order for admission on a recent evening . . . All these people, with many others, received tickets, and were admitted into the casual ward of one of our great workhouses a few minutes after this sketch was taken.'

Sir Paul Fildes, the son of Luke Fildes, explained his father's sympathy for the poor as 'due to the fact that he was brought up by his grandmother who was the Mrs Mary Fildes who was on the platform with Henry Hunt at the Peterloo Massacre of 1819. She was President of the female reformers of Manchester.'[2]

In that same year, 1869, Charles Dickens was in the process of publishing his novel, *Edwin Drood*, in monthly parts. Until 1867 he had commissioned Hablôt Browne ('Phiz') to work on his major book illustrations but Browne became paralysed in that year and Marcus Stone, who had illustrated *Our Mutual Friend* (first published 1864–65), had given up black-and-white illustration to concentrate on oil painting.

Dickens's new illustrator was Charles Alston Collins, who began on *Edwin Drood* in September 1869 but in December had to stop on the grounds of ill-health. Accounts vary as to exactly how Fildes came to be chosen in Collins's place. It seems that it was through Millais, who was staying with Dickens at Gad's Hill when the *Graphic*, containing Fildes's *Houseless and Hungry*, arrived.[3] On seeing the illustration 'Millais rushed into Dickens' room waving the paper over his head exclaiming "I've got him" – "Got who?" said Dickens. "A man to illustrate your Edwin Drood." Millais spread the paper on the desk in front of Dickens. "Who is the artist?" said Dickens. "A rising young man on the staff of *The Graphic*" said Millais. "Yes, I'll write to him" Dickens said. Fildes showed the letter to me. It ran, "I see from your illustration in *The Graphic* this week that you are an adept at drawing scamps, send me some specimens of pretty ladies." Fildes did so, and was invited to Gad's Hill.'

Edwin Drood remained unfinished owing to Dickens's unexpected death. Fildes exhibited two illustrations for the novel in the R.A. exhibition of 1870 (854). His attachment and sense of bereavement for Dickens are illustrated by the engraving which he carried out for the Christmas 1870 number of the *Graphic* entitled *The Empty Chair, Gad's Hill Ninth of June 1870*, the painting of which was exhibited at the R.A. in 1871 (628). It was at this time that Fildes abandoned black-and-white illustration.

The history of *Applicants for Admission to a Casual Ward* was told by Fildes himself after Dickens's death, which, he said 'perhaps made me turn my attention to painting sooner than I should have done and being desirous of painting 'The Casuals' I consulted Sir John Millais (then Mr) and by his advice I took[?] of some other subject that might gain some experience . . . I, however, began it in '72 and eventually it was exhibited in the Royal Academy of '74 with the title of "Applicants for Admission to a Casual Ward" considerably modified from the original drawing.'[4]

Fildes continued with how he 'used to ramble about a great deal on winter evenings visiting the Police Station where the applicants assembled with the hope of getting an order for the district workhouse and the people ranged themselves against the wall of the Police Yard taking up their stations in the order in which they arrived – Of course the earlier arrivals had the better chance, though the Inspectors used their discretion in selecting those for reasons they thought most deserving, and, in many cases no provision whatever was made to shelter the people from the inclement weather during the weary time of waiting . . . I used, on these occasions, to study the types of the people and the different incidents and select those I wanted for my picture make appointments with them, usually for the following day, to come to my studio – many a time in returning home late I have noticed my friend [sic] hanging about in my street having been unsuccessful in getting into the Casual Ward, and, I suppose feeling I was the only connecting link with existence, they were magnetically drawn to the place of appointment some 9 or 10 hours before they knew they would be wanted . . . It was a deeply interesting, yet most painful picture for me to work on for so long – for I made many more studies than appear in the picture enough for a much larger picture, my material being boundless . . .'[5]

According to L. V. Fildes's biography of his father, the figures were definitely painted from life in Fildes' studio and the idea of the man with the child on his knee which he used in *The Widower* (ex. R.A. 1876, now at Sydney Art Gallery, Australia) originated from an incident during one of the sittings for the *Applicants*.[6] The 'big old Boozer', the large central man with the top hat 'for whom a pint mug of porter at his feet, replenished at intervals by the pot-boy from the nearest pub, was an ample inducement' according to Fildes's son 'had always to be put in quarantine by being made to stand on sheets of brown paper sprinkled with Keating's Powder'.

In the R.A. catalogue for the 1874 exhibition Fildes quoted, from the not as yet published *The Life of Dickens* by John Forster,[7] an extract from a letter which Dickens had written to Fildes describing a visit to a Whitechapel workhouse on 8 November 1855, when the casual ward was full and there was no help for any of the people. The extract which Fildes quoted was 'Dumb, wet, silent horrors! Sphinxes set up against that dead wall, and none likely to be at the pains of

solving them until the general overthrow'.

Such was the overwhelming interest of the public in the painting during the R.A. exhibition that the picture had to be railed off and a policeman posted beside it to guard it from being crushed by the enthusiastic crowds. For them this was a most unusual work. The R.A. public would have been intent on reading it closely and studying every detail of a side of life about which they knew nothing. Fildes himself wrote of it 'it is one to be looked at and thought over'.[8]

The backdrop of the picture reinforces the poignancy of the hardship and poverty. Fildes perhaps deliberately included bitterly satirical posters on the wall: under a notice offering a reward of £20 for a Pug Dog, is one advertising a reward of £2 for a missing child, £50 for a murderer and £100 for one 'Absconded.' All the posters are intended to heighten the irony of these people's lot: one to the right reads 'ROYAL ARTILLERY WANTED SMART YOUNG MEN'.

The moods portrayed are generally subdued. The only sense of aggression comes from a snarling dog at the feet of the man in pin-striped trousers and the policeman who is giving directions to him. The woman in the foreground, one child in her arms and another clutching her shawl, was probably inspired by Fred Walker's *The Lost Path* (ex. R.A. 1863 [712], Private Collection). Her group is the most distinctly painted of all the figures.

The composition of the initial *Houseless and Hungry* was not much altered by Fildes to achieve *Applicants for Admission to a Casual Ward*. He added several more figures and widened and deepened the space of the picture to give a better 'view' of the street in which they are standing. He also included much more detail and gave the scene a greater sense of movement than he had allowed in the engraving. He himself had reservations about the work. It was, after all, only the third oil painting he was to exhibit at the Academy. This apprehension was expressed in a letter to his grandmother: 'I am hard at work in London and have been all this summer on my big picture for next year's Royal Academy. I am anxious about it's [sic] success. I want it to be one very much, as so much depends on it. It is a very important work and like all things that are

pretentious if they are not very successful they have corresponding failure – But I hope for the best. It promises well now and I have six more months to do all I know on it – The owner of my first one is anxious to have this one also.'[9]

A cutting from the magazine *Fun* was added to a grangerised copy of a R.A. catalogue for the 1874 exhibition by Caleb Scholefield Mann.[10] Under the authorship of 'Tymkyn RA' it ridicules *Applicants for Admission to a Casual Ward*, giving it the title 'Fly Paupers'. Mann noted that in a *Punch* issue of 1870, there was an illustration by Charles Keene entitled *Police Tyranny* based on a similar idea to Fildes's *Houseless and Hungry* and added 'so much for the originality of Comic Papers'.[11] This scene does indeed illustrate 'Murder' and 'Missing' posters and men lined up outside a Police Station with a policeman talking to one of the men who has jumped the queue.

The engraving of *Houseless and Hungry* and the painting made a great impact on Vincent van Gogh. In a letter to his brother Théo of 7 January 1882 he described how he 'discovered' Fildes's illustration of *Houseless and Hungry* to which van Gogh referred with varying titles: 'I bought them from Blok, the Jewish book dealer, and for 5 guilders I chose the best from an enormous pile of *Graphics* and *London News*. There are things among them that are superb, for instance, "The Houseless and Homeless" by Fildes (poor people waiting in front of a free overnight shelter)'.[12] In another letter of the same year, van Gogh recounted to Théo how Dickens had found Fildes to illustrate *Edwin Drood* for him. Van Gogh was obviously very moved by Fildes's black-and-white work and may well have adopted his idea for *Gauguin's Chair* of 1888 from Fildes's illustration of Dickens's empty chair at Gad's Hill.[13] A copy of that number of the *Graphic* was in van Gogh's possession.

The critics' reception of the painting at the R.A. exhibition of 1874 was mixed. For the most part they were enthusiastic, although some, such as the one writing in the *Athenaeum*, changed their minds between issues (2 May and 30 May). The *Athenaeum* wrote first that the painting was a 'painful, but not morbid, scene from London Life . . . it is not a pleasant work, but far from being a repulsive one. On the contrary, its genuineness is proved by its simplicity . . . Morally and socially speaking, this is the picture of the year. Its appeal is so powerful and its art so good, that we, whose theme is Art only, hasten to pay our tribute to the painter.' However, four weeks later, they had become considerably more cautious: 'We must not admit that it does not improve on acquaintance. Although the subject allows abundance of incident and contrasts of character, we are compelled to feel that there are too many incidents, and too great a number of contrasts of character. The picture is like an epitome of the woe and misery of London in squalor. It was not thus that Hogarth, in his finer works, impressed us. The design, fine as it is, recalls a scene in a theatre rather than anything else.'

There were those with doubts, such as the *Spectator*, who wondered if 'mere misery like this is a fitting subject for pictorial treatment'. The *Saturday Review* too thought it 'a mistake in choice of subject and a misdirection of time and talent' and: 'The worst of the matter seems to be that, when a painter is lost in emotion, he is lost to art also.'

The most vituperative comment came from the *Manchester Courier* who wrote of 'unnecessary and unnatural exaggeration . . . [the figures] are repulsive in the extreme and quite belong to the chamber-of-horrors style of art . . . they simply appal and disgust without doing the slightest good to humanity or making it more merciful . . . As regards technical execution this work is far inferior to Mr. Fildes' usual degree of care and observation . . . we turn from his work in disgust and regret the vicious experiment'.

Most of the other reviews were complimentary. *The Times* commented that Frank Holl's painting *Deserted* [(487) formerly in the collection of Captain Hill of Brighton] 'suffers from the neighbourhood of the still more sensational drama of Mr. Fildes' "Casuals"'.[14] In fact Fildes had written to Henry Woods about the news that Holl had painted a picture of a policeman with a foundling: 'It does not put me out in the least to know that he has done the same subject for when I care to paint it I should do it. He and I would look very differently at the thing I am sure.'[15]

The most concise and interesting of all the published criticism came from the *A.J.* 'This is the most notable piece of realism we have met with for a very long time. The painter has shirked nothing, he has set down the facts as he found them, and has as a result, produced the most startling impression of all wayward and unlovely reality. These deformed and wretched creatures who wait for admission to a wretched resting-place, are only admissible into art that is indifferent to beauty . . . We think Mr. Fildes has taken the only sincere course possible with a subject of this kind. He has made no attempt to make his picture pretty: he has, in truth, deliberately left it horrible and weird, but so much of artistic taste as there was room for he has bestowed upon the work. The arrangement of the different figures is as artistic as the subject permitted, the colour is quiet and in harmony . . . that admission leaves unsettled the larger question of the subject's fitness for art at all. We have no doubt that if these phases of human misery are to be perpetuated on canvas, Mr. Fildes has chosen the highest and most straightforward method of interpretation. Their use, if they have a use, is moral rather than artistic, and for the purposes of morality no picture can be too truthful or exact. But looking now, as we are bound to do, only to considerations purely artistic, there is little in a theme of such grovelling misery to recommend it to a painter whose purpose is beauty. These accidents of civilisation, regrettable enough in themselves, are not, therefore, of very profound significance for the artist, whose works are meant to endure, and whose thoughts should be of a kind that we can bear to have with us always. A picture cannot be shut up and put away like a book, and therefore a subject in painting which cannot always make an impression of satisfying beauty is so far unfitted for the purpose of artistic expression. To this extent we think Mr. Fildes' choice is indefensible. The state of things he represents to us ought rather to be removed than to be perpetuated, and its introduction into art which should be permanent is rather a matter for regret.'

Luke Fildes had studied painting as a pupil teacher at the Art School in Warrington, where, according to his son, he may have met his patron Thomas Taylor, who purchased *Applicants for Admission to a Casual Ward*.[16] From there Fildes won a scholarship to the South Kensington School of Art (now the Royal College of Art) and later moved to the R.A. Schools. He began his career with black-and-white illustrations for journals such as the *Cornhill Magazine* and *Once a Week*. *Applicants for Admission to a Casual Ward* brought Fildes considerable recognition and his genre paintings which followed also became famous through engravings. These 'social realism' works included *The Widower*, *The Return of the Penitent*, 1879 (City Hall, Cardiff), *The Village Wedding*, 1883 (not traced) and *The Doctor* of 1891 (Tate Gallery).[17]

Fildes's visit to Italy in 1874 with his wife (sister of the painter Henry Woods [1846–1921] who lived mostly in Venice) prompted him to paint subjects based on sentimentalised genre scenes of Venetian life, which form a considerable contrast to his paintings depicting life at its more raw moments of hardship and poverty. However, they proved very popular (for example, *Venetians*, which was exhibited at the R.A. in 1885 [Manchester City Art Gallery]).

In the mid-1880s Fildes turned to painting portraits almost exclusively. He exhibited a total of 119 portraits, at the Academy, which also proved extremely popular, and he was entrusted with the royal portrait commissions starting with the *Princess of Wales* in 1893 (National Portrait Gallery), followed by *Edward VII* in 1902, *Queen Alexandra* in 1905 and *George V* in 1912; these last three are in the Royal Collection. Fildes was knighted in 1906 and created a KCVO in 1918. His success and a legacy from his grandmother enabled him to commission a house in Melbury Road, Kensington, from Richard Norman Shaw (built from 1875 to 1877).[18]

In 1928, the year following Fildes's death, many of his paintings were exhibited in the Winter Exhibition at the R.A.

[1] Royal Holloway College Archives, letter addressed to Carey, dated 1 June 1888.

[2] In a letter to Graham Reynolds, dated 10 June 1970, Victoria and Albert Museum Library.

[3] According to a letter from W. H. Chambers to Howard Duffield, dated and quoted in the Introduction of *The Mystery of Edwin Drood*, ed. Margaret Cardwell, 1972.

[4] Royal Holloway College Archives, letter addressed to Carey, dated 1 June 1888, as quoted above.

[5] There is a typed manuscript in the Victoria and Albert Museum Library written by Sir Paul Fildes, entitled 'Catalogue Raisonné of the Published Reproductions of Luke Fildes's Drawings' which was revised in 1965. The existence of this manuscript was kindly brought to my attention by Professor Paul Walton of McMaster University, Hamilton, Ontario, who, at the time of going to press, was preparing an article on the painting. A number of drawings in Fildes's possession on his death have recently been discovered and are to be published by B. Myers in *Apollo*, July 1982, as 'Studies for *Houseless and Hungry* and the *Casual Ward* by Luke Fildes R.A.'.

[6] L. V. Fildes, *Luke Fildes, R.A.: A Victorian Painter*, 1968, p. 25.

[7] Finally published that year by Chapman and Hall in Vol. III, pp. 53–4.

[8] In a letter to Henry Woods dated 12 June 1874, in the Victoria and Albert Museum Library.

[9] In a letter to his grandmother of 30 September 1873, in the Victoria and Albert Museum Library, and quoted by L. V. Fildes. It is not clear who Fildes referred to. His first oil painting exhibited at the Royal Academy was *Fair, Quiet, and Sweet Rest* in 1872 (997, Corporation of Warrington) with a quotation from Tennyson. This was purchased by the dealer McLean rather than Thomas Taylor, the purchaser of *Applicants for Admission to a Casual Ward*.

[10] In the Department of Western Art, Ashmolean Museum, Oxford.

[11] *Punch*, 17 December 1870, p. 260.

[12] *The Complete Letters of Vincent van Gogh*, 1958, Vol. I, p. 302. no. 252.

[13] See exhibition catalogue, Arts Council, *Vincent van Gogh*, 1968–69, (141).

[14] For an illustration of the engraving of *Deserted* from the *Graphic*, see the exhibition catalogue, Arts Council, *English Influence on Vincent van Gogh*, 1974–75, p. 36, entitled *The Foundling*.

[15] In a letter of 1 December 1874, in the Victoria and Albert Museum Library.

[16] Taylor also owned Fildes's *The Widower* and a number of paintings which were finally bought by Holloway – namely *Licensing the Beggars* (no. 3) by Burgess (which hung opposite Fildes's *Applicants* at Aston Rowant), *Relatives in Bond* (no. 28) by Hodgson, *Sympathy* (no. 63) by Riviere, *Leaving at Low Water* (no. 32) by Hook, *A Street in Cairo* (no. 66) by Roberts and *The Banker's Private Room* (no. 33) by Horsley.

[17] See Arts Council, *Great Victorian Pictures*, 1978, p. 36.

[18] See Andrew Saint, *Richard Norman Shaw*, Yale University Press, 1976, p. 153.

BIBLIOGRAPHY

W. W. Fenn, 'Luke Fildes A.R.A.', *Magazine of Art*, 1880, pp. 49–52. Reprinted in: ed. Wilfrid Meynell, *Some Modern Artists and their Work*, 1883, pp. 103–9.

David Croal Thompson, 'The Life and Work of Luke Fildes, R.A.', *Art Annual*, 1895, pp. 1–32.

Memorial Exhibition catalogue, 1928, Royal Academy.

L. V. Fildes, *Luke Fildes, R.A.: A Victorian Painter*, 1968.

23. William Powell Frith

1819–1909, ARA 1845, RA 1852

Retired 1890, CVO 1908

The Railway Station 1862 (*pl. 6*)

oil on canvas, 46 × 101 in (116.7 × 256.4 cm)

INSCR: W. P. Frith fec[t] 1862.

PROV: Painted for Louis Victor Flatow for £4,500, agreed in 1860; sold by him to Henry Graves and Co. with copyright for £16,300, 1863; bt from him by Holloway for £2,000, 16 April 1883.

EXH: 1862 April to September, Flatow's Gallery, 7 The Haymarket and at Messrs. Hayward & Leggatt, Cornhill and then travelled over the country; 1872 London International Exhibition (73); 1876 Philadelphia (48); 1878 Paris, Exposition Universelle (78); 1911 R.A. Winter Exhibition (37); 1924 Wembley, *British Empire* (W.21); 1934 R.A. Winter Exhibition (626); 1960 Moscow and Leningrad, *British painting 1700–1960* (79); 1964 Victoria and Albert Museum, *The Growth of London A.D. 63–1964* (G.24); 1971 Guildhall Art Gallery, *London and the Greater Painters* (32); 1971 South London Art Gallery, *Mid Victorian Art Draughtsmen and Dreamers* (82); 1978 Arts Council, *Great Victorian Pictures* (15); 1979–80 Munich, *Two Hundred Years of English Painting 1680–1880* (372); 1981 Agnews (12).

LIT: *I.L.N.* 8 December 1860 p. 545, 22 December 1860 p. 584; *A.J.* 1861 pp. 61, 351; *Athenaeum* 1861 p. 122; *Critic* 1861 p. 190; *Fraser's Magazine* 1861 pp. 591–2, reprinted in William Michael Rossetti, *Fine Art, Chiefly Contemporary*, 1867 pp. 2, 265–71; *I.L.N.* 9 March 1861 p. 225, 12 October 1861, p. 365; *A.J.* 1862 pp. 95, 122–3, 147, 210, 241; *Athenaeum* 1862 pp. 502–4, 535; *Critic* 1862 pp. 397–8; *I.L.N.* 18 January 1862 p. 63, 8 March 1862 p. 245, 3 May 1962 p. 457, 20 September 1862 p. 310, 11 October 1862 p. 391; *The Times* 19 April 1862 p. 5; *Athenaeum* 1863 pp. 17, 51, 83, 113; *A.J.* 1869 p. 159; *A.J.* 1872 p. 224; *Magazine of Art* 1879 p. 82; Chesneau 1885 p. 286; ed. Wilfred Meynell, *The Modern School of Art*, 1886–88 p. 146; Frith, 1887 Vol. I, pp. 327–35; Temple, 1897 p. 152; ed. J. W. Gleeson White, *The Master Painters of Britain*, Edinburgh, 1898 and repr. p. 31; Cook and Wedderburn, 1903–12 Vol XXII, p. 338; Panton, 1908 p. 119; J. E. Pythian, *Fifty Years of Modern Painting*, 1908 p. 313, 335; Sacheverell Sitwell, *Narrative Pictures*, 1937 p. 116 and repr. pl. 118; Reynolds, 1953 pp. 24–5, 59 and repr. pl. 19; Nikolaus Pevsner, *The Englishness of English Art*, 1955 p. 25 and repr. pl. 14; ed. N. Wallis, 1957 pp. 104–5, 107; Raymond Lister, *Victorian Narrative Paintings*, 1966 pp. 23, 155 and repr. pl. 21; Graham Reynolds, *Victorian Painting*, 1966 p. 33; Maas, 1969 pp. 112, 113, 117, 164, 195; Linda Nochlin, *Realism*, 1971 p. 152 and repr. pl. 88; Jeremy Maas, *Gambart, Prince of the Victorian Art World*, 1975, pp. 135–9, 157; Wood, *Panorama*, 1976 pp. 207–11 and repr. pl. 220; Maas, 1977 pp. 13, 16, 51, 94; David Robertson, *Sir Charles Eastlake and the Victorian Art World*, Princeton, 1978 pp. 205, 209, 369, 407.

SKETCH: 1. Sepia-coloured ink on white cartridge paper

4.39 × 9.49 in (11.1 × 24 cm) (*pl. 4*)

Inscr. The first idea for the picture of the Railway Station by W. P. Frith.

Prov. Sir Arthur Elton; bequeathed to Ironbridge Gorge Museum, 1978.

2. Pen and ink on paper in a scrapbook

$3\frac{7}{8}$ × 6 in (9.8 × 15.2 cm)

Inscr. The Railway Nov[er] 7th 1860

Prov. Gilbert Davis in 1951; W. Whitney; sold to J. S. Maas 1974.

Exh. 1951 Whitechapel Gallery (55).

ENGR: 1. Francis Holl ARA, mixed style, 20 × 44 in (50.7 × 111.7 cm) published by Henry Graves and Co., 1862.

Exh. First shown at Flatow's Gallery, 1862.

Lit. Hilary Beck, *Victorian Engraving*, 1973 pp. 37, 62 and repr. no. 35.

Printseller's Association records 3,050 proofs, ranging from 8 to 15 gns.

2. Marcus Stone received £300 for two copies of the picture, one of which was treated by an engraver's outliner, for a fee of £40.

VERSIONS: 1. *The Railway Station* 1863
oil on canvas, 16¾ × 36⅛ in (42.5 × 91.4 cm)

Inscr. W. P. Frith 1863

Prov. ? Louis Victor Flatow; his sale Christie's 4 May 1867 (109) bt in 980 gns.
David Price; his sale Christie's 2 April 1892 (59) bt Agnew £325 10s; sold by them to Leicester Museum £325 10s, 4 April 1892.

Exh. 1901 Glasgow (592); 1936 Amsterdam (36); 1946 Arts Council, *Yorkshire Artists, 1600–1900* (18); 1951 Whitechapel Gallery (35) and Harrogate (39); 1955 Kidderminster Public Library (12).

2. *The Railway Station*
20½ × 44 in (52 × 50.7 cm)

Inscr. W. P. Frith.

Prov. Purchased from the artist by James Gresham CE, JP of Gallery House, Woodheys Park, Ashton-on-Mersey; his sale Christie's 12 July 1917 (67) bt Sampson £210; ? sold by Tooth and Sons to Frank Bibby for £200, 1917; presented by him to the Directors of the Great Western Railway, 1917; presented by them to King George VI, 1947 and now in the Royal Collection.

Exh. 1903 Whitechapel Art Gallery, Spring Exhibition (108).

REPLICA:
The Railway Station
(by Marcus Stone but all references are to Frith)

oil on canvas, 28 × 60 in (71 × 152.3 cm)

Inscr. Signed and dated 1862

Prov. ? Louis Victor Flatow; his sale Christie's as *The Original Sketch of the Railway Station* 4 May 1867 (94) bt Graves £147; ? Frederick William Cozens of 27 Queen's Gate, 1872; his sale Christie's 17 May 1890 (130) bt Cosens £315; Thomas Miles Restell of

Brighton; his sale Christie's 17 February 1900 (113) bt Vokins £315; Arthur Cunliffe of 169 Cromwell Road; his sale Christie's 20 June 1924 (137) bt Sampson £126; C. F. Dendy Marshall of Chinthurst Lodge, Wonersh, Guildford by 1937; his sale Sotheby's 13 November 1945 (225) bt Agnew; sold by them to W. Freeman and Son £350 27 November 1945; anon. sale Sotheby's Belgravia 9 April 1980 (25) bt in.

Exh. 1937 Leicester Galleries (97) and Birmingham City Art Gallery (84).

Lit. A.J. 1872 p. 224; ed. Michael Davie, *The Diaries of Evelyn Waugh*, 1976, p. 640; ed. Mark Amory, *The Letters of Evelyn Waugh*, 1980, p. 216.

UNTRACED WORKS:

1. *Preparatory oil sketch,*
signed and dated 1861

Prov. Mrs Gerald Arbuthnot 1938.

Exh. 1938 *Old London Exhibition* (13).

Lit. Leicester Museums and Art Gallery, *Collection of Paintings*, 1958, p. 22.

2. *Sketch,* 17 × 35 in (43.1 × 88.8 cm)

Prov. ? Frederick William Cozens of 27 Queen's Gate 1872; his sale Christie's 17 May 1980 (98) bt Cosens £68 5s; Thomas M. Restell of Brighton; his sale Christie's 17 February 1900 (114) bt M. Col £57 15s.

3. *Signed panel,* 13 × 28 in (33 × 71 cm)

Prov. anon. sale Sotheby's 18 October 1950 (99) bt Lane £110.

The setting of *The Railway Station* is the Great Western Railway terminus at Paddington, which had been built by the railway's engineer Isambard Kingdom Brunel, with Matthew Digby Wyatt, between 1850 and 1852.

Frith painted part of two of the parallel round-arched sheds and illustrated clearly the methods used in the construction of the station, and the combination of wrought iron and glass, with cast iron columns and decorative tracery in the lunettes at the end of the sheds. A diagonal view is obtained through a transept from one shed to the other, thus giving more depth to the picture surface. Frith has placed his groups of departing figures against the background of the train and carriages. The train, stationary on the down-line, is

being loaded with baggage. By tradition, the name of the locomotive was the 'Great Britain' but Frith based his painting on a photograph of the 'Sultan' engine, a 4-2-2 broad gauge engine, both of the 'Iron Duke' class. Frith used the expanse of the platform to group over 60 people, mostly divided into smaller units. These are broken further, to some degree, by the vertical partitions, created by the architecture.

Henry Russell-Hitchcock pointed out that Frith did not show Paddington Station in its original state of painted glory, for by 1861 the station had been painted over in a brown colour, obliterating the polychromy of its first years.[1]

Frith's figures are scattered, in varying scales, across the whole breadth of the canvas. The small round man engaged in conversation with the engine driver is Flatow, the dealer who commissioned the work from Frith and insisted on being included in the picture.[2] Then, in line with the train's engine, there is a family, with two children following a railway porter who is pushing their luggage on a truck. A triangular group of figures is next along the frontal plane of the painting. A parting takes place as a mother bends to kiss her son, looked on by his father and an elder brother, while their sister holds the hand of a younger brother. These figures are portraits of Frith himself and of his wife and children, whom he used as additional models.[3]

The next group, in the centre, consists of three figures, and represents what Frith described as 'a foreigner whose idea of a cab-fare differs considerably from that of the driver of the vehicle, and he is consequently subjected to a bullying not uncommon under similar circumstances'.[4] Frith added that his model was 'a mysterious individual who taught my daughters Italian'. He was from Venice, 'a man of distinguished manners'; Frith had been led to believe that he was a nobleman 'whose head was wanted in Venice to serve a very different purpose from that to which I put it in this country'. Frith had had difficulty in persuading the Italian count to sit for him for he feared 'recognition by some aristocratic friends who might come to England'. He relented after Frith had promised not to make his portrait recognisable. However, this he did not do, as he explained: 'unless I caught the character of the face, I knew my model would be useless to me'.[5] To the left is a bride leaving her two bridesmaids, while the bridegroom apparently gives directions for the luggage.

The last scene on the right is historically the most interesting. Frith painted the moment of the arrest of an ashen-faced criminal by 'two detectives well known at that time'.[6] They were Detective-sergeant Michael Haydon, on the left, with hand-cuffs in hand, and Detective-sergeant James Brett, with his hand on the criminal's shoulder. Both sat for Frith and were 'admirable sitters', because they were perfectly accustomed to 'standing on the watch, hour after hour, in the practice of their profession, waiting for a thief or a murderer.' Both were from the City of London Police.[7] Another police officer was identified as Inspector Craig, of the Great Western Railway Police, who retired from the force in 1897 and is to be seen wearing a cap, immediately to the right of the Italian count's head.[8]

Frith, as Jeremy Maas pointed out, 'liked crowds'.[9] He had two large families (his wife, Isabelle, had 12 children, and his mistress, Mary Alford, later to be his second wife, had seven), and his most successful paintings were undoubtedly those containing large numbers of people. He also believed in taking enormous care to make his figures into portraits. His next painting after *The Railway Station*, *The Prince of Wales's Wedding*, was a formidable task of crowd portraiture.

The history of *The Railway Station* has been by no means straightforward. Speculation and rumour began before it was exhibited and continued long after, and the picture became famous through its reputation and through the fierce curiosity over the price paid by the man who commissioned the work, the London art dealer Louis Victor Flatow (often spelt Flatou).

Frith felt strongly about the difference between being commissioned by an art dealer or a private patron, as was pointed out by the writer of his obituary in *The Times*.[10] The writer commented on Frith's 'relations with the dealers and . . . the transformation in the business of distributing works of art which came into existence about this time and in which he, quite unintentionally, played a very large part'. He went on to explain the history of private patronage in this country and mentioned such patrons as Sheepshanks and Vernon whose 'inevitable rule was to buy direct from the artist'. However, this had caused many problems for painters. Frith discovered that it was more satisfactory to negotiate with dealers and 'no longer to lay himself open to the caprice of the private buyer and possibly to subsequent complaints of his bargain'. Frith felt that dealers 'by courage and good organisation were able both to offer certain artists twice or thrice the sum that the private patron would have given and to secure a very handsome return for themselves'. The writer commented on how 'many of their methods were appallingly vulgar, and in the arts of puffing and pushing', and went on to claim that 'the ugly little alien', Flatow, 'is said to have made £30,000 out of *The Railway Station* but Frith made twice as much as he would have made if he had kept the management in his own hands'. Frith, they asserted, with Gambart and Flatow and some others, 'really woke up the great British public to the desirability of possessing pictures, or at least engravings'.

Over the two years, 1860 to 1862, that it took Frith to paint *The Railway Station* the press published the various stages in the picture's development and maintained a healthy interest in the fluctuations of its rumoured price. Frith, by that time, had made his reputation and generated considerable interest in his two contemporary 'crowd' pictures of *Ramsgate Sands* (ex. R.A. 1854 [157], Royal Collection) and *Derby Day* (ex. R.A. 1858 [218], Tate Gallery). Hence any information forthcoming about this new work by Frith was naturally of great fascination. Progress was reported in earnest from early 1861. Frith had begun to work on the picture before the end of August 1860. His diary recorded that 'the autumn of 1860 was taken up by studies for the picture', which he had begun on 28 August, on which day he had written: 'Commenced picture of railway platform; another long journey, to which I go with almost as good a heart as I did to the "Derby Day". May it be as successful!'[11]

By early 1861 the picture was already being discussed in the press. The *Athenaeum* published a statement given to them by Flatow, 'the eminent picture-dealer', which was addressed from Upper Albany Street and dated 19 January 1861.[12] It read: 'A variety of mis-statements having obtained circulation in the public journals respecting my arrangements with W. P. Frith, Esq. RA., for his forthcoming great picture, to be called "Life at a Railway Station", I should be obliged by your inserting in your journal, for the information of the public, the following authentic statement of the facts. – My commission secures to Mr. Frith the sum of 8,000 guineas for the picture and copyright; and as I am serious that the public should have the fullest opportunity of properly seeing this fine work, which can only be secured in a separate exhibition, I have induced Mr. Frith, at my earnest request, to forego his right to exhibit it in the Royal Academy; for which concession he receives an additional sum of 750 guineas.'

The fact that Flatow gave the figure of 8,000 guineas makes it more comprehensible how confusion arose over the price actually paid for the picture and copyright, which came to a total of £4,500. The *Athenaeum* continued this notice with a comment: 'This sum (in all £9,187 10s.) is, we suppose, the largest price ever paid for a modern picture. By means of popular exhibitions and engraving, the copyright of a picture has come to have something like the value of a book – without losing any portion of its own peculiar value as a picture. If the English school of painting fails, it will not be for lack of enterprise and patronage.'

The real price, however, was not the 'largest price ever paid for a modern picture' for Ernest Gambart, a rival dealer to Flatow, had commissioned William Holman Hunt (1827–1910) to paint *The Finding of the Saviour in the Temple* (completed in April 1860, Birmingham City Art Gallery) and paid him 5,500 guineas for the painting and copyright.[13] *The Times* compared the prices of the two paintings.[14] Their comment was that the subject and the price both 'belong to the time'. They also felt that 'Mr. Frith is helping to do for our time what Hogarth did for his'.

The *Critic* wrily commented: 'Verily, these are piping times for popular painters. What successes (of the pecuniary sort) has authorship, even the most popular, to show besides *theirs?*'[15]

The history of the painting of the picture was plainly told by Frith in his *Autobiography*, published in 1887.[16] 'The preparations' he wrote 'were on much the same lines as those for the "Derby Day". Many chalk drawings of separate figures and groups, many changes of composition and incident, before I could satisfy myself that I might commence the inevitable oil-sketch. I dont think the station at Paddington can be called picturesque, nor can the clothes of the ordinary traveller be said to offer much attraction to the painter – in short, the difficulties of the subject were very great.'

Frith then stated clearly that the agreement with Flatow had been made on 10 September 1860 for £4,500, to be paid in instalments of £500 each every three months until the painting was finished, when the remaining balance would be paid. Initially Frith retained the rights to exhibit the picture at the R.A. or elsewhere, but he later relinquished this to Flatow for a further £750. This is an admirable example of exactly how critical every financial aspect of a painting was to both dealer and painter.

Frith was constantly engaged on *The Railway Station*: 'The whole of the year 1861, with fewer interruptions than usual, was spent on "The Railway Station". My diary records incessant work, and the employment of a multitude of models.' *The Railway Station* was completed in 1862. The *I.L.N.* announced that 'the picture itself will not be required for engraving . . . but a copy will be used for that purpose'.[17] A copy was to be made and Frith had agreed to 'finish' it for the engraver. The engraver was Francis Holl (1815–84), the father of Frank Holl (q.v.). Two copies of the painting had been made meanwhile by Marcus Stone (1840–1921).[18]

There has been continual surmise over the question of whether Frith used photographs to assist him in his arduous task of painting such a densely crowded scene against a complicated architectural background. The opinion seems to be that Frith did use photographs but was not prepared to admit it. 'Every object, living or dead, was painted from nature – often imperfectly enough, as the picture proves', Frith claimed in his *Autobiography*. However, it is certain that Frith had engaged the photographer Robert Howlett (who died in

1858) for his painting of the *Derby Day*.[19] It appears that Samuel Fry took over this job for *The Railway Station*, for Frith employed him to supply a set of photographs of Paddington Station to help him with the structure of the interior, railway engine and carriages. This was stated quite explicitly in *The Photographic News* of 26 April 1861 under the title of 'Photography and Art'.[20] 'Mr. Samuel Fry has recently been engaged in taking a series of negatives, 25 inches by 18 inches, and 10 inches by 8 inches, of the interior of the Great Western Station, engines, carriages, etc., for Mr. Frith, as aids to the production of his great painting "Life at a Railway Station". Such is the value of the photograph in aiding the artist's work, that he wonders now however they did without them!'[21]

The architectural background was painted by William Scott Morton (1840–1903), who trained as an architect and also designed carpets and furniture. Early in his career, however, he painted in backgrounds for Edwin Landseer (q.v.), John Phillip (1817–67) and Frith. Scott Morton also painted the background for *The Prince of Wales's Wedding*.[22]

The *A.J.* wrote in the spring of 1862, under the title of 'Life at a Railway Station', that 'Mr. Flatow has announced his intention to devote his entire time and energies to forward the interests of this great work; and with that view he has either relinquished, or materially contracted, his business as a picture dealer, in which he has so long occupied a foremost place. "Life at a Railway Station" is now a public exhibition at the Gallery in the Haymarket, next door to the theatre. It will, in due course, make the circuit of the provinces; it is therefore destined to be examined, in process of time, by hundreds of thousands of persons, in all parts of Great Britain.'[23]

The picture was exhibited at the Haymarket Gallery from April to September 1862 and Frith found that 21,150 people had paid to see the picture in seven weeks 'and the subscription for the engraving was equally surprising and satisfactory. The critics contradicted one another as usual, without doing good to me or the picture'.[24]

The art critic, Tom Taylor, produced what the *A.J.* described as 'a charming little book, being, however,

neither more nor less than a key to Frith's picture'.[25] It was published by Graves and cost 1s bound or 6d unbound, available at the exhibition room. It informed the public visiting the exhibition what was happening in the painting, always an important factor for a Victorian subject picture.

The exhibition space was considered by the *Critic* to have been 'a most convenient room for spectators'.[25] They thought Tom Taylor's description of the picture 'an admirable stroke of policy . . . there will be a great many who will be glad to have the aid of so experienced a describer'. The painting caused a sensation. It was removed from the Haymarket Gallery to be re-exhibited at Hayward and Leggat's in Cornhill. Following its exhibition there, the painting went on a tour of provincial towns. Certainly Holloway himself reported seeing it in August 1864 in Scarborough while on a journey in the north of England.[27]

The painting still attracted attention from the press in 1863 when it changed hands. The eminent print-seller and publisher Henry Graves, of Pall Mall, bought the painting from Flatow and the price paid again caused great speculation and was the source of many rumours. An argument began in July of that year in the *Athenaeum* and was finally silenced by a letter from Graves to the journal with the title of 'Prices of Pictures'.[28] It ran: 'I paid for the picture and list of subscribers £16,300. I am to refund what has been paid to the engraver, Mr. Francis Holl, and complete up his payments to the full amount of his contract, viz., 2,000 guineas. This makes a total of £18,400 without one penny interest on the outlay until the plate is completed and published.' The *Athenaeum* added a note at the end of Graves's letter which settled the matter. It read: 'This statement ends the controversy as to the price paid by Mr. Graves. We have been invited to inspect the papers and agreements in the matter, and we find that Mr. Graves' figures are correct.'

However, the matter was by no means at an end. There was a continual history of 'piracy of engravings'. One instance in 1868 quoted in *The Photographic News* cited 25 summonses made on behalf of Graves taken against a photographer, Solomon Alber.[29] Graves had claimed that the painting of *The Railway Station* and copyright had cost him £24,000. This, in turn, set up another spate of rumours and the *A.J.* called upon Graves to contradict the 'assertion so utterly opposed to truth'.[30] Eventually interest decreased, the painting remained in Graves's possession and he continued to publish engravings of it.

It was from Graves that Holloway purchased *The Railway Station* in 1883, for the paltry sum of £2,000, presumably because the commercial possibilities of the work had been exhausted. By this time the painting had been exhibited in three major international exhibitions, London in 1872, Philadelphia in 1876 and Paris in 1878.

There are a number of replicas of, and preparatory studies for, the painting; the best known, in Leicester City Art Gallery, is dated 1863, the year after the completion of the original and is of smaller dimensions. Frith spent much time as an old man in making copies of his earlier successful works which may explain the existence of different versions of this painting.[31]

The Great Western Railway owned a number of coloured engravings of the painting, most of which were dispersed over a period of time, especially in 1947 when the Railway was nationalised. One of these was presented in 1927 to Henry Ford, the American motor car king, for his museum.[32] Another coloured engraving still hangs at Paddington Station. There is another picture of *The Railway Station*, signed by Frith, at Buckingham Palace.[33] This was housed in the Directors' Room at Paddington Station until 1947 when it was presented to King George VI.[34]

William Powell Frith was born in Aldfield, near Ripon in Yorkshire. His father had worked at Studley Royal and later, in about 1826, moved to become landlord of the Dragon Inn at Harrogate until 1837. Frith began to study at Sass's Academy in Bloomsbury in 1835 and two years later moved on to attend the R.A. Schools. He began to paint portraits at an early age, but the majority of his works were scenes taken from literature.

Frith's first R.A. exhibit in 1840 was an episode from *Twelfth Night, Malvolio before the Countess Olivia* (607). From about 1837 onwards Frith was a member of a group called The Clique, which met one evening a week to draw, mostly subjects from Byron and Shakespeare, and which included Richard Dadd (1819–87), Augustus Egg (1816–63), Alfred Elmore (q.v.) and John 'Spanish' Phillip (1817–67). Most of Frith's subjects during the decade of the 1840s were sentimentalised scenes from literary sources such as Molière, Walter Scott, Sterne or Dickens. His *Dolly Varden* (a version is at the Victoria and Albert Museum) was inspired by Dickens's *Barnaby Rudge* (published 1841): it brought him immediate success and fulfilled Frith's preference to paint contemporary subject matter and costume.

Frith was elected a Royal Academician in 1852 to fill the place left vacant by the death of Turner. Two years later he achieved great success at the R.A. with *Life at the seaside*, known as *Ramsgate Sands*, which was purchased by Queen Victoria. This was followed in 1858 by *Derby Day*, another great triumph: these two pictures, and *The Railway Station*, were regarded as mirrors of modern life.

The Railway Station was followed by *The Marriage of the Prince of Wales* (Royal Collection) exhibited at the R.A. (52) in 1865. His large-scale contemporary paintings each took a considerable length of time to execute. During the 1870s Frith continued to paint contemporary pictures, with *The Salon d'Or, Homburg* (ex. R.A. 1871 [158], Rhode Island School of Design Museum) and a series of moralistic scenes, in the tradition of Hogarth, entitled *The Road to Ruin* (ex. R.A. 1878 [291–5], Private Collection, Italy). Concurrently with these, he exhibited historical and literary subjects. However, towards the end of his life, Frith's style quickly became unfashionable and he became an easy target for criticism and mockery. One of his last great works was *The Private View (of the R.A.) 1881* (ex. R.A. 1883 [163], Private Collection) which is a good documentary illustration of a crowd at a R.A. exhibition.

[1] Henry Russell-Hitchcock, *Early Victorian Architecture*, New Haven and London, 1954, Vol. I, p. 562.

[2] See Jeremy Maas, *Gambart, Prince of the Victorian Art World*, 1975, p. 136.

[3] Frith confirmed this in a letter to Carey of 1 September 1887, Royal Holloway College Archives.

[4] William Powell Frith, *My Autobiography and Reminiscences*, 1887, Vol. I, p. 330.

[5] Frith included a figure who resembled the Italian count in *Derby Day*. He is to be found in the centre of the painting, wearing a black top hat and red waistcoat and talking to a man in a grey top hat and green coat.

[6] William Powell Frith, 1887, Vol. I, p. 330.

[7] I am indebted to the Chief Superintendent of the City of London Police and Mr. R. M. A. Brett for information concerning the detectives.

[8] British Transport Historical Records, Public Record Office, Kew, file RAIL 253/669.

[9] Jeremy Maas, *The Prince of Wales's Wedding, The Story of a Picture*, 1977, p. 43.

[10] *The Times*, 3 November 1909, p. 13.

[11] William Powell Frith, 1887, pp. 327, 329.

[12] *Athenaeum*, 1861, p. 122.

[13] See Jeremy Maas, *Gambart*, 1975, pp. 114–22 and Arts Council, *Great Victorian Pictures*, 1978, pp. 36–7.

[14] *The Times*, 19 April 1862, p. 5.

[15] *Critic*, 1861, p. 190.

[16] William Powell Frith, 1887, Vol. I, p. 327.

[17] *Illustrated London News*, 11 October 1862, p. 391.

[18] See Jeremy Maas, *Gambart*, 1975, p. 136. See also Appendix p. 141.

[19] Frith had also used an album of 62 cartes-de-visite photographs as aids with the Royal Marriage painting of 1863. These were exhibited (64) in *This Brilliant Year*, Royal Academy, 1977.

[20] *The Photographic News*, 26 April 1861, p. 204.

[21] See Helmut Gernsheim, *Masterpieces of Victorian Photography 1840–1900*, 1951, p. 12 and *Motif*, Aesthetic Trends in Photography Past and Present 3: 'Documentation and Reportage', 3 September 1959, p. 73.

[22] I am most grateful to Miss Beatrice Morton for kindly providing me with information regarding her grandfather.

[23] *Art Journal*, 1862, pp. 122–3.

[24] William Powell Frith, 1887, Vol. I, p. 334.

[25] *Art Journal*, 1862, p. 147.

[26] *Critic*, 1862, p. 397.

[27] Noted in Holloway's Travel Diary of 1848 onwards, housed at Surrey Record Office.

[28] *Athenaeum*, 25 July 1863, p. 113.

[29] *The Photographic News*, 4 December 1868, p. 587.

[30] *Art Journal*, 1869, p. 159.

[31] See Jeremy Maas, *Gambart*, 1975, p. 284.

[32] British Transport Historical Records, Public Record Office, Kew, file RAIL 253/669.

[33] Its medium is unknown but the picture is currently undergoing investigation.

[34] It is listed in the 'Descriptive Catalogue of the Pictures at

Paddington and Other Relics' by D. V. Levin in 1926 in the British Transport Historical Records, Public Record Office, Kew, file RAIL 253/669.

BIBLIOGRAPHY
'British Artists: Their Style and Character, No. XVII, William Powell Frith, R.A.', *Art Journal*, 1856, pp. 237–40.
W. W. Fenn, 'Our Living Artists: William Powell Frith, R.A.', *Magazine of Art*, 1879, pp. 80–3; reprinted and enlarged in: ed. Wilfrid Meynell, *The Modern School of Art*, 1886–88, pp. 144–51.
W. P. Frith, *My Autobiography and Reminiscences*, 3 Vols., 1887–88.
Jane Ellen Panton, *Leaves from a Life*, 1908.
Exhibition catalogue, *Paintings by William Powell Frith R.A. 1819–1909*, 1951, Whitechapel Gallery and Harrogate.
ed. N. Wallis, *A Victorian Canvas: The Memoirs of W. P. Frith, R.A.*, 1957.
Jeremy Maas, *The Prince of Wales's Wedding; The Story of a Picture*, 1977.

24. Thomas Gainsborough

1727–88, Founder Member R.A. 1768

Peasants going to Market: Early Morning c. 1770 (*pl. 62*)

oil on canvas, 48 × 58 in (121.8 × 147.2 cm)

PROV: 6 July 1773 Henry Hoare of Stourhead paid William Hoare, R.A., £84; by descent; Sir Henry Hoare; his sale Stourhead Heirlooms Christie's 2 June 1883 (16) *Peasants and Colliers going to Market*, bt Martin £2,835.

EXH: 1814 B.I. *Old Masters* (44); 1870 R.A. Winter Exhibition (124); 1962 University of Nottingham, *Landscapes by Gainsborough* (18); 1968–69 R.A. *Bi-Centenary Exhibition* (143); 1972 Paris, *La Peinture Romantique Anglaise et Les Raphaelites* (124); 1975 Milan, *British Paintings 1660–1840* (51); 1979–80 Munich, *Two Hundred Years of English Painting 1680–1880* (35); 1981 Paris, *Gainsborough 1727–1788* (45).

LIT: William Gilpin, *Observations on the Western Parts of England, etc.*, 1798, p. 119; Fulcher, 1856 p. 195; Armstrong, 1898 p. 206; ed. Emily J. Climenson, *Passages from the Diaries of Mrs. Philip Lybbe Powys*, 1899, p. 173; Whitley, 1915 pp. 43, 357–8; Woodall, 1939 pp. 45, 49–51, 55 and repr. pl. 50; Woodall, 1949 pp. 93–4; Ellis Waterhouse, *Painting in Britain 1530–1790*, 1953 p. 188; Waterhouse, 1958, no. 911, p. 114, and repr. pl. 115; John Hayes, 'Gainsborough and Rubens', *Apollo*, Vol. LXXVIII, 1963, pp. 92–3 and repr. p. 94; St. John Gore, 'A Worthy Heir to Greatness', *Country Life*, 6 February 1964, p. 278; Hayes, 1971 p. 17, nos. 502, 826, detail repr. pl. 301; Luke Herrmann, *British Landscape Painting of the Eighteenth Century*, 1973 p. 97; Hayes, 1975, no. 80, p. 25, and repr. pl. 115; Barrell, 1980 pp. 53–4.

REPR: M. Kitson, *The Age of Baroque*, 1966, pl. 68.

DRAWING AFTER: *Open Landscape with Peasants Going to Market* or *Peasants Returning from Market* early 1780s
grey, grey-black and brown washes
7⅝ × 9⅝ in (19.6 × 24.7 cm)
Prov. Sir Jeremiah Colman; 1935 with Walker's Galleries; P. M. Turner; Colnaghi; Viscount Eccles; sold Agnew's 1977; Private Collection, U.S.A.
Exh. 1935 Walker's Galleries, *31st Annual Exhibition of Early English Watercolours* (26); 1949 Aldeburgh Festival, *Drawings by Thomas Gainsborough* (23); 1962 University of Nottingham Art Gallery, *Landscape by Thomas Gainsborough* (42); 1963 Colnaghi's, *English Drawings and Watercolours in Memory of the late D. C. T. Baskett* (30); 1977 Agnew's, *104th Annual Exhibition of Watercolours and Drawings* (7).
Lit. Hayes, 1971 p. 225, no. 502, and repr. pl. 156; *Connoisseur*, February 1977, p. 68.

This painting was formerly at Stourhead, Wiltshire, in the famous collection of Sir Henry Hoare, one of Gainsborough's earliest patrons.[1] It was the last purchase that Holloway made for the College in June 1883 and is the earliest in date of all the paintings in the collection. The painting had been in the Hoare family since 1773, when, on 6 July, Henry Hoare paid William Hoare RA, the Bath portrait painter (1706–99; no relation) the sum of £84 for a 'Gainsborough Picture'.[2] Gainsborough himself banked with Messrs. Hoare in Temple Bar from 1762 to 1785.

Henry Hoare (called the 'Magnificent'), together with his grandson, Richard Colt Hoare, had built up a fine collection of paintings, purchased both in England and on the Continent. It included Poussin's *Rape of the Sabines* (now in the Metropolitan Museum, New York) and Mengs's *Caesar and Cleopatra* (still at Stourhead).[3] The sale of the Stourhead Heirlooms at Christie's in 1883 was instigated by the fifth Baronet, Sir Henry Ainslie Hoare, possibly to finance his political career.[4] The painting is first recorded as having been seen at Stourhead in 1776 by Mrs Lybbe Powys, a doctor's daughter, whose diaries and travel journals, according to their editor, 'cannot fail to interest the general reader, containing as they do such interesting anecdotes of royalty, and other notable people, descriptions of country seats, places, towns, manufactures, amusements, and general habits of the period which now form history.' She reported the painting as hanging in the Picture Gallery at Stourhead and described it as a 'fine landscape by Gainsborough, of Bath'.[5]

The Reverend William Gilpin, in his account of country houses in the West country, first published in 1798, also commented on *Peasants Going to Market*.[6] He referred to it as 'some Market peasants' and praised both the figures and the effect as 'pleasing'.

The Bath portrait and history painter Prince Hoare (1755–1834) wrote about this painting while commenting on the fact that Gainsborough's early landscapes were overlooked by patrons who were reluctant to buy them.[7] He stated that Gainsborough was 'so disgusted at the blind preference paid to his powers of portraiture, that, for many years of his residence at Bath, he regularly shut up all his landscapes in the back apartments of his house, to which no common visitors were admitted. The landscape, that first found its way into any collection, was purchased of him by the late Henry Hoare, Esq. of Stourhead, on a friend's *recommendation* !! and so little even then was the merit of Gainsborough duly estimated, the Mr. [Coplestone Warre] Bampfylde, a dilettante in Painting, being on a visit at Stourhead, offered to *mend Gainsborough's sheep*, by repainting them, and was allowed to do so. They have been restored to their original *deficiencies*, by the taste and good sense of the present possessor [Sir Richard Colt Hoare] of that beautiful place.' 'Gainsborough's sheep' must refer to this painting of *Peasants Going to Market*, which was the only painting

Catalogue

which inlcuded sheep in the Hoare collection.

As to the content of the painting, John Hayes has pointed out that both Gainsborough's great friend William Jackson, the composer, and also William Hazlitt had remarked on the fact that his peasant figures were basically too sophisticated for truly rustic characters.[8] He quoted from Hazlitt's *Criticisms in Art* where he wrote that Gainsborough attributed 'the air of an Adonis to the driver of a hay-cart, and models the features of a milkmaid on the principles of the antique'.[9] This Hayes sees as a reference to *Peasants Going to Market*.

The scene represents an early morning with the effects of the first light of the day being shed on a band of country people appearing over the brow of a hill on their way to market. In 1962 John Hayes wrote that he felt that Gainsborough had taken from Rubens ideas for the painting of the dawn light in his landscapes and named Rubens's *Birdcatchers* in the Louvre in particular.[10] The precise date of the painting is uncertain but it is considered to have been painted in the last years of Gainsborough's stay in Bath, that is, between 1769 and the date of payment in mid–1773.[11]

A wash drawing relating closely to the oil painting of *Peasants Going to Market* is in a Private Collection in America. It is strongly felt however[12] that this drawing of *Open Landscape with Peasants Going to Market* (also catalogued as *Peasants Returning from Market*)[13] was executed by Gainsborough after the completion of the oil painting and not as a study for it. John Hayes has dated this drawing as belonging to the early 1780s. It represents three figures on horseback, a dog to the left of them and two donkeys in the right foreground. The sheep are omitted in the drawing but the tree on the right is common to both works. The effect of the figures silhouetted against the sky is also similar.

A drawing in pencil and watercolour of two figures on horseback and a dog in the Leeds City Art Gallery was catalogued in 1949 as being by Gainsborough and a possible study for *Peasants Going to Market*.[14] However, it is no longer considered to be by him.[15]

Thomas Gainsborough was born at Sudbury in Suffolk, the son of a cloth merchant. He was sent to London in 1740 to study under the French draughts-man and engraver, Hubert Gravelot (1699–1773); here he painted *The Charterhouse* (Foundling Hospital), a topographical roundel painting which he presented to the Foundling Hospital in 1748.

Some time before 1750 he settled in Ipswich, where he began to paint portraits, and where he remained until the autumn of 1759, when he moved to Bath. In 1761 he began to send paintings, full-length portraits and some landscapes, to London to be exhibited in the first public exhibitions held by the Society of Artists. In 1768 when the R.A. was founded by George III, Gainsborough was one of its original members. He exhibited there first in the following year, at their inaugural exhibition, with the *Countess of Sefton* (Private Collection). Gainsborough was elected to the Council of the Academy, but, after a quarrel in 1773, he did not exhibit there for four years. Another argument in 1784 led him to hold his own private exhibitions at his home at Schomberg House, Pall Mall, until his death four years later.

Gainsborough's Bath portraits show van Dyck's influence as, in much the same way, his landscapes acknowledge his debt to Rubens.

In 1774 Gainsborough left Bath to establish himself in London as a portrait painter of some reputation and three years later he received his first commission from the Royal Family: the *Duke* and *Duchess of Cumberland* (ex. R.A. 1777 [131] and [132], Royal Collection).

Gainsborough's greatest rival in London was Sir Joshua Reynolds (1723–92) whose approach and style however were completely at variance with his own. Reynolds paid great tribute to Gainsborough in his *Fourteenth Discourse*, in which he said: 'If ever this nation should produce genius sufficient to acquire us the honourable distinction of an English School, the name of Gainsborough will be transmitted to posterity, in the history of the Art, among the very first of that rising name.'[16]

[1] See Mary Woodall, *Thomas Gainsborough, His Life and Work*, 1949, p. 93.
[2] According to Hoare's Bank Ledger. This was kindly looked up for me by the Archivist, Mr R. McD. Winder.
[3] See the *Country Life* articles by St. John Gore, 'Prince of Georgian Collectors', 30 January 1964, pp. 210–12 and 'A Worthy Heir to Greatness', 6 February 1964, pp. 278–80.
[4] See Kenneth Woodbridge, *Stourhead*, The National Trust Guidebook, 1975.
[5] Ed. Emily J. Climenson, *Passages from the Diaries of Mrs. Philip Lybbe Powys*, 1899, p. 173.
[6] William Gilpin, *Observations on the Western Parts of England etc.*, 1798, p. 119.
[7] Prince Hoare, *Epochs of The Arts Including Hints on the Use and Progress of Painting and Sculpture in Great Britain*, 1813, pp. 76–7.
[8] John Hayes, *The Drawings of Thomas Gainsborough*. 1971, p. 17.
[9] William Hazlitt, *Criticisms in Art*, 1843, p. 195.
[10] In the Introduction to the catalogue of the exhibition of Gainsborough's landscapes at the University of Nottingham.
[11] See Mary Woodall, *Gainsborough's Landscape Drawings*, 1949, p. 49, and Ellis Waterhouse, *Gainsborough*, 1958, p. 114.
[12] John Hayes, *The Drawings of Thomas Gainsborough*, 1971, no. 502.
[13] In Agnew's exhibition catalogue of *104th Annual Exhibition of Watercolours and Drawings*, 1977, no. 7.
[14] Mary Woodall, *Gainsborough's Landscape Drawings*, 1949, pp. 45, 49–51, no. 78 and repr. pl. 49.
[15] John Hayes, *The Drawings of Thomas Gainsborough*, 1971, p. 319.
[16] Ed. Robert R. Wark, Discourse XIV, *Sir Joshua Reynolds Discourses on Art*, Yale University Press, 1975, p. 248.

BIBLIOGRAPHY
Philip Thicknesse, *A Sketch of the Life and Paintings of Thomas Gainsborough*, Esq., 1788.
George Williams Fulcher, *Life of Thomas Gainsborough R.A.*, ed. by his son, 1856.
Allan Cunningham, *Lives of the Most Eminent British Painters*, revised edition by Mrs Charles Heaton, 1879, Vol. I, pp. 258–81.
Walter Armstrong, *Thomas Gainsborough*, 1894.
Walter Armstrong, *Thomas Gainsborough and his Place in English Art*, 1898.
Lord Ronald Gower, *Thomas Gainsborough*, 1903.
James Greig and Mortimer Mempes, *Thomas Gainsborough*, 1909.
William T. Whitley, *Thomas Gainsborough*, 1915.
Mary Woodall, *Gainsborough's Landscape Drawings*, 1949.
Mary Woodall, *Thomas Gainsborough, His Life and Work*, 1949.
Oliver Millar, *Gainsborough*, 1949.
Ellis Waterhouse, *Gainsborough*, 1958.
ed. Mary Woodall, *The Letters of Thomas Gainsborough*, 1963.
John Hayes, *The Drawings of Thomas Gainsborough*, 2 Vols., 1971.
John Hayes, *Gainsborough, Paintings and Drawings*, 1975.
John Barrell, *The Dark Side of the Landscape*, 1980.

25. Peter Graham

1836–1921, ARSA 1860, HRSA 1877, ARA 1877, RA 1881

A Highland Croft 1873 (*pl. 75*)

oil on canvas, 48 × 72 in (121.8 × 182.8 cm)

INSCR: Peter Graham 1873

PROV: Commissioned by Baron Albert Grant for 1,100 gns; his sale Christie's 28 April 1877 (146) bt Holmes £640 10s; William Lee; his sale Christie's 26 May 1883 (69) bt Martin £630.

EXH: 1873 R.A. (980); 1922 R.A. Winter Ex. (180); 1981 Agnew's (13).

LIT: *Athenaeum* 31 May 1873 p. 701; *Examiner* 31 May 1873 p. 576; *I.L.N.* 24 May 1873 p. 487; *The Times* 19 May 1873 p. 6; W. Matthews Gilbert, 'Peter Graham, R.A.', *Art Annual* 1899 p. 23.

STUDY: Oil; Repr. W. Matthews Gilbert, 'Peter Graham, R.A.', *The Art Annual*, 1899 p. 23.

Seven years before this painting was exhibited at the R.A., Graham had achieved a tremendous success with *A Spate in the Highlands* (ex. R.A. 1866 [373] and now in the City of Manchester Art Galleries).[1] He never again painted a dramatic natural landscape with the same impact.

By contrast, *A Highland Croft* is a peaceful un-challenging composition, tame in the light of the possibilities which Highland subjects offer and which were so often taken up by painters in the 19th century. The painting was well liked by the critics of the 1873 Academy exhibition. The *I.L.N.* called it 'remarkable for the fresh limpidity of the atmospheric effect and lighting'. The *Examiner* recorded that it 'is an effect that he has often painted before, but probably never more beautifully, and the picture is further note-worthy on account of the fine group of calves huddled together beside the stile that opens on the corn-yard'. More lyrical yet was the review in *The Times*, which described it as a painting 'in which the sentiment of a hard harvest wrung from an ungrateful soil by intense industry, and the repose of animal life, as contrasted with the unending toil of man, its master, are power-fully and pathetically conveyed'.

The paintwork of the picture is more feathery than in most of Graham's other works, looking almost as if it had been painted at some speed. It precedes his more successful pictures of Highland cattle on wild moors, which constitute the bulk of his work.

Graham was born in Edinburgh, the son of an accountant, and was one of the many well known Scottish painters who began their career at the Trustees' Academy in Edinburgh under the able tutelage of Robert Scott Lauder (1803–69) and his assistant John Ballantyne (1815–97). Graham studied there from 1850 to 1856; in 1859 he changed from figure to landscape painting. He always had the habit of making his preliminary studies from nature, as P. G. Hamerton pointed out in *Thoughts about Art*: 'He believes, and so do I, that the shortest road to good landscape-painting is an indirect road, and that he himself got his first initiation into the mysteries of landscape effect through constant observation of the delicate play of light and shade in a gallery of statues.'[2]

Graham went to live in London in 1866 and after a while found it more convenient for his numerous commissions to be controlled by one of the foremost dealers in London, William Agnew, who had moved his firm from Manchester in 1861. By this means he could systematically produce a succession of Scottish landscapes for an eager market, and he became very prosperous. *A Spate in the Highlands* was his first painting to be exhibited at the R.A. Two years later he accepted a commission from Queen Victoria to paint *Bowman's Pass, Balmoral Forest*.

According to the Irwins, Graham would constantly visit Scotland, especially the Highlands.[3] He had a studio in the country at Gerrards Cross in Buckinghamshire, where he kept a herd of Highland cattle to be studied at first hand. For the rest of his career he did not deviate from his Scottish landscapes and coastal scenes and many of them became well-known to the public through engravings.

[1] See Arts Council, *Great Victorian Pictures*, 1978, pp. 41–2.
[2] P. G. Hamerton, *Thoughts about Art*, 1889, p. 34.
[3] David and Francina Irwin, *Scottish Painters at Home and Abroad, 1700–1900*, 1975, p. 363.

BIBLIOGRAPHY

W. W. Fenn, 'Peter Graham, A.R.A.', *Magazine of Art*, 1879, pp. 144–8; reprinted almost exactly in: ed. Wilfrid Meynell, *The Modern School of Art*, 4 vols., 1886–88, pp. 158–63.

Walter Armstrong, 'Scottish Painters IX', *Portfolio*, 1887, pp. 211–12.

W. Matthews Gilbert, 'Peter Graham R.A.', *Art Annual*, 1899.

Sir James L. Caw, *Scottish Painting, Past and Present, 1620–1908*, Edinburgh, 1908, pp. 255–6.

David and Francina Irwin, *Scottish Painters at Home and Abroad, 1700–1900*, 1975, pp. 362–3.

26. Frederick Daniel Hardy

1826–1911

Expectation: Interior of a Cottage with a Mother and Children 1854 (*pl. 36*)

panel, 9 × 12 in (22.8 × 30.4 cm)

PROV: Samuel Mayou of Birmingham; his sale Christie's 21 April 1883 (19) as *Interior of cottage with a mother and children* bt Martin £99 15s.

EXH: 1854 R.A. (505) as *Expectation*; 1981 Agnew's (14).

LIT: *A.J.* 1854 p. 169.

This view into a peaceful, rustic cottage interior is characteristic of F. D. Hardy's work in the 1850s, early in which he began to exhibit at the R.A. and the B.I. These paintings were mostly small in scale, on panel, and the still-life quality of the groups of figures reflects his awareness of 17th-century Dutch genre painting. In this instance the figures are represented at a fairly close range. In similar paintings of the next decade, Hardy tended to introduce more figures and a greater degree of activity generally. The fireplace, framed by brickwork and a timber beam, was a favourite setting in his work, and some of the accessories in this painting appear in others of the 1850s.[1]

The closeness of detail was commented on by the *A.J.* in the review of the R.A. exhibition of 1854, where it was exhibited with the title *Expectation*. They re-ferred to its '. . . unimpeachable exactitude. The walls and the brick floor have been most assiduously wrought into microscopic imitation of these surfaces . . . The work is entitled to rank among the best of this class of subject.' Two years later Ruskin, reviewing another 'Interior' painting of Hardy's, declared in his *Academy Notes*: 'With his powers of execution, a little more faithfulness will make Mr. Hardy a perfect painter in this kind.'[2]

Frederick Daniel Hardy was born in Windsor, where his father played in the Private Band of Music of the Royal Household and was also an amateur oil painter. He began to study at the Academy of Music in Hanover Square when he was seventeen but three years later, in 1846, he took up painting. His brother, George Hardy (1822–1909) had studied at the R.A. Schools, and, with Thomas Webster (1800–86), a relation by marriage, was painting the sort of rustic genre subjects which F. D. Hardy was soon to adopt. The brothers became members of the Cranbrook Colony in Kent, together with Webster, J. C. Horsley (q.v.), A. E. Mulready (1843?–after 1903) and G. B. O'Neill (1828–1917). Hardy lived in Cranbrook for over 20 years, painting mostly scenes of cottage life, which became extremely popular. Many of his scenes including children were intended to be humorous, such as *The Young Photographers* of 1862 (The Ashton Bequest, Tunbridge Wells Museum), and many were set in interiors and show in detail the appearance of Victorian houses and cottages.

Though he developed his pictures' size and content in the 1860s, Hardy's style changed little and he continued to exhibit the same kind of subject until 1889, after which, except for the year 1898, he no longer exhibited at the R.A.

[1] See the exhibition catalogue *The Cranbrook Colony*, Wolverhampton Art Gallery, 1977, pls. 1 and 2 of *Interior of a Sussex Farmhouse* (Leicestershire Museums and Art Gallery) and *The Clergyman's Visit* (Wolverhampton Art Gallery).
[2] John Ruskin, *Academy Notes*, ed. 1856, p. 24.

BIBLIOGRAPHY
James Dafforne, 'The Works of Frederick Daniel Hardy', *Art Journal*, 1875, pp. 73–6.
The Cranbrook Colony, exhibition catalogue, 1977, Wolverhampton and Newcastle.

27. James Hardy (the younger)
1832–89

A young Gillie, with setters and dead game 1877 (*pl. 77*)

oil on canvas, 28 × 39 in (71 × 99 cm)

INSCR: J. Hardy / 77

EXH: 1981 Agnew's (15).

PROV: William Lee; his sale Christie's 26 May 1883 (16) bt Martin £204 15s.

This painting is typical of James Hardy's subject matter. Hardy came from Bristol. His father was probably the landscape painter James Hardy who worked in London and exhibited his work there from 1842 to 1867. James Hardy the younger made his name with paintings of outdoor scenes connected with sport.

He painted in oil and watercolour and became a member of the New Watercolour Society in 1877. He exhibited his work at the R.A. (1862 to 1886), the B.I. and the Society of British Artists. Many of his works contained the same elements as seen here, scattered dead game, dogs and occasional figures in sporting costumes. They were mostly set in the Scottish Highlands and have a marked still-life quality.

28. John Evan Hodgson
1831–95, ARA 1873, RA 1879, HFRPE

Relatives in Bond 1877 (*pl. 21*)

panel, 37 × 26 in (93.9 × 66 cm)

INSCR: J .E. Hodgson 1877

PROV: Purchased by Thomas Taylor of Aston Rowant Gallery, Oxfordshire, from the artist; his sale Christie's 28 April 1883 (60) bt Martin £556 10s.

EXH: 1877 R.A. (415); 1981 Agnew's (16).

LIT: *A.J.* 1877 p. 199; *Athenaeum* 5 May 1877 p. 582, 12 May 1877 p. 615; *The Times* 12 May 1877 p. 6; *Mag. of Art* 1882 p. 312.

This picture is another example of Holloway's interest in buying works of an Oriental flavour, a type of painting extremely popular from the middle of the 19th century onwards.[1]

According to the 1877 *Athenaeum* Academy review, the scene is set outside a Tunisian prison. The figures in the main foreground are attaching baskets of provisions to ropes to be hauled up to their relations, who can be seen piteously looking out of the grated opening at the top left side of the painting. 'The details of the design explain the doleful condition of the latter, and show how sore is the need for a Tunisian Howard. The background comprises highly picturesque groups of buildings, a vista enriched with sunlight and shadow, thus producing a very agreeable effect.'

The *A.J.* described the painting as 'full of character and local colour'. Hodgson has combined in the foreground group a good variety of expressions and a convincing interest in Eastern detail. He visited North Africa – Tunis, Algiers, Tangier and Morocco – in 1868 and after that visit began to paint Eastern subjects.

John Evan Hodgson was born in London but was brought up in Russia, where his father was in business. In 1855 he entered the R.A. Schools as a student. He began painting genre subjects and his first exhibited work at the R.A. was *The notice of ejectment* (1213) in 1856, and in 1861 he exhibited his first historical subject, *A visit to Holbein's studio – Sir Thomas More and his daughters looking at his portrait* (608). It was followed the next year by the *Return of Francis Drake to Plymouth, with his prisoners and prize, after the naval expedition to Cadiz in 1587* (523), (none of which have been traced).

North Africa made a deep impression on Hodgson. There were many Arabian subjects at the R.A. following his journey there in 1868. From 1882 until his death in 1895 he was Librarian and Professor of Painting at the Academy. He published his *Academy Lectures* in 1884, and in 1887 *Fifty Years of British Art, as illustrated by the pictures and drawings in the Manchester Royal Jubilee Exhibition, 1887*. He was co-author with Sir Frederick A. Eaton (Secretary of the R.A.) of *The Royal Academy and Its Members, 1768–1830*, which was published in 1905.

[1] See the exhibition catalogue *Eastern Encounters: Orientalist Painters of the Nineteenth Century*, Fine Art Society, 1978.

BIBLIOGRAPHY

Tom Taylor, 'English Painter of the Present Day, XIX', *Portfolio*, 1871, pp. 17–19.

Art Journal, 1895, p. 256 (Obit.)

Bevis Hillier, 'The St. John's Wood Clique', *Apollo*, June 1964, pp. 490–5.

Sidney Charles Hutchinson, *The History of the Royal Academy, 1768–1968*, 1968, pp. 137, 143.

29. Frank Holl

1845–88, ARA 1878, RA 1883

Newgate: Committed for Trial 1878 (*pl.* 1)

oil on canvas, 60 × 83 in (152.3 × 210.7 cm)

INSCR: Frank Holl 1878; on verso: Number 1 / Newgate–Committed for Trial / Frank Holl / 4, Camden Square NW / April 1878.

PROV: Edward Hermon M.P. of Wyfold Court, Henley-on-Thames; his sale Christie's 13 May 1882 (60) bt Martin £808 10s.

EXH: 1887 R.A. (423); 1889 R. A. Winter Exhibition *A Special Selection from the Works of Frank Holl, R.A.* (221); 1968–9 R.A. *Bi-Centenary Exhibition* (317); 1981 Agnew's (17).

LIT: *Academy* 25 May 1878 p. 470; *A.J.* 1878 p. 168; Blackburn, *R.A. Notes* 1878 p. 43 (and repr. same page); *Examiner* 4 May 1878 p. 568; *I.L.N.* 1878 p. 459; *Mag. of Art* 1878 p. 100 and repr. opp. p. 100; *Spectator* 8 June 1878 p. 730; *The Times* 11 May 1878 p. 6.; *Mag. of Art* 1880 p. 189 reprinted in Meynell, 1883 pp. 172–3 and repr. p. 169; *The Times* 16 May 1882 p. 4; Quilter, 1892 p. 130; Temple, 1897 p. 339; Reynolds, 1912 pp. 144–6; Redgrave, 1947 p. 363; Reynolds, 1953 pp. 28, 93 and repr. pl. 83; Maas, 1969 p. 237; Gaunt, 1972 p. 29 and repr. pl. 126; Arts Council, *English Influences on Van Gogh*, 1974–5, p. 40; Forbes, *R.A. Revisited*, 1975 p. 70; Wood, 1976 p. 58 and detail repr. pl. 51; Arts Council, *Great Victorian Pictures*, 1978 pp. 35, 44.

STUDY: 27 × 37 in (68.5 × 93.9 cm); 1878

Prov. Captain Hill of Brighton by 1882; his sale Christie's 25 May 1889 (134) bt Agnew £388 10s; sold by them 25 May 1889 to W. C. Quilter M.P.; his sale Christie's 29 April 1893 (116) bt in £231: Sir Cuthbert Quilter Bart. of 74 South Audley Street, London; his sale Christie's 12 May 1900 (87) bt in £99 15s; his sale Christie's 9 July 1909 (58) bt Heape 90 gns.

Exh: ? Brighton 1884

Lit: Charlotte J. Weeks, *Magazine of Art* 1882 p. 3.

VERSION: oil on canvas, 71 × 97 in (180.2 × 246.2 cm)

Inscr: Frank Holl 1878

Prov: Sir Cuthbert Quilter Bart. of 74 South Audley Street; Robert Taylor Heape gift to Rochdale Museum in 1910.

This painting of Holl's made his reputation when it was exhibited at the R.A. in 1878 and he was elected an ARA. The picture was the result of direct experience. Holl visited Newgate Prison, the Governor being a friend of his, and was deeply moved by what he saw. Writing from The Three Gables, his house in Hampstead, Holl described his painting as 'the part of Newgate prison, called the cage – in which prisoners whilst on trial are permitted at certain hours, & on certain days, to see their friends – on the inner side the prisoners are placed, & in the passage – their friends are conducted to them when their relations or friends are at once brought out – A Warden walks between the 2 gratings, who can hear and see everything that takes place between the friend & prisoner – It is particularly impressive for scenes of such pathos & agony of mind on both sides take place . . . I witnessed this scene some years before I painted the picture – visiting the prison through the interest of the then Governor – [Mr Sidney Smith] & I shall never forget the impression it made upon me . . . Prisoners of all sorts of crime were there – the lowest brutal criminal – swindlers, forgers, & boy thieves – all caged together, awaiting the results of their separate trials, & in one or two cases, the misery of their friends in seeing them in this hopeless condition, fell but lightly on their brains dulled by incessant crime . . .'[1]

Holl underlined the 'pathos and agony' with the dark tones of the painting and with the angle of the composition, directing the spectator's view straight into the scene, to confront the victims at close range. Newgate as a subject would necessarily have had emotional overtones. Newgate subjects had been exhibited at the R.A. before Holl's painting. For example, Henrietta Ward (Mrs E. M. Ward) exhibited *Newgate 1818* in 1876 (120, illustrated in ed. Elliott O'Donnell, *Mrs E M Ward's Reminiscences*, 1911, opp. p. 164), which depicted Elizabeth Fry visiting the women prisoners. This was greeted with optimism rather than gloom and was given a long notice in the *A.J.* of that year.[2]

Holl's painting, however, was not lightly dismissed: the *A.J.* of 1878 curtly commented: 'how an artist, personally so healthy, bright, and manly, can year after year give way to this melancholy habit of mind and brush is beyond our comprehension.'

The *Examiner* did not approve either. 'This is a text that might be illustrated by reference to a number of other works that are dignified with the title of "strong realistic pictures". In too many instances, though they may be very strong, they are not pictures at all, and the force of the sentiment that is in them only serves, where it serves any purpose at all, to blind our eyes to the failure of the artist.'

'Realistic' pictures by painters such as Fildes (q.v.) and Hubert von Herkhomer (1849–1914) never wholly gained the approval of the critics, as opposed to the exhibition-going public who were always fascinated by them. Of the other journal reviews the *I.L.N.* and the *Academy* saw the painting from a different point of view. The *I.L.N.* described it as a 'most powerful and pathetic but irrepressibly dismal picture . . . [but] Mr Holl's picture is so technically excellent as to deserve all the honours of engraving either on steel or on wood . . . we do not withhold from the painter . . . the very highest praise that it is within our power to bestow for the fidelity and the assiduity which he displayed.' The *Academy* commented on the realistic qualities too, but more kindly than the *Examiner*. 'Mr Holl's principle seems to be realism without insistency . . . he is entitled to ungrudging praise.' *The Times* wrote of the Holl painting that it had 'at least, the action of melodrama'. The *I.LN.* and *The Times* both mentioned Dickens in their appraisals of the painting. The *I.L.N.* compared Holl's painting with a woodcut illustration by 'Phiz' for *The Old Curiosity Shop* of a meeting in the prison between Mrs Nubbles and her son Christopher, who was on a charge of felony. Dickens often introduced Newgate into his novels.

A larger version of the painting of 1878 is now in Rochdale; a small study for it of the same year (untraced) was formerly in the collection of Captain Henry Hill of Brighton.[3] Hill was a great friend of Frank Holl and owned many works by him, including his own portrait. The survey of the Hill collection in *The Magazine of Art* described Holl's study for *Newgate* as 'perhaps of all his compositions the most direct in feeling and the most painter-like in execution. As regards workmanship this study is, to our mind, in some respects preferable to the finished picture.'[4]

Thomas Holloway himself had spent some time in Whitecross Street debtors' prison in the early stage of his career.

Frank Holl died at the age of 43 of a heart disease, having achieved great success in limited time. He was born in Camden Town, London, the son of Francis Holl (1815-84) a well-known engraver. Holl went to University College School until 1860 and then learnt to paint from his father and at the R.A. Schools. There he won a silver medal in 1862 and a gold medal the following year. From the beginning Holl painted scenes of poverty and misery and did much illustration work for the *Graphic* and other journals.

In 1868 Holl was awarded a travelling scholarship to Italy but after spending only one year in Rome he returned to England. He produced a succession of dramatic paintings. *No Tidings from the Sea* (ex. R.A. 1871 [595]) was bought by Queen Victoria, who had been impressed by *The Lord Gave and The Lord Hath Taken Away* (ex. R.A. 1868 [210] Guildhall Collection) which had won Holl his travelling scholarship. Then followed *Her First Born* (ex. R.A. 1876 [286] in Dundee) and the *Newgate* picture.

In the same year as *Newgate*, Holl began to paint portraits. He later wrote in a letter: 'Whilst I was painting this said Newgate picture, an old friend of mine came and asked me to paint a portrait of a friend of his . . . he pressed me to do it and I painted a head portrait which I exhibited at the same time as the Newgate picture.' Congratulations were such that 'I felt almost a little regret that it seemed to gain me more

praise than my picture'.[5] From then on Holl met with a huge demand for portraits which left him little time for subject pictures. He painted the Prince of Wales, the Duke of Cambridge, Gladstone, Joseph Chamberlain, many fellow-painters, Millais for example, and, amongst dealers, William Agnew.[6] He painted them mostly with dark tones and strong chiaroscuro, having been influenced by 17th-century Dutch and Spanish work.

His financial success enabled Holl to employ Richard Norman Shaw to build for him The Three Gables in Fitzjohn's Avenue in 1881-82, and a house in the country, Burrows Cross, near Comshall in Surrey.[8]

Part of the Winter Exhibition of 1889 at the R.A. was devoted to *A Special Selection from the Works of Frank Holl R.A.* in which 53 of his works were shown, subject paintings and portraits together.

[1] In a letter to Carey of 1 September 1887, Royal Holloway College Archives. This was published by Carey.

[2] *Art Journal*, 1876, p. 216.

[3] For his collection, see Alice Meynell, *Magazine of Art*, 1882, pp. 1-7, 80-84, 116-21 and Ronald Pickvance, *Apollo*, December 1962, pp. 789-91.

[4] *Magazine of Art*, 1882, p. 3.

[5] Autograph letter from Holl to A. M. Broadley, dated 30 November 1887, published by kind permission of The Pierpont Morgan Library, New York.

[6] See Arts Council, *Great Victorian Pictures*, 1978, p. 44.

[7] Andrew Saint, *Richard Norman Shaw*, Yale University Press, 1976, pp. 158-9.

BIBLIOGRAPHY

James Dafforne, 'The Works of Frank Holl', *Art Journal*, 1876, pp. 9-12.

Wilfrid Meynell, 'Our Living Artists – Frank Holl A.R.A.', *Magazine of Art*, 1880, pp. 187-91; reprinted in ed. Wilfrid Meynell, *Some Modern Artists and Their Work*, 1883, pp. 167-73.

Portfolio, 1888, pp. 183-4 (Obit.)

Gertrude E. Campbell, 'Frank Holl and His Works', *Art Journal*, 1889, pp. 53-9.

A Special Selection from the Works of Frank Holl R.A., Winter Exhibition 1889, Royal Academy.

Harry Quilter, *Preferences in Art, Life and Literature*, 1892, pp. 124-34.

A. M. Reynolds, *The Life and Work of Frank Holl*, 1912.

30. James Holland

1800-70, ARWS 1835, RWS 1857, RBA

Piazza dei Signori, Verona; with the Market Place 1844 (*pl. 16*)

oil on canvas, 40 × 30 in (101.5 × 76.1 cm)

INSCR: J. Holland 1844 / VERONA

PROV: Peter Potter of Walsall; his sale Christie's 9 July 1881 (128) bt Mason £913 10s.

EXH: 1844 Society of British Artists, Suffolk Street (544); 1981 Agnew's (18).

LIT: *Art Union* 1844 p. 99; *Spectator* 1844 p. 306.

REPR: Gaunt, 1972 pl. 55.

STUDIES:

1. watercolour and pencil 10 × 7¾ in (25.3 × 19.6 cm)
   Inscr. Verona Jas. Holland 1835.
   Prov. 1925 bt from Agnew by The Trustees of the John Wigham Richardson Bequest for the Walker Mechanics Institute and placed on permanent loan to the Laing Art Gallery, Newcastle.
   Lit. R. Davies, 'James Holland', *Old Watercolour Society*, Vol. VII, 1929-30, p. 46 and repr. pl. XIV.

2. *Verona*, watercolour, 13⅜ × 10⅜ in (33.7 × 26.1 cm)
   Inscr. J. Holland VERONA 1844.
   Prov. Salting Bequest to British Museum 1910.
   Repr. C. E. Hughes, *Early English Watercolours*, rev. and ed. by Jonathan Mayne, 1950, pl. 56.

3. *Verona*? 1862? 12½ × 11½ in (31.7 × 29.1 cm)
   Prov. F. Huth; Robert Arnold Cosier; his sale Christie's 4 March 1887 (175) bt Colnaghi (with [176] *Venice*) £315; anon. sale Sotheby's 21 Feb. 1934 (152) bt Vicars of Bond Street (with [151] *Venice Scene*) as *Street Scene in Verona*.

4. *Verona*, watercolour and pencil, 9½ × 6⅞ in (24.1 × 17.1 cm)
   Inscr. Verona (part of the inscription is lost by trimming. The drawing is stuck on a board signed James Holland).
   Prov. C. B. O. Clarke; anon. sale Christie's 11 March 1960 (86) bt Agnew 55 gns as *A View in Verona from the Piazza della Signoria towards the Piazza dell'Erbe*; by descent to the present owner.

UNTRACED VERSIONS:
1. 1852 ex. B.I. (460), 29 × 29 in (73.6 × 73.6 cm).
2. 1840 ex. Society of Painters in Watercolours (201).
3. 1868 ex. Society of Painters in Watercolours (285).
4. J. Carpenter Smith of Edgbaston, Birmingham; his sale Christie's 15 May 1880 (110) bt Agnew £90.
5. Charles Frederick Huth; his sale Christie's 6 July 1895 (85) by Agnew £157 10s (painted for Huth 1855, 14¼ × 11 in (36.1 × 27.9 cm); sold by them 8 Dec. 1896 to T. W. Bacon £111.
6. watercolour; James Holland; his sale of remaining works at Christie's on 26 May 1870 (191) bt White £25 14s 6d.

This subject was a recurring theme in Holland's work, for there is evidence of many pictures of this title between 1835 (the watercolour and pencil drawing in the Laing Art Gallery, Newcastle) and 1868 (one exhibited at the Society of Painters in Watercolours). Holland seems to have painted this view of the Piazza dei Signori in Verona mostly in watercolour. The works traced vary only very slightly in detail from the much larger oil painting in this collection. This painting is a polished version of the studies in watercolour and is nearest in composition to that in the British Museum of the same date. It shows minor alterations in small details – accessories and minor figures.

The painting, exhibited at the Society of British Artists in 1844, was well received. The *Art Union* described it as 'powerfully painted, and so unaffectedly that we may readily conceive a just representation of the place'. Similarly the *Spectator* called it 'His best picture . . . a piece of architectural perspective, full of character and admirably drawn, with a pleasing effect of cool shade in the foreground, contrasted with sunny brightness in the distance'. But they had reservations: 'though the colouring is opaque and the light is deficient in warmth'.

The composition is decidedly theatrical with the layers of activity and the central view through the buildings into the far distance framed by the two round arches. The figures appear merely as incidental foreground objects, secondary to the architecture.

31. James Holland
1800–70, ARWS 1835, RWS 1857, RBA

Venice : Piazza di San Marco 1850 (*pl. 17*)

panel, 9 × 11 in (22.8 × 27.9 cm)

INSCR: on verso
PIAZZETTA di S. MARCO, VENEZIA
James Holland 1850
"To Peter Potter Esq.
   This picture is a genuine work of,
      yours very truly
         James Holland Jany 22^d 1855"
(with a red seal of wax)

PROV: Peter Potter of Walsall 1855; Thomas Frederick Walker of Birmingham; his sale Christie's 21 April 1883 (98) bt Martin £189.

This small-scale painting is characteristic of Holland's views of the city which he visited many times. It was one of his favourite places to paint in both oil and watercolour.

Peter Potter of Walsall owned the other Holland in this collection, the *Piazza dei Signori, Verona*, as well as paintings by Hayter, Millais, LeJeune, H. O'Neil, Hook and Dobson, each with an autograph letter attached to the back of the picture.

A painting with the title of *Piazzetta di San Marco*, but larger dimensions (28 in square, 71.1 cm) was exhibited at the B.I. (211) in 1850; it was possibly a finished picture for which this small painting may have been a sketch. This larger work, according to the *A.J.*, was chosen by the Art Union for a prize of £40.[1] From the descriptions of the painting in the journal reviews of the B.I. exhibition, the work exhibited there was very similar to the one in the collection here. The *A.J.* wrote: 'This view presents the quay of the Grand Canal, at Venice, having the palace on the left. The composition derives life from numerous figures of senators and citizens, in the costume of the palmy days of the City of the Sea'.[2] This reinforces the supposition that the Royal Holloway College painting was a preparatory oil sketch for the larger exhibited work.

James Holland, born in 1800, was known equally for his work in watercolour and in oil. His family was connected with the pottery industry in Burslem, and he began his career by painting flowers on porcelain. In 1819 he moved to London, firstly teaching flower painting and later painting landscapes, coastal and architectural views.

In 1831 he went to France, one of many Continental tours he was to make. Some of his topographical work was published: for *The Landscape Annual*, Holland illustrated William Henry Harrison's *The Tourist in Portugal* published in 1839. He exhibited many of his works, at the R.A. from 1824 to 1865 and also at the B.I., the Society of British Artists and the two watercolour societies. He was elected Associate of the Royal Watercolour Society in 1835 and a full member in 1857.

[1] *Art Journal*, 1850, p. 212.
[2] *Art Journal*, 1850, p. 91.
[3] I would like to acknowledge information received from Mr Alfred Vicars and Mr Evelyn Joll in connection with the preparation of these entries.

BIBLIOGRAPHY
Art Journal, 1870, p. 107 (Obit.)
H. Stokes, 'James Holland', *Walker's Quarterly*, Vol. XXIII, 1927.
R. Davies, 'James Holland', *Old Water-Colour Society*, Vol. VII, 1929–30.
M. Tonkin, 'The Life of James Holland', *Old Water-Colour Society*, Vol. XLII, 1967, pp. 35–50.
Martin Hardie, *Water-Colour Painting in Britain, Vol. III: The Victorian Period*, 1968, pp. 31–5.

32. James Clarke Hook
1819–1907, ARA 1850, RA 1860, Ret. 1907, HFRPE

Leaving at Low Water 1863 (*pl. 31*)

oil on canvas, 27 × 42 in (68.5 × 106.6 cm)

INSCR: 18 ⏦ 63

PROV: Frederick Thomas Turner; his sale Christie's 4 May 1878 (51) bt Thomas Taylor of Aston Rowant Gallery, Oxfordshire £1,186 10s; his sale Christie's 28 April 1883 (61) bt Martin £1,365.

EXH: 1863 R.A. (335); 1981 Agnew's (19).

LIT: *A.J.* 1863 p. 113; *Athenaeum* 2 May 1863 p. 590; *Examiner* 2 May 1863 p. 280; *Fraser's* June 1863 pp.

785, 791, reprinted in William Michael Rossetti, *Fine Art, Chiefly Contemporary* 1867 p. 27; *I.L.N.* 16 May 1863 p. 542; *Saturday Review* 30 May 1863 p. 694, reprinted almost exactly in Francis Turner Palgrave, *Essays on Art* 1886 pp. 22–4; *The Times* 2 May 1863 p. 11, *Mag. of Art* 1882 p. 314; Dumas, 1882–4 p. 239; *The Times* 30 April 1883 p. 6; Stephens, 1888 p. 24; Hook, 1929–32 Pt. II p. 145 and Appendix C p. xxxiii; Bethel, 1975 pp. 26–7, checklist no. 69 and repr. pl. 25a.

According to Hook this 'was painted at Tresco one of the Scilly Islands'.[1] Despite the title opinions varied as to exactly whether the scene was one of preparation for departure or of arrival. Most likely it was departure, with the father carrying a child out to the waiting sailing boat and the mother and child on the shore, having done some errands, about to make their own way to the boat at the end of the stone jetty.

Hook's son, Allan James Hook, recorded in his biography of his father that for most of the summer of 1862, the year before the painting was exhibited at the R.A., Hook rented rooms in a cottage at Tresco in order to paint there. He wrote that 'the three pictures painted at Scilly formed the whole of my father's contribution at the Academy Exhibition in the following year, 1863'. The other two paintings were *The Prawn Catchers* (Private Collection) and *A Sailor's Wedding Party* (Brighton Art Gallery). They are characteristic of Hook's work from about the late 1850s onwards, when he began to paint genre sea pieces. *The Times* reviewer of the 1863 R.A. exhibition observed that the three paintings 'have his wonted charms of freshness and truth, daylight, and salt sea air'.

The *Athenaeum* critic reported that *Leaving at Low Water*, of the three, was 'the most brilliant' and the *I.L.N.* called it 'the most entirely satisfactory . . . There is true poetry and pathos in this common incident of humble seafaring life'. The idea of the picture representing 'common' and 'humble' life was reiterated by *Fraser's Magazine* who, in reference to this painting and *The Prawn Catchers*, stated that Hook 'though, sometimes, more striking, has never been better . . . never a greater master of the riches of simplicity, and the beauty of common things'.

The two fullest descriptions and appraisals of the painting came from the *A.J.* and the *Saturday Review*, and they differed only slightly in their praise and hesitations. The *A.J.* wrote that the painting 'includes one of this artist's noblest figures – a fisherman's wife preparing to join a boat as the tide goes down. Mr. Hook raises his rustics by aid of a certain nobility of type, infusing beauty into their rude frames, which become thus exalted into a natural, and yet in some degree into an ideal, manhood and womanhood. The figures he introduces are like to peasants of Arcadia, only they happen, instead of tending flocks in Greece, to be boating at Bideford or Clovelly, or fishing among the Scilly Islands.' Francis Turner Palgrave in the *Saturday Review*, however, chose to criticise 'some want of accuracy in drawing the figure'. But like all the other critics, he found that 'the freshness and charm of the idea and the execution appeal to us, almost too strongly, to overlook these deficiencies in the sight of so much excellence. Few . . . can do justice to the admirable fidelity with which Mr. Hook has caught the peculiar features of the little Archipelago . . . we heartily rejoice that he has transferred his easel to so new and picturesque a region.'[2]

Hook's grandfather was Dr Adam Clarke, the Wesleyan preacher, commentator and theological writer, and his father was a merchant and judge in Sierra Leone. Hook entered the R.A. Schools in 1836 and his first exhibit, in 1839, was *The Hard Task* (now lost). He won a R.A. travelling scholarship in 1846 and spent his two years in Italy. His work at this time was influenced by Venetian painters, especially Carpaccio, and consisted mostly of historical and literary subjects. During the early 1850s Hook changed his subject matter to rural and coastal scenes: his *Luff, Boy* of 1859 (ex R.A. [369], Private Collection) was a great success. Ruskin wrote of him in *Modern Painters* that his designs 'are, perhaps, the only works of the kind in existence which deserve to be mentioned in connection with the pastorals of Wordsworth and Tennyson'.[3]

Graham Reynolds summed up Hook's work with: 'This once well-known and influential artist was one of those singled out by Baudelaire for praise in the English contribution to the 1855 Exhibition in Paris . . . His forte, for which he may still be appreciated, lies in his painting of the sea; he has a rich Venetian tone, no doubt appropriated from his historical paintings, and a surface which is in agreeable contrast to the linoleum-like finish of some of his contemporaries . . . he spoke highly in praise of the Pre-Raphaelites and, though his work had no affinity with theirs was, as a sort of un-covenanted reward, himself praised by Ruskin. To have been praised both by Baudelaire and Ruskin is no common achievement . . . the merit of his later style rests in its clear understanding of the sea, his ability to link human action with coastal scenery, and the genuinely attractive character of his brushwork.'[4]

Ruskin and Reynolds do not mention Hook's ability to balance colour, and this painting is a good example of a very clever sparing use of red, dabbed carefully, to liven interest, only in small areas of the canvas.[5]

[1] Stated in a letter to Carey of 3 September 1887, Royal Holloway College Archives.
[2] This was re-printed almost exactly three years later in Palgrave's *Essays on Art*.
[3] John Ruskin, *The Works of John Ruskin*, Library Edition, ed. E. T. Cook and Alexander Wedderburn, 1903–12, Vol. V, p. 23.
[4] Graham Reynolds, *Victorian Painting*, 1966, p. 152.
[5] I am grateful to Miss Denise Bethel for information regarding this painting.

BIBLIOGRAPHY
'British Artists: Their Style and Character, no. XII, James Clarke Hook, A.R.A.', *Art Journal*, 1856, pp. 41–4.
F. G. Stephens, 'English Artists of the Present Day, XXXII, James Clarke Hook, R.A.', *Portfolio*, 1871, pp. 181–6.
W. W. Fenn, 'James Clarke Hook', *Magazine of Art*, 1879, pp. 10–14; reprinted in: ed. Wilfrid Meynell, *Some Modern Artists and their Work*, 1883, pp. 160–5.
F. G. Stephens, *Illustrated Biographies of Modern Artists*, ed. F. G. Dumas, 1882–84, Vol. II, pp. 219–40.
A. H. Palmer, 'James Clarke Hook, R.A.', *Portfolio*, 1888, pp. 1–9, 35–43, 74–82, 105–11, 165–70.
F. G. Stephens, 'J. C. Hook, R.A., His Life and Work', *Art Annual*, 1888, pp. 1–32.
Allan James Hook, *Life of James Clarke Hook, R.A.*, 1929–32, 3 vols.
Denise Bethel, *James Clarke Hook R.A., 1819–1907*, Courtauld Institute of Art, University of London, Unpublished M.A. Report, 1975.

33. John Callcott Horsley

1817–1903, ARA 1855, RA 1864, Ret. 1897

The Banker's Private Room: Negotiating a Loan 1870
(*pl. 56*)

oil on canvas, 40 × 50 in (101.5 × 126.9 cm)

INSCR: J C Horsley 1870

PROV: Painted for George Fox of Harefield, Wimslow; his sale Christie's 12 May 1877 (161) bt Marsden £1,165 10s; Thomas Taylor of Aston Rowant Gallery, Oxfordshire; his sale Christie's 28 April 1883 (59) bt Martin £850 10s.

EXH: 1870 R.A. (147); 1872 London Int. Ex. (325); 1887 Manchester Royal Jubilee Ex. (240); 1897 Guildhall (81); 1977 Wolverhampton Art Gallery and Laing Art Gallery, Newcastle *The Cranbrook Colony* (39); 1981 Agnew's (20).

LIT: *A.J.* 1870 p. 165; *Athenaeum* 28 May 1870 p. 714; *Graphic* 11 June 1870 p. 663; *I.L.N.* 7 May 1870 p. 487; *Saturday Review* 4 June 1870 p. 737; *The Times* 30 April 1870 p. 12; *A.J.* 1872 p. 117; *A.J.* 1887 p. 251; Walter Armstrong, *Celebrated Pictures Exhibited at the Manchester Royal Jubilee Ex. Fine Arts Section* 1888 p. 33; Temple, 1897 p. 57 and repr. opp. p. 56.

How the idea for this picture came to Horsley was explained by him in a letter to Carey.[1] Horsley outlined in some detail what he called the 'anecdote': 'I have been asked to state any incident connected with my picture of "The Banker's Parlour, Negotiating a Loan" that might possess some amount of general interest as an insertion in the Catalogue of the pictures at The Royal Holloway College ... One day, wishing to speak to the Manager of the Bank I deal with, I passed through the Office to the door of his Private Room, which, being a glass one I could see through without opening it, and my attention was at once arrested by observing my old friend, a staid Scotchman, sitting at his desk just in the action of the picture, with an expression of doubt and hesitation on his face, whilst before him was a lady, with papers around her on the table, leaning forward and apparently stating her case with much earnestness – I could not see her face but the momentary glance I had of the lines of her figure, and handsome garments, suggested the presence of a decidedly fine woman . . . before I got outside the Bank I was filled with the idea that I had seen an excellent subject for a picture, and ere I reached Oxford St from Stratford Place I saw the completed work, (much as I have painted it) – "in my mind's eye".'

In an earlier letter to Carey of 5 June of the same year, Horsley wrote that he considered this painting 'one of the best I ever painted'.[2]

It seems from the *A.J.* description of George Fox's collection that it was a 'companion' picture to *Pay for Peeping* (ex. R.A. 1872 [5], of the same dimensions, now at Cartwright Hall, Bradford Art Galleries and Museums).[3] This was also painted for George Fox, a Manchester cotton king, as had been *The Banker's Private Room*. In both paintings, Horsley based his ideas on Dutch 17th-century painting, especially in his use of clear divisions of strong light to dramatise the effects of suspense and tension.

A detail of *The Banker's Private Room* inspired by Dutch motifs is, for instance, the man seen on the right through the half-open door, caught in the action of taking a book off the shelf, and the glimpse through into the room beyond. In fact, the painting has been put together very cleverly with the use of various ideas from Dutch and Flemish painters. The head-dress of the chaperone seated on the left of the picture suggests a hat which Rubens had painted in a portrait of his second wife, Hélène Fourment, although Horsley has reversed it for his figure. The banker's attire is perhaps inspired by Rembrandt's Syndics figures and Horsley has painted a Metsu-like fur-trimmed jacket for the pleading lady. He took great interest and delight in the costumes that he used and is known to have borrowed them from a 'costumier'. He also travelled a good deal and recorded much about the pictures he saw. His knowledge of 16th- and 17th-century painting must have been extensive to combine these elements and extract so skilfully what he wanted from them.

The painting hanging above the chaperone or 'duenna' is very similar to works by the Flemish 17th-century painter, David Teniers II, of *The Temptation of St Anthony*, which might possibly have been intended by Horsley to have some significance for this subject.[4]

According to Andrew Greg, A. E. Mulready, one of the members of the Cranbrook Colony, posed for the figure of the banker whilst he was staying with the Horsley's in 1870.[5] The catalogue for the George Fox sale in 1877 states that Horsley selected *The Banker's Private Room* for exhibition at Vienna which indicates that Horsley himself was pleased with this work.

The painting was very well received at the R.A. exhibition of 1870. The *A.J.* was particularly enthusiastic. They considered it one of the best pictures Horsley ever painted and: 'The old usurer is worthy of the scholars of Rembrandt; the figure is powerful, individual, and, in common with the rest of the picture, capitally turned out of hand. The execution is not that of the small Dutchman, such as Teniers and Ostade: it is large and broad, and yet realistic. Here and there may be noticed a watchful eye for niceties of detail . . . The distinctions of colour and of light are here delicate as they are liberal.'

The quality of the colour and light was reiterated by the *Saturday Review*. They pointed out that the 'quiet unobtrusive study of texture, light, shade, and colour can scarcely be praised too highly'. Certain other critics chose details to comment on, as in the *Athenaeum* who, though considering the composition 'poor', conceded that 'the expression of the banker is the best Mr. Horsley has produced within our recollection'. The *Times* praised the details, with 'Mr. Horsley has painted nothing better than the two figures and still life of the picture – in particular the trunk, sword, and parchments, and the banker himself' and 'the lady, too, is very bewitching'. The *Graphic* summed up most concisely how 'Mr. Horsley distinguishes himself' with: 'The Story is clearly told, the characters well represented, the painting very firm and bright. The fair borrower, in her radiant dress, contrasts happily with the sombre lender, soberly attired, with a keen business look in his face, and yet an air about him of grave courtesy. The fittings of the banker's apartment are reproduced with fond care.'

John Callcott Horsley was the son of a musician, William Horsley, nephew of the landscape painter Sir Augustus Wall Callcott (1779–1844) and brother-in-law of the famous civil engineer Isambard Kingdom

Brunel. He was born in London and first studied at Dr Sass's Academy and then from 1831, at the R.A. Schools. He exhibited his first painting at the R.A. in 1839, *The Pride of the Village* (58, Tate Gallery) and continued to exhibit there until 1896. He was awarded prizes for his entries in the competition for the Palace of Westminster decorative scheme during the 1840s and continued to paint historical or contemporary genre subjects throughout the following two decades.

During the 1850s Horsley was painting portraits (to which he returned later, in the 1880s and 1890s, when his style of genre painting had become unfashionable). In the later years of the 1850s he settled in Cranbrook, Kent, and began to paint with those who had formed themselves into the Cranbrook Colony (amongst whom was F. D. Hardy [q.v.]), though he remained with the Colony only for a short time.

In 1864 Horsley employed the architect Richard Norman Shaw to extend his Cranbrook house, Willesley – Shaw's first commission for a country house. Horsley provided Shaw with more commissions from his friends, and his son, Gerald Callcott Horsley, became a pupil of Shaw's. *The Banker's Private Room* could well have been painted at Willesley, which had a panelled room with windows similar to those in the painting.[6]

Horsley was deeply committed to the R.A.: he organised their first Old Master Winter exhibition in 1867 and continued to do so for the next 27 years. He also was officially appointed Rector of the Academy from 1875 to 1890 and was Treasurer from 1882 to 1897. He died in 1903 and in the same year his memoirs were published posthumously as *Recollections of a Royal Academician*, edited by Mrs. Edmund Helps.

[1] Dated 18 June 1888, Royal Holloway College Archives. This was quoted in part by Carey.
[2] Royal Holloway College Archives.
[3] *Art Journal*, 1872, p. 117.
[4] I am grateful to Dr Lorne Campbell for suggestions he has made concerning this painting.
[5] See the exhibition catalogue, *The Cranbrook Colony*, Wolverhampton Art Gallery, 1977, no. 39.
[6] See the illustration in Andrew Saint, *Richard Norman Shaw*, Yale University Press, 1976, p. 35.

BIBLIOGRAPHY
'John Callcott Horsley, A.R.A.', *Art Journal*, 1857, pp. 181–4.
John Callcott Horsley, *Recollections of a Royal Academician*, ed. Mrs Edmund Helps, 1903.
The Cranbrook Colony exhibition catalogue, 1977, Wolverhampton and Newcastle.

34. Sir Edwin Landseer
1802–73, ARA 1826, RA 1831, KT 1850

Man proposes, God disposes 1864 (*pl.80*)

oil on canvas, 36 × 96 in (91.4 × 243.7 cm)

PROV: Painted for Edward John Coleman of Stoke Park, Buckinghamshire; his sale Christie's 28 May 1881 (49) b₁ Thomas £6,615.

EXH: 1864 R.A. (163); 1874 R.A. Winter Ex. *Landseer* (222); 1878 Paris Int. Ex. (128); 1897 Guildhall (92); 1925 Wembley, *British Empire Ex.*, in Polar Section of Court of Heroes; 1981–82 Philadelphia and Tate Gallery *Sir Edwin Landseer 1802–73* (151).

LIT: *Annual Register* 1864 pp. 332, 333; *A.J.* 1864 p. 168; *Athenaeum* 7 May 1864 p. 650; *Blackwood's* July 1864 p. 95; *Examiner* 30 April 1864 p. 280; *Fine Arts Quarterly Review* 1864 pp. 27–8; *Fraser's* July 1864 p. 67; *I.L.N.* 7 May 1864 p. 455; *The Reader* 7 May 1864 pp. 595, 596, 724; *Saturday Review* 4 June 1864 p. 689 reprinted in Francis Turner Palgrave, Essays on Art, 1866 p. 78; *Spectator* 14 May 1864 p. 564; *The Times* 30 April 1864 p. 14; Stephens, *Early Works*, 1869 p. 71; *Portfolio* 1871 pp. 165–70; Dafforne, 1873 pp. 57 and listed pp. 82, 89; Stephens, *Memoirs*, 1874 pp. 138–9 and 3rd ed., 1881 pp. 105–6; Graves, 1875 no. 417; Monkhouse, *Pictures*, 1877 p. xi; Monkhouse, *Studies*, 1877 pp. 83, 86; Monkhouse, *Works*, 1879, 80 pp. 106, 112; Sweetser, 1879 pp. 123–4, 138; Cunningham, 1880, Vol. III p. 387; *The Times* 30 May 1881 p. 8; Temple, 1897 pp. 45–6; Gilbey, 1900, Vol II pp. 67, 78, 80; Manson, 1902 pp. 161–2; Scott, 1903 pp. 34, 71; Chester, 1920 pp. 51–2 and repr. p. 54; Hill, 1973 pp. 39–40 and repr. p. 38; Lennie, 1976 pp. 207, 209, 243 and repr. detail pl. 15; Arts Council, *Great Victorian Pictures*, 1978 p. 48; David Robertson, *Sir Charles Eastlake and the Victorian Art World*, Princeton, 1978 pp. 402–3, 416–7.

REPR: Gaunt, 1972 pl. 122.

ENGR: By Thomas Landseer ARA, entitled *Man Proposes – God Disposes (Polar Bears)*. Line style, 42 × 15 in (106.6 × 39.8 cm) Published by Agnew's, declared 31 July 1871.
  Exh. 1887 Manchester Royal Jubilee Ex. (1109)
  Lit. Gilbey, 1900 p. 67; *Agnew's 1817–1967*, Intro. Sir Geoffrey Agnew, 1967, p. 65.

Painted for Edward John Coleman of Stoke Park, near Stoke Poges, Buckinghamshire, for the sum of £2,415, which included the copyright, this is one of the most enigmatic of all Landseer's works.[1]

Described in 1902 as a 'bitter satire upon the vanity of human effort', it supposedly depicts the destruction by two polar bears of the scattered remains of some of Sir John Franklin's party who perished in their attempt to discover the North-West Passage.[2] A distinguished naval officer, Sir John Franklin (1786–1847) undertook a series of enterprising explorations determined to discover the Passage. In May 1845 he set out in command of two specially-equipped ships, the *Erebus* and the *Terror*, with 138 men and provisions for three years. Both ships disappeared. It was not until the expeditions of Dr John Rae, a factor in the Hudson Bay Company, in 1854, and Sir Leopold McClintock, in 1858–59, that any concrete evidence was established as to the fate of Franklin's quest. McClintock's expedition was the more conclusive, finding proof of Franklin's death and physical remains of his expedition.[3] Among McClintock's discoveries were human skeletons, some of which had been destroyed by 'large and powerful animals, probably wolves'.[4] They also found a small British red ensign and the tracks of bears and arctic foxes. Another expedition of the 1850s, Inglefield in the *Isabel*, had reported seeing 'a huge bear sitting motionless on one of the graves at Beechey Island'. Further evidence was the discovery by Rae of a telescope. One appears in the bottom left hand corner of Landseer's painting.

Interest and curiosity in the Franklin mystery was perpetuated by further expeditions and their reports, and by the wide coverage by the press throughout the 1850s and 1860s. It would not have been unusual, therefore, for a painter such as Landseer to have adopted this popular subject. Cosmo Monkhouse put this down to Landseer's 'power of seizing a subject in everybody's thoughts' which was 'due to the influence of passing events and feelings on his mind', and made up the 'elements of his popularity'.[5] Holloway, too, it seems, was fascinated by the story, for among his personal possessions are contemporary documents relating to the disappearance of Franklin in the form of newspaper cuttings, charts, letters and so on.[6]

For a comparative treatment of the subject, David Robertson cites E. W. Cooke's (q.v.) *H.M.S. "Terror" in the Ice of Frozen Strait, April 1837* (ex. R.A. 1860 [248], not traced).[7] Cooke, however, shows a ship wedged amongst icebergs, with no sign of life, and no polar bears.

The *A.J.* of 1866 (two years after Landseer's picture was exhibited) announced a forthcoming chromo-lithograph after the painting entitled *Deserted*, by Captain Walter William May (1831–96).[8] May, a marine painter and watercolourist and member of the Royal Society of Painters in Watercolours, had taken part in one of the search expeditions in 1852–54 and painted what he saw. Some of his work was later used as book illustrations.[9] *Deserted* depicted an abandoned ship frozen in the ice. The description in the *A.J.* read: 'The only signs of life are two polar bears, which have been attracted to the spot in the hope of finding food.' Neither the painting nor the print have been traced but this is a further rare example of the polar bear being represented in pictorial form at an early date. Landseer's brother, Thomas, had produced an awkward and unconvincing impression of a polar bear standing on an iceberg, for a set of engravings published under the title of *Characteristic Portraits of Animals*.[10] 'The Polar Bear, Zoological Gardens' is amongst this set and is dated January 1831.[11] Edwin Landseer would have seen polar bears in the London Zoo in the early 1860s, for there was a pair of adult bears there which had a cub in 1865.[12]

Apart from the written sources available to Landseer for re-enacting on canvas a possible moment of the sad story, and the live polar bears in the Zoo, there would have been a good many illustrations of icebergs and the scenery of the polar regions. There is, however, very little documentary evidence extant concerning this painting, and no studies or preliminary material have been traced. There does exist the receipt for the painting, dated 'London April 28, 1864' and signed by Thomas Hyde Hills, Landseer's friend and agent.[13]

Years before, Landseer had been reminded that 'Man proposes, God disposes', in a letter the sixth Duke of Bedford had written to him on 24 March 1837, reporting the non-arrival of 'your sister's miniature copy by this time, *mais l'homme propose, Dieu in-idispose*'.[14] The epigram appears in a variety of sources, amongst them Thomas à Kempis's *De Imitatione Christi*, William Langland's *Piers Plowman*, Ariosto's *Orlando Furioso* and Cervantes's *Don Quixote*.

There is evidence of Landseer having referred to the skull of a polar bear, which he borrowed from the famous palaeontologist Hugh Falconer (1808–65), for there are two letters at the Forres Museum, Morayshire, in one of which, of 16 March 1864, Landseer writes to Falconer 'Your skull has been invaluable'. The other of 2 (? Feb) 1864 says: 'The P. Bear skull is exactly what I wanted – when my Picture is in a . . . state you must do me the favour to come and tell me if I have done justice to the grand Head you have kindly trusted me with.'[15] Landseer was 62 when he painted this important picture. He had not exhibited at the R.A. since 1861, possibly due to his illness, his preparation for *Man Proposes, God Disposes* or his preoccupation with the work for the Nelson Monument lions in Trafalgar Square (1858–67).[16] He submitted four works for the 1864 exhibition. The other three, *Piper and pair of Nutcrackers* (82, untraced), *Windsor Park* (134, Wolverhampton Art Gallery) and *Pensioners* (371, untraced), would not have required the attention which he needed for this painting. In comparison to his other subjects this picture is almost a reversal of role, since he had spent much of his life painting and drawing the animal as a victim hunted by man and at his mercy.

The man who commissioned this painting from Landseer, Edward John Coleman (1834–85) lived at Stoke Park, a magnificent unusual house built for John Penn, the grandson of William Penn of Pennsylvania. It seems that Landseer visited the house frequently and, according to Vernon Heath's *Recollections*, used the banqueting hall of the Old Manor House at Stoke Poges for a studio.[17] In 1881 Coleman sold four paintings by Landseer, three of which had been painted for him, and two major Clarkson Stanfields, *The Battle of Roveredo* and *The Pic du Midi d'Ossau*, both of which were bought by Holloway.

A postscript to a letter from Coleman to Landseer reads thus: 'I hope the picture of the Polar Bears arrived safely. I suppose you will be good enough to send Graves the enclosed names who have all asked me to place their names down for a proof. I suppose you have also many friends who are waiting to subscribe.' A list of five names and addresses follows:
'Lord Bishop of Oxford, Caddesdon Palace
R B Harvey Esq. MP Lanley Park
J W Knight Jr. 57 Cleveland Square, Hyde Park
J E Coleman Esq. Hollanden Park, Tunbridge, Kent
T H Hills Esq. 45 Queen Anne Street.'[18]

From the point of view of composition, there are few works by Landseer to compare with *Man Proposes, God Disposes*. The broken mast provides a strong diagonal force and separates the activities of the two bears, neither of which is painted in full, to create what Cosmo Monkhouse called a 'terribly suggestive picture'.[19] It was he who compared the fundamental idea behind *Man Proposes, God Disposes* with 'the almost unbearable torture' of the *Otter Hunt* (ex. R.A. 1844, Laing Art Gallery Newcastle) and the *Random Shot* (ex. R.A. 1848, Bury Art Gallery), all of which he considered the result of 'a nightmare of imagination'.[20]

The dimensions of the canvas are unusual for Landseer too. A. G. Temple suggested that the disproportionate three feet by eight feet 'was adopted presumably as calculated to give a better idea of the immensity of that lone region stretching right and left into which the daring of the Arctic explorers had led them to penetrate'.[21] Many writers felt too that the large scale of the work emphasised the impression of pathos and terror.

One of Landseer's works closest to *Man Proposes, God Disposes* in idea and composition was his *War* of 1846, painted as one of a pair with *Peace* (presented to the nation by Robert Vernon, both destroyed in the Tate Gallery flood in 1928).[22] *War* depicted a similar balance of a dead horse on either side of the painting, with a dead soldier lying beside each amid débris and smoke. It was a painting of destruction, despair and isolation, much as *Man Proposes, God Disposes* is.

A few weeks before the opening of Royal Holloway College by Queen Victoria in 1886, there appeared in *Punch* a rearrangement of the painting in the form of a cartoon entitled *The Grand Old Man Proposes, and –*.[23] It had been adapted, with the words UNION and MORLEY added, to comment on Gladstone's problem of Ireland.

Most of the exhibition reviews, of which there were many, gave some sort of description of Landseer's painting itself, possibly because it was felt that an explanation of the subject matter was needed. One of the most lyrical of the reviews was in the *A.J.* who described 'the terror-striking ice-fields where Franklin and his companions found in death snow for their grave and winding-sheet. Two hungry bears have come upon the relics of the expedition – a mast, a sail, a telescope, and a flag. One of the savage brutes tears the red union jack, the other crunches the rib bones of an unfortunate navigator. The cold mountains of ice, vast and desolate, are illumed by gleams of sunlight. Altogether the picture is remarkably impressive by its poetry, pathos and terror.' They were the only journal to point out that 'in execution the work is a little slight, and the bodies of the bears are certainly wanting in substance'.

It was, however, considered an imaginative and courageous painting. Francis Turner Palgrave in the *Saturday Review* wrote: 'What, to our thinking, gives it supremacy in rank is the force and height of the idea.' William Michael Rossetti in *Fraser's Magazine* went so far as to claim that the polar bear 'will henceforth be a majestic personality in fine art'. The *Fine Arts Quarterly Review* wrote: 'Like some of his previous works, but still more decidedly, it places the painting of brute life upon a new and higher platform, hardly inferior in lofty suggestiveness to human subjects.'

The painting was taken very seriously, as seen in the review in *Blackwood's Edinburgh Magazine*, who probed deeper than most in their summary of the picture: 'It is

not for some years that this consummate painter of animal life has been so much himself. As of old, he here not only gives smoothness of coat and texture of hair, but seems at the same time, by an art too subtle for analysis, to portray the inner nature and mute consciousness of the brute creation, making the silent actors in the scenes he delineates move the spectator to terror; or, on the other hand, by beauty and pathos awaken to sympathy.'

However, the question of how appropriate a subject it was to paint was evident, presumably given that it was painted at such an early date following the certain knowledge of Franklin's death and considering that his widow, Jane, Lady Franklin, was still alive. The *Athenaeum* wrote, following a lengthy discusion of the painting's quality and merits, simply: 'So much for the picture, and the artist's craft. As to his choice of subject, we protest against it.' Further to this objection came one, on the same day, in the *I.L.N.* which read: 'Extraordinarily original and imaginative as is this picture, it may be questioned whether the representation is not too purely harrowing for the proper function of art.' The *Examiner* had already written that this element of the picture was not perhaps crucial enough to be important, for they wrote: 'Let us protest in advance against all mock squeamishness over the very natural behaviour of these two bears.'

The issue was raised again seven years later by F. G. Stephens in his *Portfolio* article on Landseer in 1871. His view summed up Landseer's achievement in a less subjective manner. He wrote that the painting 'was ineffably pathetic, its effect is due to more obvious means . . . [it] brings, in the slow, shouldering, stride of the heavy, yet silent-footed brutes over the shining blocks of ice which hold the bones of our countrymen, something, the horror of which is beyond the aims of art, nevertheless it is not the less powerful because it is revolting. This horror-invoking process may be taken as indicating where Sir Edwin, in one of his most potent pictures, touched the very verge of melodrama, that pest of modern design, and furnished an instance which is the more worthy of note because it is one of a very few offences against noble and pure taste distinguishable in the long list of his works.'

Man Proposes, God Disposes came towards the end of Landseer's career. He was to exhibit works at the R.A. for only eight more years, having begun in 1815 with two works, at the prodigiously early age of 13. He was the only British painter to receive a first-class gold medal at the 1855 Exposition Universelle in Paris. His Highland subjects especially had enchanted Queen Victoria, who owned a large collection of his work, and Landseer was never without patrons either for his animal paintings (mostly for dogs, horses and deer) or for his portraits.

Landseer profited greatly from the income from engravings of his paintings, most of which were done by his brother Thomas, as well as from the high prices he secured for the paintings themselves. From 1860 onwards his pictures at auction brought prices well into the thousands. What Holloway paid in 1881 for *Man Proposes, God Disposes* (£6,615) was at the time a record auction price for a Landseer painting. This was unequalled in the saleroom until 1892, when Agnew paid £7,245 for *The Monarch of the Glen* (ex. R.A. 1851 [112] now the property of John Dewar & Sons, Ltd.) at the sale of Lord Cheylesmore.

[1] Edward John Coleman also owned Landseer's 1864 B.I. exhibit *Well-bred Sitters, that never say they are 'bored'.*

[2] James A. Manson, *Sir Edwin Landseer R.A.*, 1902, pp. 161–2.

[3] See Captain McClintock, RN, LLD, *A Narrative of the Discovery of the Fate of Sir John Franklin and his Companions*, 1859.

[4] See Roderic Owen, *The Fate of Franklin*, 1978.

[5] W. Cosmo Monkhouse, *Pictures of Sir Edwin Landseer*, A New Series, 1877, p. xi.

[6] These papers are now housed at the Surrey Record Office at Kingston-on-Thames.

[7] David Robertson, *Sir Charles Eastlake and the Victorian Art World*, Princeton, 1978, pp. 402–3, 416–17. For an illustration of the painting by E. W. Cooke, see *Art Journal*, 1869, p. 254.

[8] *Art Journal*, 1866, p. 126.

[9] In *Fourteen Sketches made during the voyage up Wellington Channel in search of Sir John Franklin*, 1855 and F. L. McLintock, *The Voyage of the Fox in the Arctic seas*, 1859.

[10] Published by Moon, Boys and Graves, Pall Mall.

[11] I am grateful to Dr Catherine Gordon for drawing my attention to this engraving.

[12] This information was kindly provided by Mr R. Fish, Librarian of the Zoological Society of London.

[13] I am extremely grateful to Mr. A. J. Forrest for telling me of the existence of this receipt and to Mr B. D. J. Walsh for allowing me to publish it.

[14] In the Landseer correspondence at the Victoria and Albert Museum Library.

[15] I am grateful to Mr Richard Ormond for pointing out these letters which were catalogued by Mr Patrick Boylan for the Forres Museum in 1977, nos. 245 and 267. Permission to publish has kindly been granted by the Moray Museums Service.

[16] Another letter at the Forres Museum (cat. no. 117) from Falconer to 'My Dear Grace', no year given, states that Landseer 'failed to get a bear's skull – and his picture was too late for the Exhibition!'

[17] Vernon Heath, *Recollections*, 1892, p. 78.

[18] This letter has no date but is thought to be about 1864, in the Victoria and Albert Museum Library.

[19] W. Cosmo Monkhouse, *The Studies of Sir Edwin Landseer*, 1877, p. 86.

[20] Op. cit. p. 83.

[21] A. G. Temple, *The Art of Painting in the Queen's Reign*, 1897, pp. 45–6.

[22] For an illustration, see Chesneau, 1885, opp. p. 97.

[23] *Punch*, 10 April 1886, p. 171. I am grateful to Mr Malcolm Warner for drawing this to my attention.

BIBLIOGRAPHY

F. G. Stephens, *The Early Works of Sir Edwin Landseer, R.A.*, 1869.

The Landseer Gallery; A Series of Twenty Autotype Reproductions of Engravings after the Celebrated Early Paintings of Sir Edwin Landseer R.A., 1871, new and enlarged edition, 1878.

F. G. Stephens, 'English Artists of the Present Day, Sir Edwin Landseer', *Portfolio*, 1871, pp. 165–70.

Art Journal, 1873, pp. 326–7 (Obit.).

James Dafforne, *Pictures by Sir Edwin Landseer*, 1873.

'The Works of Sir E. Landseer at Burlington House', *Art Journal*, 1874, pp. 55–6.

Caleb Scholefield Mann, *The Works of Sir E. Landseer*, unpublished manuscript Victoria and Albert Museum Library, 1874.

F. G. Stephens, *Memoirs of Sir Edwin Landseer*, 1874.

Exhibition catalogue, *Landseer*, 1874, Royal Academy.

Algernon Graves, *Catalogue of the Works of Sir Edwin Landseer*, 1875, (the manuscript for which is in the British Museum Print Room).

R. N. Wornum, 'The National Gallery XVII – Sir Edwin Landseer', *Portfolio*, 1876, pp. 18–19.

W. Cosmo Monkhouse, *The Studies of Sir Edwin Landseer*, Illustrated by Sketches from the Collection of Her Majesty the Queen and Other Sources, 1877.

W. Cosmo Monkhouse, *Pictures of Sir Edwin Landseer*, A New Series, 1877.

W. Cosmo Monkhouse, *The Works of Sir Edwin Landseer*, Illustrated by Forty-Four Steel Engravings and about Two Hundred Woodcuts from Sketches in the Collection of Her Majesty the Queen and Other Sources, 1879, 1880.

M. F. Sweetser, *Landseer*, Boston, 1879.

Allan Cunningham, *Lives of the Most Eminent British Painters*, Revised edition by Mrs Charles Heaton, 1880, Vol. III, pp. 377–90.

F. G. Stephens, *Sir Edwin Landseer*, 1880.

F. G. Stephens, 'Landseer, The Dog-Painter', *Portfolio*, 1885, pp. 32–4.

William John Loftie, *Landseer and Animal Painting in England*, 1891.

Sir Walter Gilbey, *Animal Painters of England from the year 1650*, 1900, Vol. II, pp. 47–84.

James A. Manson, *Sir Edwin Landseer R.A.*, 1902.

MacDougall Scott, *Sir Edwin Landseer*, 1903.

Austin Chester, *The Art of Edwin Landseer*, 1920.

Exhibition Catalogue, *Sir Edwin Landseer R.A.*, 1961, Royal Academy.

Exhibition Catalogue, *Landseer and His World*, 1972, Mappin Art Gallery, Sheffield.

Ian Barras Hill, *Landseer, An Illustrated Life of Sir Edwin Landseer*, Aylesbury, 1973.

Campbell Lennie, *Landseer, The Victorian Paragon*, 1976.

Richard Ormond, *Sir Edwin Landseer 1802–73*, 1981.

35. Benjamin Williams Leader

1831–1923, ARA 1883, RA 1898

The Rocky Bed of a Welsh River 1874 (*pl. 8*)

oil on canvas, 48 × 36 in (121.8 × 91.4 cm)

INSCR: B. W. LEADER 1874

PROV: Painted for Thomas Frederick Walker of Birmingham; his sale Christie's 21 April 1883 (110) bt Martin £283 10s.

EXH: ? Birmingham Society of Artists

LIT: Lusk, 1901, p. 23

ENGR: David Law, 1898, published Virtue & Co.

Leader wrote in a letter to Carey in 1888 that this picture 'was painted in 1874 for Mr. T. F. Walker of Birmingham. It is a view on the river Llugy at Bettws y Coed, and was painted on the spot. I was there in the company of Sir Robert Collier afterwards Lord Monkswell and we painted the same subject together. The river is low in the picture, after rain a foaming torrent covers the whole of the rocks and the subject is entirely changed.'[1] Robert Porrett Collier, Lord Monkswell (1817–86), was a well-known judge. According to the *D.N.B.*, 'it was chiefly in painting, of which he was passionately fond, that he was distinguished . . . he exhibited frequently at the Royal Academy and Grosvenor Gallery.' He was the father of the painter the Hon. John Collier (1850–1934).

The painting, described by Lusk as Leader's 'finest upright picture', is one of many similar representations by him of that area and these paintings varied but little in their style and content.

[1] Dated 3 June 1888, Royal Holloway College Archives. This was published by Carey.

36. Benjamin Williams Leader

1831–1923, ARA 1883, RA 1898

Unterseen, Interlaken: Autumn in Switzerland 1878 (*pl. 11*)

oil on canvas, 34 × 48 in (86.3 × 121.8 cm)

INSCR: B. W. LEADER 1878

PROV: Painted for Agnew; sold by them to William Lee 29 March 1878 for £393 15s; his sale Christie's 26 May 1883 (48) bt Martin £357 as *Autumn in Switzerland*.

EXH: 1878 R.A. (122) as *Autumn in Switzerland – on the road from Meyringen to Rosenlaui*; 1981 Agnew's (21).

LIT: *A.J.* 1878 p. 147; Blackburn, *Academy Notes* 1878 p. 19 and repr. (with wrong dimensions); *Graphic* 18 May 1878 p. 498; *I.L.N.* 15 June 1878 p. 551; *Saturday Review* 25 May 1878 p. 660; *The Times* 11 May 1878 p. 6; Lusk, 1901 p. 32.

In the letter to Carey already quoted, Leader wrote 'I did not know that my picture of the old (?) houses at Unterseen, Interlaken, was in the possession of the Royal Holloway College, neither that I called it

"Autumn in Switzerland" but it was painted from studies made in the autumn of 1876. It is an unusual subject for me but I was struck with the picturesque old buildings and thought they would make a good picture, the picture was painted for Messrs. Agnew & Sons.'

In August 1876 Leader had married Miss Mary Eastlake, the niece of the painter and former President of the R.A., Sir Charles Eastlake (1793–1865), and they spent their honeymoon in Switzerland. The studies which Leader mentioned in his letter have not been traced.

The painting, finished in 1878 and exhibited at the Academy that year, was received with mixed criticism. The *A.J.* called it 'a magnificent landscape', the *Graphic* described it as 'remarkable' and the *I.L.N.* regarded it and his other exhibit of that year, *Summertime – in Worcestershire* (135), as 'two admirable landscapes'.[1] The *Saturday Review*, however, was not so complimentary. The 'picturesque old buildings' did not suit them, for they commented on 'a certain effect of what passes for prettiness'. They thought he lacked imagination: 'the spirit of nature is, according to Mr. Leader, always the same. To whatever part of the world he takes us we find in his pictures the same strange angularity and shallow glitter.'

Benjamin Williams Leader was one of a family of painters called Williams. In 1857, to distinguish his work from other Williams paintings, he changed his name to Leader. His major interest was landscape and he was especially fond of the district around Betws-y-Coed, but also painted much in the West Midlands, especially Worcestershire, and in Scotland.

Leader's works were very popular in his own time, being admired for their 'truth to nature'. His outstandingly successful picture was *February Fill Dyke* (ex. R.A. 1881 [42] Birmingham City Art Gallery), of all Victorian paintings one of those most reproduced, through engravings, and most popular.[2] His success enabled him in 1890 to purchase the house built for Frank Holl (q.v.) by Richard Norman Shaw, Burrows Cross, near Gomshall in Surrey.

[1] There is an illustration of *Summer-time – in Worcestershire* in the Witt Library, Courtauld Institute of Art.

[2] See Arts Council, *Great Victorian Pictures*, 1978, p. 49.

BIBLIOGRAPHY
'British Artists: Their Style and Character, No. XCVII, Benjamin Williams Leader', *Art Journal*, 1871, pp. 45–7.
Lewis Lusk, 'The Life and Work of B. W. Leader R.A.', *Art Annual*, 1901.
Frank Lewis, *Benjamin Williams Leader R.A., 1831–1923*, Leigh on Sea, 1971.

37. Edmund Blair Leighton

1853–1922

A Flaw in the Title 1878 (*pl. 52*)

oil on canvas, 24 × 36 in (60.9 × 91.4 cm)

INSCR: E. BLAIR LEIGHTON. 1878.

PROV: ? Purchased from the artist by Thomas Taylor of Aston Rowant Gallery, Oxfordshire; his sale Christie's 28 April 1883 (14) bt Martin £162 15s.

EXH: 1878 R.A. (650); 1981 Agnew's (22).

LIT: *Academy* 25 May 1878 p. 471; *A.J.* 1878 p. 179; Blackburn, *Academy Notes* 1878 p. 60; *I.L.N.* 1 June 1878 p. 507; *Spectator* 22 June 1878 p. 795; Yockney, 1913 p. 9 and 28 (with wrong dimensions) and repr. p. 1; *Connoisseur* 1922 p. 125.

This painting was E. Blair Leighton's first exhibited work at the R.A. and was remarkably well-received by the critics. Henry Blackburn in his *Academy Notes* called it 'especially noticeable' and the *Spectator* 'a thoroughly well-painted work'. The *I.L.N.* gave more space, to comment that: 'The mingled expressions of shrewdness, patience, and anxiety in the faces are limned with well-nigh Holbein-like minuteness; and the details of furniture and drapery are all handled with exact care; but the general effect of the work is, nevertheless, broad and powerful; and the chiaroscuro is, in particular, luminous and well balanced.'

The painting certainly contains many interesting ingredients to attract the attention of the spectator to detail. Each item is painted with extreme care to create a still-life quality and Leighton has obviously been anxious to vary the expressions of the three men's faces. A clever compositional device continues the action beyond the foreground triangular group to the seated

man and the view through the window of the houses opposite, thus escaping a completely stage-like effect. Leighton evidently took great delight in reconstructing the historical costumes.

Edmund Blair Leighton was the son of Charles Blair Leighton (1823–55), a portrait and history painter who did much research into colour lithography and was a senior partner of Leighton Bros., a firm specialising in lithographic art. The family was not related to Lord Frederic Leighton (1830–96) who became President of the R.A. in 1878.

In a letter to Carey of 1888 Leighton wrote: 'Tho' it was always my wish to follow his [father's] profession, I was sent at 15 years of age to a Tea Merchants in the City, where I had to remain 'till I was 21 when having saved a little money out of my salary I left the City, gained permission to make some drawings at the British Museum, in order to obtain a studentship at the Academy; that end I attained the following year; & in two years painted "The Flaw in the Title", the *first* work I exhibited on the walls of Burlington House.'[1]

His works were usually historical or literary in subject, often full of romance and drama, heightened by the use of bright colours and close attention to detail. Between 1878 and 1920, Leighton exhibited many of his works at the R.A. where they were very popular.

[1] Dated 12 October 1888, Royal Holloway College Archives.

BIBLIOGRAPHY
Fred Miller, 'The Work of E. Blair Leighton', *Art Journal*, 1900, pp. 133–8.
Alfred Yockney, 'The Art of E. Blair Leighton', *Art Annual*, 1913.
Connoisseur, Vol. LIV, 1923, p. 125 (Obit.).

38. Henry Lejeune

1819–1904, ARA 1863

Early Sorrow 1869 (*pl. 40*)

panel, 12 × 10 in (30.4 × 25.3 cm)

INSCR: 18 ⫙ 69

PROV: Thomas Frederick Walker of Birmingham; his sale Christie's 21 April 1883 (113) bt Martin £54 12s.

EXH: 1961 Agnew *Victorian Painting 1837–87* (69); 1981 Agnew's (23).

ENGR: Arthur L. Cox, 1932.

Henry Lejeune was particularly known for his paintings of children. The *A.J.* of 1858 commented: 'We will not say that his art is altogether engrossed by his love of children, but they certainly occupy a very large portion of his ideas, and, there is little doubt, from the most numerous class of models in his studio, they are the most pleasant and welcome fancies of his Art-dreams.' Amongst other painters of children 'he stands without an equal . . . for truth, beauty, and natural expression'.[1]

Lejeune was born in London of Flemish extraction. At 14 he went to study at the R.A. Schools, where he achieved great success, winning silver and gold medals. In 1845 he was appointed drawing master at the R.A., a post he held for three years. In 1848 he became Curator of the R.A. School of Painting. His earlier subjects included literary, historical and biblical works, but he turned increasingly to pure genre scenes such as the painting here. He also painted in watercolour.

[1] *Art Journal*, 1858, p. 265.

BIBLIOGRAPHY

'British Artists: Their Style and Character, No. XXXVIII, Henry LeJeune', *Art Journal*, 1858, pp. 265–7.

39. John Linnell

1792–1882

Wayfarers 1849 and 1866 (*pl. 60*)

oil on canvas, 28 × 36 in (71 × 91.4 cm)

INSCR: J Linnell 1849 / 66

PROV: Painted for Joseph Gillott for £210; Thomas Rought; George Pennell; Mr Collis of Alderly Edge; James Eden JP of Fairlawn, Lytham, Nr Preston, Lancashire by 1866; his sale Christie's 30 May 1874 (99) bt Agnew as *A Road Scene with Cattle at a pool*; sold by them 6 June 1874 to George Fox of Harefield, Wimslow for £992 5s; his sale Christie's 12 May 1877 (176) bt Agnew £714 as *A Landscape*; sold by them 16 May 1877 to William Lee; his sale Christie's 26 May 1883 (24) bt Martin £819.

EXH: 1981 Agnew's (24).

LIT: Story, 1892, Vol. II, p. 269.

This painting has a varied and interesting history. Formerly entitled *A Country Road* and *A Road Scene*, it is inscribed with two dates. The first is 1849, the year in which it was painted although not exhibited at the R.A., and the second date is 1866, the year in which the painting was retouched and cleaned for its new owner by Linnell. According to Linnell's *Sketchbook*, *A Country Road*, of standard kitcat proportions,[1] was painted in 1849 for Joseph Gillott, the famous steel-pen maker from Birmingham who also had the reputation of being something of a picture dealer.[2] Gillott was mentioned by Linnell's biographer, Alfred T. Story, as one of his major patrons: 'Mr. Gillott had very fine perceptions in art, and seldom made a wrong judgement; and it is to his credit that he was among the first to give Linnell large prices.'[3]

The painting went through many different hands. Gillott sold it to the dealer Thomas Rought. The Gillott papers record that on 15 January 1849 the *Fishing Party* and *A Country Road* were sold to Rought together, for £472 10s.[4] Gillott appears to have paid Linnell for the paintings later, on 30 March 1849. The price is uncertain because they were paid for along with other pictures. In the front cover of Gillott's 'Picture Transactions' book is pasted a small pen sketch of *A Country Road* with the inscription 'this sold TR' (i.e. Thomas Rought). Rought in turn sold the painting to George Pennell, a printseller and art dealer friend of Gillott's. It was later sold by a Mr Collis of Alderley Edge, Cheshire, to the collector and art patron James Eden, J.P., of Lytham, Lancashire, who also owned Richard Ansdell's *The Drover's Halt* (in the College collection). In a letter to Linnell about the painting Eden wrote: 'I believe this Picture has been tost [sic] about in the hands of Dealers for years and frequently in pawn until it has got into a most filthy state'.[5] Hence his request for Linnell to clean and retouch the picture, which he did in 1866 for the sum of £50.

The title of the painting had been changed to *A Road*

Scene by the time of Eden's sale at Christie's in 1874. It was later bought by the collector George Fox of Harefield, Wimslow, Cheshire, who had a large number of modern English paintings and also owned J. C. Horsley's *A Banker's Private Room*, which Holloway bought.[6] From his collection the Linnell picture found its way into that of William Lee, who owned many of the paintings later bought by Holloway.

Story listed, under the heading of 'Landscape and Subject Pictures', a 'Replica' and a 'Sketch' of 1849, neither of which have been traced.[7] He also listed a panel (28 × 39 in, 71.1 × 99 cm) of 1864, entitled *A Country Road*, for which there were a 'Replica' (drawing 10 × 14 in, 25.4 × 35.5 cm) of 1863 and a 'Drawing', as companion to *Cows in a Road*.[8] This panel was most likely to have been *A Country Road*, exhibited in 1864 at the R.A. (402), and was not the painting in the Holloway collection. Another picture of the same title was exhibited at the R.A. of 1873 (1083). *The Country Road* was lent by David Jardine to the Liverpool Art Club exhibition of 1881 (134). None of them, however, appears to be this particular picture. Linnell was certainly in the habit of making up to six replicas of a painting if necessary, and it was also usual for him to retouch paintings at a later date.

Story related how Linnell, having lived all his life in London, 'resolved to gratify his love for the country to the full . . . In May, 1849, therefore, he went with his son James to Edenbridge [in Kent] to look out for a suitable locality in which to settle within easy reach of London.

At Redhill Junction there was a delay, and they took the opportunity to walk up the hill to Redstone Wood. Linnell had previously noticed a wooded knoll on the left of the line from London to Brighton, and had remarked that it seemed just the place for an artist's cottage . . . By June 20 he had agreed upon the purchase.'[9] This painting may well have been an outcome of Linnell's move to the country. How much of it was 're-painted' in 1866 by Linnell is difficult to ascertain.

John Linnell was born in Bloomsbury in 1792, the son of James Linnell, a wood carver and picture dealer. He started to draw at ten, mostly portraits in chalk and pencil, and copied some of Morland's paintings. He began to study at the R.A. Schools in 1805 and later under John Varley (1778–1842). He first exhibited at the R.A. in 1807 (two small oil landscape sketches) and was represented there all his life.

Linnell exhibited many paintings at the B.I. and his watercolours at the Old Watercolour Society. He also did engravings and portraits in order to make a living. His major interest, however, was in landscape painting, which he was able to turn to only in middle age. His landscapes were mostly painted in Surrey and the majority depict people at work. He usually chose peaceful rather than wild or stormy rural scenes, had a precise style and based his compositions generally on conventional means. In 1818 Linnell met William Blake, who became a life-long friend, as did Samuel Palmer, who married Linnell's daughter, and whose work influenced Linnell's.

The Winter R.A. exhibition of 1883, a joint one with Rossetti, included a total of 161 works by Linnell.

[1] 28 × 36 in, 71 × 91 cm. The *Sketchbook* is with the Linnell papers in the possession of his descendants.
[2] For Gillott's collection, see *Art Union* 1846, pp. 328–9.
[3] A. T. Story, *The Life of John Linnell*, 1822, Vol. I, p. 21.
[4] The Gillott Papers, unpublished, in the possession of Mr Jeremy Maas who kindly allowed me to quote from them.
[5] Linnell papers.
[6] For Fox's collection, see *Art Journal*, 1872, pp. 117–20.
[7] A. T. Story, op. cit. 1892, Vol. II, p. 269.
[8] Op. cit. p. 278.
[9] Op. cit. pp. 30–1.

BIBLIOGRAPHY
'British Artists: Their Style and Character, No. XLIV, John Linnell', *Art Journal*, 1859, pp. 105–7.
F. G. Stephens, 'John Linnell', *Portfolio*, 1872, pp. 45–8.
F. G. Stephens, 'John Linnell, Painter and Engraver', *Art Journal*, 1882, pp. 261–4, 293–6.
Portfolio, 1882, p. 61 (Obit.).
F. G. Stephens, 'The Aims, Studies, and Progress of John Linnell, Painter and Engraver', *Art Journal*, 1883, pp. 37–40.
Rossetti and Linnell Winter Exhibition catalogue, 1883, Royal Academy.
A. T. Story, *The Life of John Linnell*, 2 Vols., 1892.
A. T. Story, 'John Linnell's Country', *Art Journal*, 1892, pp. 301–5.
A. T. Story, 'John Linnell', *Magazine of Art*, 1892, pp. 130–4.
A Loan Exhibition of Drawings, Watercolours, and Paintings by John Linnell and His Circle, 1973, Colnaghi, London.

40. Edwin Longsden Long
1829–91, ARA 1876, RA 1881

The Suppliants. Expulsion of the Gypsies from Spain 1872 (*pl. 48*)

oil on canvas, 72 × 113 in (182.8 × 286.9 cm)

INSCR: EDWIN LONG 1872

PROV: Purchased from the artist by Edward Hermon MP of Wyfold Court, Henley-on-Thames for ? £1,575; his sale Christie's 13 May 1882 (67) bt Martin £4,305 with copyright.

EXH: 1872 R.A. (64); 1981 Agnew's (ex. cat.).

LIT: *Annual Register* 1872 p. 363; *A.J.* 1872 p. 149; *Art Pictorial and Industrial* Vol. III, 1872 p. 89; *Athenaeum* 4 May 1872 p. 564 and 11 May 1872 pp. 595–6; *Examiner* 1 June 1872 p. 549; *Fraser's* July 1872 pp. 27–8; *Graphic* 1 June 1872 p. 518; *I.L.N.* 18 May 1872 p. 486; *Punch* 25 May 1872 p. 213; *Saturday Review* 8 June 1872 p. 729; *The Times* 4 May 1872 p. 5; *The Times* 16 May 1882 p. 4 (sale report); *Graphic* 9 June 1888 p. 612; Quick, 1931 pp. L3–4, 44 and repr. L12 (p. 14).

The 1872 R.A. catalogue had the reference 'Vide – "Expulsion of Gypsies from Spain", by Doctor Sancho de Moncada, Toledo, 1619' next to the title. However, as Long pointed out in a letter to Carey, *The Suppliants* were inspired by the writings of Pacheco, the Secretary to the Holy Inquisition of Spain in 1624, preserved in the archives of Simancas.[1] The documents told of the proposal by Philip III to expel the gypsies from Spain. Long wrote: 'The Gypsies in Spain have always been considered a very degraded race, they were at that time excommunicated & consequently not allowed to enter a church. It is supposed the edict of expulsion would have been carried out, as in the case of the Jews in the time of Ferdinand & Isabella, but for the timely deputation which the picture attempts to represent when the King & the Cardinal [Gonzales] were descending the steps of the Santa Annunciata in Valladolid, and for the compassionate intervention of the young queen, who may be seen in the corridor above.'

Intent on maximum accuracy, Long studied portraits in the Prado to reconstruct the figures of the King and Queen and the Cardinal. The gypsies were painted from 'probably descendants of the Suppliants themselves living near Granada in 1871'.

Long had painted a similar theme some years before, in 1864, but *The Suppliants, Spanish Gypsies* (Russell Cotes Museum, Bournemouth) bears no resemblance to this painting. The picture here was purchased from Long by Edward Hermon, of Wyfold Court in Oxfordshire (who also commissioned the *Babylonian Marriage Market* from Long three years later) and was bought by Holloway from the sale of Hermon's collection at Christie's for the outstandingly high price of £4,305. According to Long, there are no studies or sketches extant for this painting.[2]

The grouping of the figures in the picture was considered a great success. The division of the two completely different groups by the rounded arches created a marvellous contrast between the finery and elegance of the Queen and the innocent curiosity of the children peering through the central arch, and the bare feet, pleading faces and peasant costumes of the gypsies. Further, the King and Cardinal have been not only placed on steps above the gypsies but also removed from them by the sudden area of blank wall between the King and the leading gypsies on their knees. There is much of general interest in the work, and it fascinated the public and the critics alike when exhibited at the Academy of 1872.

The *A.J.*, above all, was impressed by *The Suppliants*. They described it as 'a manifestation of the new power that is rising in English Art', and continued with: 'It is a picture of a very high class, painted by E. LONG, who could not have produced a composition like this without having already shown tokens of being on the road to high achievement . . . It is an admirable work, and we cannot compliment Mr. Long more highly than by saying there is not a person in his picture who has not something appropriate to urge.'

In the other reviews opinions were mixed. Most of them thought the subject matter interesting, the characters lively and the colour and the composition successful. The author of the notice in the *Annual Register* compared the painting to Veronese's *Family of Darius before Alexander* (National Gallery, London), though the only feature in common is people pleading on their knees for mercy. *Fraser's Magazine* felt that the subject was too obscure for the ordinary spectator to be able to comprehend, despite being given the reference in the catalogue. The *Graphic* concurred: if the picture did not win the acclaim it deserved, 'the inferiority of the subject must be held accountable'.

1873, the year after the show, marked the end of Long's interest in Spanish subjects. Until then he had travelled to Spain annually from 1857 onwards, in search of subjects. From 1874 he turned to oriental, classical and biblical themes. Long had been much encouraged by John 'Spanish' Phillip (1817–67), and his first Spanish subject exhibited at the R.A. was *Bravo, el Toro!* (ex. R.A. 1859 [312], untraced). He had studied the work of Velasquez and Murillo in particular.

¹Dated 14 September 1887, Royal Holloway College Archives. This letter was published by Carey.
²Letter to Thomas Holloway, dated 1 June 1882, Royal Holloway College Archives.

41. Edwin Longsden Long
1829–91, ARA 1876, RA 1881

The Babylonian Marriage Market 1875 (*pl. 50*)

oil on canvas, 68 × 120 in (172.6 × 304.6 cm)

INSCR: EDWIN LONG 1875

PROV: Commissioned by Edward Hermon MP of Wyfold Court, Henley-on-Thames for ? £7,350; his sale Christie's 13 May 1882 (66) bt Martin with copyright for £6,615.

EXH: 1875 R.A. (482); 1887 Manchester Royal Jubilee Ex. (540); 1897 Guildhall Ex. (40); 1977 R.A. *This Brilliant Year* Queen Victoria's Jubilee 1887 (150), 1981 Agnew's (25).

LIT: *Academy* 8 May 1875 p. 486; *Annual Register* 1875 p. 374; *A.J.* 1875 p. 250; *Athenaeum* 1 May 1875 pp. 590–1 and 29 May 1875 p. 726; Blackburn, *R.A. Notes* 1875 pp. 34–5 and repr. p. 35; *Blackwood's* June p. 763; *Examiner* 1 May 1875 p. 501 and 22 May 1875 p. 585; *Graphic* 1 May 1875 p. 415 and 29 May 1875 p. 518; *I.L.N.* 1 May 1875 p. 415; Ruskin, 1902 ed. pp. 233–5; *Saturday Review* 1 May 1875 p. 567 and 15 May 1875 p. 625; *Spectator* 22 May 1875 pp. 661–2; *The Times* 1 May 1875 p. 12 and 24 May 1875 p. 5; *The Artist* 1 June 1882 p. 173; *A.J.* 1882 p. 317; *The Times* 16 May 1882 p. 4; Chesneau, 1885 p. 268; Hodgson, 1887 pp. 82–3; *A.J.* 1887 p. 252; Walter Armstrong, *Celebrated Pictures exhibited at the Manchester Royal Jubilee Exhibition*, 1888 p. 45; *Graphic* 9 June 1888 p. 612; Quilter, 1892 pp. 317, 318–9; Temple, 1897 pp. 291–2; *A.J.* 1908 p. 175; Quick, 1931 pp. L4, L5, L44 and repr. p. L13; A. C. R. Carter, *Let Me Tell You*, 1940 pp. 37–40; Maas, 1969 p. 184; Wood, *Dictionary*, 1971 p. 91 and repr. p. 319; Arts Council, *Great Victorian Pictures*, 1978 pp. 12, 45.

ENGR: Photogravure, 32½ × 18 in (82.5 × 45.7 cm); published Fine Art Society Ltd.; declared 10 December 1889.

As with *The Suppliants*, this painting was commissioned by Edward Hermon, for a reputed 1,700 guineas which must have been one of the highest prices paid to a painter for one work. An account of the Hermon sale at Christie's in 1882 described the painting as 'placed before the audience at the end of the room, being too large and, being under plate-glass, too heavy, to put upon the easel. It was received with a round of applause ... The hammer fell ... amid loud cheering.'¹ The sum which Holloway paid, £6,615 including the copyright, was always considered to have been quite exceptional and was, indeed, a sale-room record until 1892.

Long wrote to Thomas Holloway 10 days after the sale at Christie's 'to say how gratified I feel at the very handsome way in which you have purchased my two pictures, and that they are to be placed in your noble collection. I am aware that there has been a desire on the part of one or two firms to engrave the "Babylonian Marriage Market" and I dare say it might answer to them as a speculation, but I feel sure you will agree with me that unless it were done in a *first rate* way it would be a great vexation, and I am afraid it would be a very difficult work to get done properly.'² No action was taken to reproduce it on a large scale until 1889 when a photogravure was published by the Fine Art Society. The College Governors' Report for 1888–89 records that the Scholarship Fund received £1,000 from the Fine Art Society for the sale of the copyright and that the sum was invested for a permanent Entrance Scholarship.

Long took his subject from George C. Swayne's *The History of Herodotus*.³ The entry for the painting in the R.A. catalogue of 1875 included a long extract from Swayne describing the custom of the marriage market.⁴ The convention of the Babylonians was to auction off the young women in an order judged on their appearance, so that the prettiest girl would be auctioned first and so on until 'the damsel who was equidistant between beauty and plainness, who was given away gratis. Then the least plain was put up, and knocked down to the gallant who would marry her for the smallest consideration, – and so on till even the plainnest was got rid of to some cynical worthy who decidedly preferred lucre to looks.' In that way, Swayne pointed out, 'the rich man's taste was the poor man's gain'. He felt that this method of finding a husband was, financially, a good idea for 'it at least possesses the merit of honesty and openness, and tends to a fair distribution of the gifts of fortune'.

This vastly ambitious work, a subject not attempted before, proved an enormous success for Long and gained him an Associateship of the R.A. It took him two years to complete the painting. M. H. Spielmann recounted how one evening Long was playing whist when he had a sudden vision in his mind of how he would organise his subject and how it developed from there.⁵ As with *The Suppliants*, there are no studies or sketches extant for this painting.⁶

One of the most interesting of all the criticisms of this work came from Ruskin, who described *The Babylonian Marriage Market* as being worthy of purchase by the Anthropological Society.⁷ They did not, however, take up his suggestion. Ruskin considered the work 'of great merit', and continued: 'For the varieties of character in the heads are rendered with extreme subtlety; while as a mere piece of painting, the work is remarkable, in the modern school, for its absence of affectation: there is no insolently indulged indolence nor vulgarly asserted dexterity – the painting is good throughout, and unobtrusively powerful . . . intensely subtle observation of physical character and expression . . . necessitates the isolation of the artist's thoughts from subjects of intellectual interest or moral beauty . . . anatomical precision . . . of the twelve waiting girls, from great physical beauty to absolute ugliness . . . As a piece of anthropology, it is the natural and very wonderful product of a century occupied in carnal and mechanical science . . . a specific piece of the natural history of our own century.'

The notices in the journals of 1875 concerning the painting were, without exception, ecstatic. The *Saturday Review* wrote: 'No composition has proved so popular, save Miss Thompson's battle-piece' (Elizabeth Thompson [later Lady Butler]'s famous *Quatre Bras* [853] in Melbourne Art Gallery, Australia). The critics agreed on the quality of the colour, its 'spirit and dramatic power' (*Athenaeum*) and its rare and adventurous subject matter. Considering its large scale, it was judged by many to have been painted in the most ingenious way.

The *A.J.* wrote many lines of high praise and ended: 'The picture, in our eyes, is historic in the best sense, and does honour to the British school.' Henry Blackburn in his *Academy Notes* questioned whether the picture was in good taste but otherwise was obviously genuinely delighted with it, and called it 'a great technical triumph, especially in the management of details, in the painting of the tiled walls, and the ornaments and jewels worn by the women. There is a touch of genius in concealing the faces of the Alpha and Omega of comeliness.' Many of the critics commented on how popular the painting was at the Academy, 'the town-talk of a season' (*Academy*), and on the large crowds which gathered round it. The colourful details obviously attracted much attention and as William Michael Rossetti (in the *Academy*) pointed out, its success lay in the 'richness and archaeology, scenic

drama and amusement, much beauty and some grotesque by-play, antique fact and modern innuendo. Besides, his very large picture is a work of uncommon force and tact, meeting without stint the great demands which it involves upon the executive faculty.' Indeed, it is a painting which seems to inspire endless interest and fascination.

The Babylonian Marriage Market was a turning-point in Long's work and he turned his attention to *An Egyptian Feast* (ex. R.A. 1877 [83], ill. Quick, 1931, p. L18), another subject inspired by Herodotus, and other equally successful compositions of middle-Eastern life.

According to his son Maurice Stelair Long, Edwin Long was born in Bath and bought up as an 'Independent' or 'Congregationalist' dissenter.[8] The celebrated William Jay, Minister of Argyle Chapel, Bath was one of the first portraits which he painted. In 1858 Long moved to London. Throughout his career he exhibited portraits together with subject pictures. He first exhibited (three portraits) at the R A in 1855 He was continually in demand as a portrait painter especially amongst the gentry and aristocracy. Such was his success that he was able to commission the architect Richard Norman Shaw to design two houses for him in Hampstead. The first was built in 1878 at 61 Fitzjohn's Avenue, and the second, begun nine years later at 42 Netherhall Gardens, was sited in the garden of the Fitzjohn's Avenue house.[9]

[1] *The Artist*, 1 June 1882, p. 173.
[2] Letter dated 23 May 1882, Royal Holloway College Archives.
[3] George C. Swayne, *The History of Herodotus*, 1870, pp. 36–7.
[4] This was reprinted in the Manchester Royal Jubilee Exhibition catalogue of 1887 and again by Carey.
[5] *Graphic*, 9 June 1888, p. 612.
[6] Letter from Long to Holloway, dated 1 June 1882, Royal Holloway College Archives.
[7] John Ruskin, *Academy Notes*, ed. 1902, pp. 233–5.
[8] Letter to Carey, 12 October 1888, Royal Holloway College Archives.
[9] See Andrew Saint, *Richard Norman Shaw*, Yale University Press, 1976, p. 155.

BIBLIOGRAPHY
Art Journal, 1891, p. 222 (Obit.).
M. H. Spielmann, 'Painters in their Studios', *Graphic*, 9 June 1888, pp. 612–14.
Richard Quick, *The Life and Works of Edwin Long, R.A.*, Bournemouth, 1931, reprinted 1970.

42. Daniel Maclise
1806–70, ARA 1835, RA 1840

Peter the Great at Deptford Dockyard 1857 (*pl. 49*)

oil on canvas, 60 × 96 in (152.3 × 243.7 cm)

PROV: Henry Woods of Warnford Park; his sale Christie's 5 May 1883 (145) bt Martin £388 10s.

EXH: 1857 R.A. (78); 1967 Arts Council *GB/USSR* (33); 1981 Agnew's (26).

LIT: *Annual Register* 1857 p. 79; *A.J.* 1857 pp. 166–7; *Athenaeum* 9 May 1857 pp. 601–2; *Critic* 15 May 1857 pp. 232–3; *Examiner* 2 May 1857 p. 278; *I.L.N.* 9 May 1857 p. 444; *Literary Gazette* 9 May 1857 p. 450; *Monthly Review* 1857 pp. 416–17; *Saturday Review* 30 May 1857 pp. 497–8; *Spectator* 2 May 1857 p. 463 and 9 May 1857 p. 502; *The Times* 2 May 1857 p. 9; Dafforne, 1873 pp. 44 5; ed. J. W. Gleeson White, *The Master Painters of Britain*, Edinburgh, Vol. II, 1898 p. 21 and repr. bet. pp. 21–2; Ruskin, 1902 ed. pp. 81–2; Walter G. Strickland, *Dictionary of Irish Artists*, Dublin and London, Vol. II, 1913 pp. 69, 77; C. H. Collins Baker, *British Painting*, 1933 p. 191; Arts Council, *Great Victorian Pictures*, 1978 p. 75; David Robertson, *Sir Charles Eastlake and the Victorian Art World*, Princeton, 1978 pp. 391–2.

REPR: Redford, 1888, Vol. I p. 355 N.

STUDY: Pencil study of boat sheds, 4 × 10½ in (10.1 × 26.6 cm) with annotations V & A Museum, Forster Bequest 1876 no. F.48.F.63 no. 12.

When this painting was exhibited in the R.A. in 1857 it was given no title in the catalogue (nor in the Christie's sale catalogue of 1883, when Holloway bought it). This was common for Maclise's exhibited works, many of which were supplied with explanatory descriptions. The lengthy explanation, published also by Carey, was fully justified, in that the scene represented is not, at first glance, obvious. Maclise's inspiration comes from Bishop Gilbert Burnet's reminiscence of the Czar Peter the Great of Russia.[1] Burnet, when Bishop of London, had 'waited often on him, and was ordered, both by the King and the archbishop and bishops, to attend upon him, and to offer him such informations of our religion and constitution as he was willing to receive.' Burnet (as quoted in the R.A. catalogue) wrote of Peter: 'He is mechanically turned, and seems designed by nature rather to be a ship carpenter than a great prince: this was his chief study and exercise while he stayed here: he wrought much with his own hands, and made all about him work at the models of ships.'

The R.A. catalogue adds that Czar Peter was working at Deptford Dockyard during a three-month stay in England in the winter of 1698–9. He is on the left of the painting with his foot resting on the wooden bench. Those around him are apparently his 'rough retinue', and they are designed to contrast with the elegant figure of the King, William III, who is visiting Deptford wearing a black costume and holding a cane. According to Burnet, William is accompanied by Lord Carmarthen, the President of the Council, and Lord Shrewsbury, his Foreign Secretary.

Peter the Great's 'rough retinue' were named in the R.A. catalogue as Menzikoff, Golownin, Galatzin and Prince Siberski. Siberski was famous for his 'skill to rig a ship from top to bottom'. The rest of the group, a dwarf, a negro boy, a monkey and a young Drury Lane actress are part of his 'jolly company', as they were called, a group of friends and acquaintances who shared both the lighter and the more serious moments of his life.

The description ended: 'In St. Petersburgh are still kept the coarse woollen stockings and sailor's coat in which he worked, and the Annual Register of 1769 preserves the testimony of an old man, a Deptford shipwright in those days, who remembered well hearing his father say forty years before, that the Czar of Muscovy worked with his own hands as hard as any man in the yard.' Maclise's own undated notes (and a pencil study of the boat-sheds in the picture) are in the Victoria and Albert Museum Library.[2] They include two ink sketches for Peter's head and details of his features, as well as general historical material, much of which was published as the R.A. catalogue entry.

Peter the Great (1672–1725) began his reign in 1682 and was anxious to develop a powerful army, and, in particular, a navy for his empire; he set out in 1697 to work in Holland as a shipwright with the intention of gaining first-hand experience of naval building. After his stay in Holland, he went on to England, where he and his assistants worked at Deptford Dock in the Port of London, called 'The King's Yard' after Henry VIII. He returned to Russia taking with him engineers, scientists and future officers for his navy. While living in London Peter the Great stayed in John Evelyn's house, Sayes Court, at Deptford,[3] and his visit to England was followed with interest and fascination.

The subject of this painting was not novel for visitors to the R.A. exhibition. Sir William Allan had exhibited *Peter the Great teaching his subjects the Art of Shipbuilding* at the R.A. in 1844 (87). This painting is missing.[4] After it was exhibited at the R.A. it was taken to St. Petersburg but there has been no trace of it since. For Maclise the subject offered possibilities which might have been irresistible.

A letter of 25 March 1857 from Maclise to the dealer and print-seller Henry Graves must concern *Peter the Great*, because the painting mentioned, although not named, is referred to as his R.A. exhibit for that year, when *Peter the Great* was his only oil painting.[5] Maclise offered Graves the painting and the copyright for an additional £1,000 over a figure which had obviously already been proposed. He outlined how he would like these to be paid to him in three instalments. However, it is not known if Graves bought it from him.

The painting was parodied in *Punch* by 'John Trot at the Royal Academy' with a verse which read:

'I zee a lot o' people a standun, starun hard
At one gurt grand big pictur, resemblun a dockyard.
Wi carpentern a gwiun on, chaps workun, buildun ships,
How naterel their shavuns wus, and rayal all the chips!'[6]

Their view of the painting was echoed to some extent by Ruskin, who wrote in his *Academy Notes* of that year: 'This is a less exaggerated and more conscientious work than Mr. Maclise has yet produced. But I hope his conscience will become keener yet; for it is difficult to understand how a painter who goes through so much hard work can persist in the idea that there is no indistinctness in Nature, or that there ought to be none . . . he appears to see, not more, but a great deal less, than the world in general.'

In an article on Maclise in the *Burlington Magazine*, Richard Ormond compared *Peter the Great* with Maclise's *Caxton's Printing Press* (ex. R.A. 1851 [67], Knebworth House, Hertfordshire).[7] He described them as 'more conventional history paintings' and in many ways they are similar: in their abundance of figures and details and in the static quality of those represented, who are not, in either case, actively at work.

The many reviews of the painting were more or less universal in their criticisms. Most remarked on the same weaknesses: the worst, in their opinion, were the exaggeration and the over-crowding. They emphasised the same strengths of the picture, especially its fine draughtsmanship. The *A.J.* wrote: 'The observation is suggested by the bewildering plenitude of objects, which in this really splendid picture importune the eye . . . the drawing and painting of the items are a kind of perfection in Art which it is difficult to describe . . . But, withal, we know of no other painter of our school who could send forth such a composition. We know not the destiny of the picture, but the subject is national, and it is well worthy to form one of the historical series in the New Houses of Parliament.'

The *I.L.N.* stated their disapproval strongly and disliked particularly the 'multifarious paraphernalia of shipbuilding . . . the chief defect of the picture. The difficulty of concentrating the attention is further increased by every separate object being painted with equal force. Colour is also everywhere crude and unqualified by general tone. Indeed a footlight effect seems to glare upon the whole; and this, together with the general *mise en scène*, the attitudinising, and the painted faces, would lead us for a moment to fancy we were assisting at a representation of "L'Etoile du Nord", and that this incident was included.' The general opinion was that the parts were painted well but made up an imperfect whole. Certainly Maclise has mistaken the scale in many areas of the picture. An obvious example is the difference between the faces and figures of the two major characters, William III and Peter the Great. They are, of course, designed to be contrasted. The dapper elegance of the English King is intended to appear out of place beside the massive bulk of his casually dressed Russian counterpart. Some of the gestures and expressions are exaggerated and Maclise has not successfully achieved the transition from the boat sheds in the background to the crowded stage-like activities in the foreground.

The *Saturday Review* hailed *Peter the Great at Deptford Dock*, exclaiming that it 'irresistibly calls forth the remark that Maclise is a provoking painter'. They singled out his capabilities of draughtsmanship for praise: 'He is perhaps at the very head of living artists – his firmness and decision of touch, and precision of outline, have never been excelled.'

The *Literary Gazette* began their review by calling the picture 'second to none in importance or interest ... Mr. Maclise also is one of those artists who paints for all time, and whose works impress the facts of history more surely on the general mind than even Macaulay's vivid and ornate pages ... In this and other late pictures there seems to be even more of that flatness, overcrowding, exaggeration, and feeling of unreality that is to be found in the earlier works ... There is no depth, no breadth, no air – no massing of light and shade, no tone ... No defects, however, serious even as these, can destroy the effect of a work of real genius, and transformed and heightened by imaginative power, this picture will doubtless be a permanent rendering of the event in the minds of all its beholders.'

Maclise's style was explained by J. T. Turpin: 'Both iconographically and stylistically, German idealism and German composition lay behind his great series of subjects on the history of these islands, executed in the 1850s ... The Idealist approach to history which informed the 1850s subjects derived partially from the policies of the Commissioners who listed most of the titles for execution in the new Houses of Parliament.'[8]

Maclise had been involved in the decorations for the new Palace of Westminster since 1844, when he exhibited *The Knight* at Westminster Hall. Two years later he began the fresco of the *Spirit of Chivalry* in the House of Lords, and in 1848 the *Spirit of Justice* fresco. His major contributions to the scheme for the Parliament buildings were the two vast paintings in the Royal Gallery in the House of Lords: *The Meeting of Wellington and Blucher after the Battle of Waterloo* (completed 1861) and *The Death of Nelson* (completed 1865) which he worked in waterglass technique. They were the last of his great history pictures, a genre he had been attracted to all his life.

Maclise was born in 1806 in Ireland. In 1822 he joined the Cork School of Art and in 1828 the R.A. Schools; he exhibited his first painting at the R.A. in 1829: *Malvolio Affecting the Count* (untraced). He became known for his book illustrations, his portraits in pencil and watercolour, and his caricatures for *Fraser's Magazine*. He retained an absorbing interest in Shakespearean and other literary subjects and a wide variety of historical themes. His best known history paintings were those of the 1850s (*Caxton's Printing Press*, 1851, *Alfred in the Camp of the Danes*, 1852 [Laing Art Gallery, Newcastle] and *The Marriage of Strongbow and Eva*, 1854 [National Gallery of Ireland]).

[1] Bishop Gilbert Burnet, *History of his Own Time*, ed. 1818, Vol. III, p. 245 (first published 1724).
[2] Forster Collection 385, pp. 407, 408, 412, 413.
[3] See Arts Council, *Great Britain U.S.S.R.*, 1967, pp. 8, 15.
[4] David and Francina Irwin, *Scottish Painters at home and abroad, 1700–1900*, 1975, p. 436, n. 85.
[5] Add. MS. 46140 f. 251, Department of Manuscripts, British Museum, reproduced by permission of the British Library.
[6] *Punch*, 16 May 1857, p. 200.
[7] Richard Ormond, *Burlington Magazine*, 1968, Vol. CX, p. 685 and in his catalogue of the Arts Council exhibition, *Daniel Maclise*, 1972, p. 95.
[8] J. T. Turpin, 'German Influence on Daniel Maclise', *Apollo*, 1973, pp. 169–75.

BIBLIOGRAPHY
'Portraits of British Artists', *Art Union*, 1847, p. 164.
Art Journal, 1870 pp. 181–2 (Obit.).
William Justin O'Driscoll, *A Memoir of Daniel Maclise*, 1871.
James Dafforne, *Pictures by Daniel Maclise R.A.*, 1873.
Allan Cunningham, *Lives of the Most Eminent British Painters*, rev. ed. by Mrs Charles Heaton, Vol. III, 1880, pp. 406–33.
Richard Ormond, 'Daniel Maclise', *Burlington Magazine*, December 1968, Vol. CX, pp. 684–93.
Richard Ormond, 'Diploma Paintings from 1840 Onwards', *Apollo*, January 1969, pp. 56–63.
J. T. Turpin, University of London, Unpublished M.A. Report, 1969. J. T. Turpin, University of London, Unpublished PhD., 1973.
Arts Council, *Daniel Maclise, 1806–1870*, 1872, National Portrait Gallery.
Richard Ormond, 'Daniel Maclise (1806–1870) – a major figurative painter', *Connoisseur*, March 1972, pp. 165–71.
J. T. Turpin, 'German Influence on Daniel Maclise', *Apollo*, February 1973, pp. 169–75.

43. John MacWhirter

1839–1911, ARSA 1867, ARA 1879, HRSA 1880, RA 1893

'*Night, most glorious night, thou wert not made for slumber*' 1874 (*pl. 61*)

oil on canvas, 39 × 65 in (99 × 165 cm)

INSCR: MacWhirter.

PROV: Edward Hermon M.P. of Wyfold Court, Henley-on-Thames; his sale Christie's 13 May 1882 (69) bt Martin £283 10s as *Moonlight*.

EXH: 1874 R.A. (709); 1922 R.A. Winter Ex. (86); 1968–69 R.A. Bi-Centenary Ex. (336).

LIT: *I.L.N.* 6 June 1874 p. 543; Caleb Scholefield Mann, Ms copy of Exhibition of the Royal Academy of Arts 1874 (Ashmolean Museum) p. 121; Sinclair, 1903 p. 11 and listed p. 30; Irwins, 1975 p. 364 and repr. pl. 186; Hardie, 1976 p. 58.

STUDY: *On a Moonlight Beach*
13 × 25 in (33 × 63.4 cm)
Signed. Anon. sale 30 August 1974 Sotheby's Gleneagles (230) and repr. bt L. Hicks.

Sold in 1882 from the Edward Hermon collection at Wyfold Court to Holloway as *Moonlight*, this painting had been exhibited at the R.A. in 1874 (the same year as Fildes's *Applicants for Admission to a Casual Ward*, Pettie's *A State Secret* and Webb's *Carthagena*, all in this collection) with the quotation from Byron, above, as its title.[1] MacWhirter himself referred to the painting as *Summer Midnight* and it would seem most likely that he represented the night-time of June in Scotland, when it is never fully dark.[2] The picture was painted at Corrie in the Isle of Arran but, as MacWhirter wrote, 'of course it was the glitter on the water that was my principal aim'.[3]

A small sketch (which has not been traced) shows a very similar scene, with the same effect of moonlight across the water, and the two figures huddled close to each other, but without the boat.[4] The idea reappears in a volume illustrating MacWhirter's watercolours, *The MacWhirter Sketch Book*.[5] A watercolour entitled *Loch an Eilan, Moonlight* depicts a similar beached boat and shore against the moonlit water, but the view is the enclosed landscape background of a loch, and there are no figures. As William Hardie pointed out in *Scottish Painting*, it was unusual for MacWhirter to paint figures into his landscapes.[6]

The reviewers of the Academy exhibition hardly noticed the painting, but 1874 was a year in which there were some vastly important works shown, such as Elizabeth Thompson's (Lady Butler) *Calling the roll after an engagement, Crimea (The Roll Call)* (142, Royal Collection), *The North-West Passage* (320, Tate Gallery), Alma-Tadema's *The Picture Gallery* (157, Towneley Hall Art Gallery and Museum, Burnley) and Briton Rivière's *Apollo* (260, Bury Museum and Art Gallery).

[1] *Childe Harold's Pilgrimage* Canto III, Verse XCIII begins 'And this is the night: – Most glorious night! Thou wert not sent for slumber!'
[2] Letter to 'The Directors' of Royal Holloway College, dated 23 January 1888, Royal Holloway College Archives.
[3] Letter to Carey of ? 1887, Royal Holloway College Archives, and published in part by Carey.
[4] This was sold at Sotheby's Gleneagles, 30 August 1974 (230).
[5] John MacWhirter, *The MacWhirter Sketch Book*, Introduction by Edwin Bale, 1906 and 1908.
[6] William Hardie, *Scottish Painting*, 1976, p. 58.

44. John MacWhirter

1839–1911, ARSA 1867, ARA 1879, HRSA 1880, RA 1893

Spindrift 1876 (*pl. 70*)

oil on canvas, 32 × 56 in (81.2 × 142.1 cm)

INSCR: MacWhirter

PROV: Edward Hermon M.P. of Wyfold Court, Henley-on-Thames; his sale Christie's 13 May 1882 (70) bt Martin £215.

EXH: 1876 R.A. (427); 1897 Guildhall (45); 1922 R.A. Winter Ex. (104); 1978 Arts Council *Great Victorian Pictures* (32); 1981 Agnew's (27).

LIT: *A.J.* 1876 p. 262; Blackburn, R.A. Notes 1876 p. 40; *I.L.N.* 20 May 1876 p. 498; *The Times* 31 May 1879 p. 5; *A.J.* 1879 p. 11; Stephens, 1884 p. 59; Temple, 1897 pp. 218–19 and repr. opposite p. 218; Sinclair, 1903 pp. 11, 30 and repr. p. 10; Hardie, 1976 p. 58.

ENGR: Wood engraving; *Graphic* 30 September 1876 p. 328.

STUDY: *A Seaweed Collector*
20 × 32 in (50.7 × 81.2 cm) signed with initials. Anon. sale 30 August 1974 Sotheby's Gleneagles (231) and repr.; bt Eroscot Art, Glasgow.

This painting, bought from the Edward Hermon collection like the previous MacWhirter picture, shows two seaweed carts being pulled by horses along the seashore. According to MacWhirter, *Spindrift* was 'painted from studies made in this island, Arran . . . "Spindrift" – means the spray of the sea caught up and whirled away by the wind.' He continued: 'I saw the seaweed cart coming along where I was walking on a stormy day – and made a note of it in my sketch book. I afterwards made careful studies of the wet road, gravel etc. The scene is near Loch Range, Arran.'[1]

MacWhirter spent part of each year in the Highlands of Scotland or in Arran. He would devote much time and study to his landscape paintings, which in some cases contain elements of more interest than simple landscape views.

Animals going along a road beside the sea are seen in another work by him at the Orchar Art Gallery at Broughty Ferry, Dundee: *Stray Sheep*, a sketch of a flock of sheep walking down a road away from the spectator. It is related to a painting, sold at an auction in 1976, entitled *Bringing Home the Sheep*.[2]

MacWhirter repeated the theme of the white horse against the sea in *Sunday in the Highlands* (ex. R.A. 1881 [483] photograph in Witt Library). It has many more figures than *Spindrift*: a line of people, headed by an elderly bearded man on a horse, returning from a distant kirk in the rain. The atmosphere is like that of *Spindrift*: a harsh damp Scottish day.

MacWhirter probably took the title for this painting from one of a volume of poems by J. Noel Paton published in 1867 by William Blackwood and Sons. *Spindrift* was dedicated to Paton's wife and dated 10 December 1866. Earlier, in 1865, Noel Paton had executed a sketch for a group in clay of two sea nymphs in an attempt to personify the breaking wave.[3]

James Dafforne in an article on MacWhirter in the *A.J.* described *Spindrift* as being a companion picture to *The Lady of the Woods* (ex. R.A. 1876, the same year as *Spindrift*, Manchester City Art Gallery), a landscape of a silver birch in a wood.[4] However, it seems unlikely that MacWhirter would have paired these two works, and no further support for this view has been found.

Henry Blackburn's *Academy Notes* review of the R.A. exhibition mistakenly attributed the painting to H. R. Robertson but described it as 'a good landscape'. The *I.L.N.* called it 'very spirited' but *The Times* was more descriptive and more romantic: 'A dreary road by the sea, flogged with pelting rain, with which the spray blown by the wind from the crests of the waves blends in gray discomfort.'

John MacWhirter was born at Slatesford, near Edinburgh, the son of a paper manufacturer at Colinton. He studied for three years, 1851 to 1854, at the famous Trustees' Academy in Edinburgh under Robert Scott Lauder (1803–69), who was responsible for training some of the best Scottish painters after 1850.

MacWhirter was one of the youngest exhibitors at the R.S.A. when, at 15, he showed a painting entitled *Old Cottage of Braid* (untraced). In the 1850s he was a member of the same sketching club as Orchardson, Pettie, Chalmers and McTaggart which reformed in London in the 1870s. From 1855 onwards MacWhirter spent a good deal of time in Europe, Turkey and America. In 1860, together with John Pettie (q.v.), William Quiller Orchardson (1832–1910) and other Scottish painters, he was commissioned to provide illustrations for *Good Words*, a new journal first published in Edinburgh, and from 1862 onwards in London.

MacWhirter's first R.A. exhibit came in 1865, when he submitted *Temple of Vesta, Rome* (untraced), the first of many landscapes to be shown there. He moved to London in 1869, and lived there until his death.

Ruskin admired his early watercolour studies of botanical subjects, mostly flowers, and in about 1870 he bought 25 of them to use as examples of light and shade in his lectures on landscape at the Oxford School of Art. According to Cook and Wedderburn, 'the virtue of it [MacWhirter's sketchbook] is in *Drawing and shading the white or colour*'.[5] Ruskin compared MacWhirter's studies to Dürer drawings.

MacWhirter's favourite locations for his paintings were Scotland and the Alps. His work varied greatly, between the wilder aspects of nature, as in *The Track of a Hurricane*[6] (ex. R.A. 1885, Forbes Magazine Collection) and calmer poetic representations like *The Three Gables* (ill. Sinclair, 1903, p. 7) or *Out in the Cold* (Dundee Art Gallery). Sinclair categorised MacWhirter's work under seven headings: 'The Highland, The Generally Scottish, The Italian, Pictures from other Countries, Domestic and Subject, Trees and Flowers'.[7]

Neither of the two paintings in the College collection fully represents MacWhirter's interest in the botanical details shown in many of his works. *June in the Austrian Tyrol* (ex. R.A. 1892, Tate Gallery) purchased by the Chantrey Bequest, illustrates how he could paint exact and minute detail into a landscape against a grandiose mountain setting. These details were very important for him and he devoted much time and study to their execution. Caw described MacWhirter's paintings as having 'daintiness of colour, delicacy of drawing and elegance of design'.[8]

Such was MacWhirter's success and popularity that, like so many contemporary painters, he had a house built for him in fashionable St. John's Wood by William Flockhart FRIBA: a vast Italian Renaissance mansion at 1 Abbey Road.

[1]Letter to Carey, of ?1887, Royal Holloway College Archives, and published in part by Carey.
[2]Sotheby's Gleneagles, 23 August 1976 (370). It measured 23½ × 41½ in. (59.6 × 105.4 cm).
[3]*Art Journal*, 1895, p. 124.
[4]*Art Journal*, 1879, p. 11.
[5]John Ruskin, *The Works of John Ruskin*, ed. E. T. Cook and Alexander Wedderburn, (Library Edition) 1906,. Vol. XXII, p. 33n.
[6]See catalogue Christopher Forbes, *The Royal Academy (1837–1901) Revisited*, 1975, no. 44.
[7]Dr. William MacDonald Sinclair, 'John MacWhirter R.A.', *Art Annual*, Christmas 1903, pp. 11–14.
[8]Sir James L. Caw, *Scottish Painting Past and Present 1620–1908*, 1908, p. 257.

BIBLIOGRAPHY
James Dafforne, 'The Works of John MacWhirter, A.R.S.A.', *Art Journal*, 1879, pp. 9–11.
Walter Armstrong, 'Scottish Painters: John MacWhirter', *Portfolio*, 1887, pp. 208–10.
John MacWhirter, *Landscape Painting in Watercolour*, 1900.
Dr William Macdonald Sinclair, 'John MacWhirter R.A.', *Art Annual*, 1903.
M. H. Spielmann, *The Art of J. MacWhirter, R.A.*, 1904.
John MacWhirter, *The MacWhirter Sketch Book*, Introduction by Edwin Bale, 1906 and 1908.
Sir James L. Caw, *Scottish Painting Past and Present, 1620–1980*, Edinburgh, 1908, pp. 256–8.
John MacWhirter, *Sketches from Nature*, Introduction by Mrs MacWhirter, 1913.
David and Francina Irwin, *Scottish Painters at Home and Abroad, 1700–1900*, 1975, pp. 359–60, 364–5.

45. Joshua Hargrave Sams Mann
fl. 1849–84, RBA

The Cauld Blast 1876 (*pl. 78*)

oil on canvas, 36 × 24 in (91.4 × 60.9 cm)

INSCR: J. h. S. Mann 1876; on verso: The Cauld Blast / by Jh S Mann / 1876.

PROV: Edward Hermon M.P. of Wyfold Court, Henley-on-Thames; his sale Christie's 13 May 1882 (36) bt Martin £152 5s.

EXH: 1876 R.A. (1); 1981 Agnew's (28).

Exhibited at the R.A. in 1876, *The Cauld Blast* went unnoticed by the critics.

Mann was a little-known London genre painter. His range of subjects was wide, taking themes from the poetry of Tennyson, Byron, Coleridge and Burns. The following poem by Burns could have been the inspiration behind this painting. Entitled *O Wert Thou in the Cauld Blast*, it begins:

> O Wert Thou in the cauld blast
> On yonder lea, on yonder lea,
> My plaidie to the angry airt,
> I'd shelter thee, I'd shelter thee.
> Or did Misfortune's bitter storms
> Around thee blaw, around thee blaw,
> Thy bield should be my bosom,
> To share it a', to share it a'.[1]

Mann also painted portraits, some of them with fancy titles like *Day Dreams* and *Startled*. He exhibited mostly at the Society of British Artists, the R.A., the B.I. and elsewhere.

[1]I am grateful to Miss Janet Christie for drawing the poem to my attention.

46. Sir John Everett Millais
1829–96, ARA 1853, RA 1863, PRA 1896

The Princes in the Tower 1878 (*pl. 44*)

oil on canvas, 58 × 36 in (147.2 × 91.4 cm)

INSCR: 18ȹ78

PROV: Bought from the artist by the Fine Art Society, 27 March 1878 for £1,000 including copyright; their sale at Christie's 28 May 1881 (88) bt Thomas for £3,990.

EXH: 1878 R.A. (21); 1879 Agnew Exhibition, Feb–Apr; 1881 Fine Art Society *The Collected Works of John Everett Millais* (14); 1885 Manchester; Corporation Art Gallery, *Third Autumn Exhibition* (392); 1886 Grosvenor Gallery, *Works by Sir John E. Millais, Bt.* (63); 1898 R.A. *Works by Sir J. E. Millais, Bt., P.R.A.*; 1967 Liverpool, Walker Art Gallery and R.A. *Millais PRB–PRA* (93); 1977 Brighton *Royal Children* (d3); 1979 Jersey, *Sir John Everett Millais Commemorative Exhibition* (56); 1981 Riverside Studios, Hammersmith, London *Victorian Paintings at Riverside* (33); 1981 Agnew's (29).

LIT: *Academy* 11 May p. 423; *A.J.* 1878 pp. 145–6; *Athenaeum* 4 May pp. 576–7; Blackburn, *R.A. Notes* 1878 p. 8 and thumbnail sketch; *Examiner* 4 May 1878 p. 569 and 11 May 1878 p. 600; *Graphic* 11 May 1878 p. 467; *I.L.N.* 4 May 1878 p. 410; *Mag. of Art* 1878 p. 42 and repr; *Punch* 25 May 1878 p. 237; *Saturday Review* 11 May 1878 p. 592; *The Times* 4 May 1878 p. 12; Spielmann, 1898 pp. 134, 173 and listed no. 191; Baldry, 1899 pp. 32, 57, 69 and repr. p. 32; Millais, 1899 Vol. II, pp. 88–91, 478 and repr. p. 103; Reid, 1909 pp. 81–2; Roy Strong, *And when did you last see your Father?*, 1978, pp. 60.

ENGR: 1. Samuel Cousins R.A., mezzotint, 16⅛ × 26¼ in (40.9 × 66.6 cm) Fine Art Society 1879
Repr. Millais, 1899, Vol. II, p. 103
2. Lumb Stocks R.A., line engraving, *A.J.* 1884, frontispiece.

In 1878 Millais exhibited five paintings at the R.A. One was *The Princes in the Tower*. Three were portraits: the *Earl of Shaftesbury* (242), painted for the Bible Society in London and still in their possession, *A Jersey Lily*, a portrait of Mrs Langtry (307, The States of Jersey) and *The Countess of Carysfort* (1021, Private Collection). The fifth exhibit was *St. Martin's Summer* (465, whereabouts unknown).

The two princes shown in the painting are King Edward V, aged 13, and his brother, Richard, Duke of York, aged 10, the sons of King Edward IV. Their father died in 1483, and in the same year their uncle, Richard, Duke of Gloucester, imprisoned them in the Tower of London and took the throne for himself, as Richard III. The boy captives did not long survive.

The child is a recurrent theme throughout Millais's work. However, *The Princes in the Tower* and *Princess Elizabeth* (q.v.) are exceptional in showing particular children known to history: all three are royal children destined to die in captivity. The only important precedent of Millais painting children from history is *The Boyhood of Raleigh* (ex. R.A. 1870 [334], Tate Gallery). In British 18th- and 19th-century art as a whole, however, such subject-matter is commonplace, and the two princes were depicted by a number of prominent artists before Millais, including John Opie

(1761–1807) and James Northcote (1746–1831). These painters chose episodes from the princes' story other than the moment of apprehension before their presumed murder, the subject of this painting. But a work by a less well-known painter, Henry Courtenay Selous (1811–90) seems to have anticipated Millais' subject more precisely. *The Rustle of the Tapestry – Scene in the Tower of London, Anno Domini 1483* (whereabouts unkown) was exhibited at the R.A. in 1853 (169), and may have been noticed by Millais since he probably knew Selous.[1]

The major pictorial source for *The Princes*, however, was the painting by the French Paul Delaroche (1797–1856) of 1831, entitled *Edward V and the Duke of York in the Tower*, the Wallace Collection's version of which Millais would certainly have seen.[2] This also deals with the tense moment just before the arrival of the assassins, whose approach is indicated in both works by ominous shadows. Moreover, there are points of similarity in the costumes, especially the boots, which suggest that Millais's painting was at least in part derived from the Delaroche. The garter worn by Edward is another feature common to both paintings, although the critic of the *Athenaeum* implied that his wearing the Order of the Garter was recommended to Millais by 'the highest authority on such subjects', J. R. Planché.

According to Spielmann, Millais's most immediate inspiration was seeing the two children who were to be his models 'thus arrayed when playing in *tableaux vivants*'. Spielmann identified the models as the son and daughter of Thomas Dallas-Yorke of Walmsgate, Lincolnshire (the daughter, Winifred Anna, later became the Duchess of Portland). J. G. Millais, however, claimed that they were the children of a professional model who had sat for Millais's *White Cockade* of 1862 (Delaware Art Museum, U.S.A.).[3] J. G. Millais made no mention of *tableaux vivants* and stated that the artist himself had 'cast' them as the princes upon being offered them as models by their mother.

The most familiar accounts of the princes' story describes their being found sleeping by their murderers and suffocated with pillows.[4] Millais's picture implies

that the murder will take place by a staircase, a setting chosen presumably because of the discovery by workmen in 1674 of the skeletons of two children (never identified) in a wooden chest buried under a staircase in the White Tower. In the interests of historical accuracy, Millais sent his son to the Bloody Tower to make sketches of the interior; the result was unsatisfactory, and the first canvas was discarded.[5] Millais then began the work afresh, basing the background on his own drawings of the Bloody Tower. A letter to his daughter, Mary, of 3 February 1878, mentioned that *The Princes* was in progress.[6] It was presumably complete or near completion on 20 February, when the Managing Director of the Fine Art Society reported having been in touch with Millais about buying it, and in early April it would have been submitted for the R.A. exhibition.[7]

The reviews of the 1878 R.A. exhibition were numerous and, almost without exception, enthusiastic. Some objected to the gloom and lack of expression in the painting. The critics recognised that the success of the composition lay in its simplicity and its pathos, and it was this which resulted in its enormous popularity as an engraving.

The *A.J.* pointed out that Millais had not painted a historical subject for some time. They described it as 'very pretty' but objected to the costumes as 'only an approximation of that belonging to the period'. The *Magazine of Art* also commented: 'The black in the costume is treated with a fine reticence of tone, the artist has kept well within the force at his command; more black paint, however, and less red and blue in the composition of the black, would, it appears to us, produce a more satisfactory result.'

William Michael Rossetti in *The Academy* considered that *The Princes in the Tower* 'redeems this section [of the exhibition] out of mediocrity' and 'gives indeed a certain prestige to the whole exhibition ... [it] looks at first a rather trifling affair – it carries simplicity of treatment to the verge of bareness: but the simplicity is so masterly, the sentiment so natural and touching, the whole thing comes so much home to one as one gazes, that no room and no inclination for critical dissent remain at last . . . There is absolutely no accessory, except two shreds of straw upon the principal stair. Such are the simple means by which the author produces his tragic impression: he hardly tells a story, indeed, but he strikes pathetically the chord of innocence and doom.'

The *I.L.N.* was more condescending and described 'the two charming little boys' as possibly 'the sons of a modern nobleman or gentleman, and ready dressed for a fancy ball'. This was echoed by *Punch*, who gave the boys the names of Sandford and Merton, dressed in 'fancy Costumes . . . going out to a ball without the permission of their revered tutor, Mr. Barlow'. But they did add that it was 'a noble work styled by the Artist'.

Of all the reviewers *The Times* was the most generous with praise. They forecast that *The Princes* 'will probably be the picture of the first room . . . The painter has admirably expressed in these young faces the trouble of continued fear blent with the agitation of sudden alarm, and it is greatly to his praise that, even after the "Enfants d'Edouard" of De la Roche, his work should awaken no thought of plagiarism. The execution is consummate, and thoroughly carried through the picture.'

[1] Both artists came from old Jersey families, and Millais' son wrote a biography of Selous's nephew in 1918, which suggests there may have been compatriotic links.

[2] The Wallace Collection version was exhibited at Bethnal Green Museum from 1872 to 1875, and subsequently at Hertford House. The original version of the Delaroche is in the Louvre.

[3] The model for the *White Cockade* was identified by Millais, Vol. II p. 91, as a Miss White, later Mrs Davis.

[4] Shakespeare, *Richard III*, Act IV, Scene 3 and Paul M. Kendall, *Richard the Third*, 1955, pp. 393–418.

[5] This was later taken up again as the background for *The Grey Lady* of 1883 which was sold anonymously at Christie's, 15 December 1972 (156) bt Stanley.

[6] Letter in Millais Papers, B.20, reproduced by kind permission of The Pierpont Morgan Library, New York.

[7] Fine Art Society Minute Book.

47. Sir John Everett Millais
1829–96, ARA 1853, RA 1863, PRA 1896
Princess Elizabeth in prison at St. James's 1879 (*pl. 45*)
oil on canvas, 57 × 40 in (144.7 × 101.5 cm)

INSCR: 18⚓79
PROV: Bought from the artist by the Fine Art Society, agreed 28 March 1879 for £1,000 including copyright; bought from them by Holloway, 30 June 1881 for £3150.

EXH: 1881 Fine Art Society, *The Collected Works of John Everett Millais* (12); 1885 Manchester, Corporation Art Gallery, *Third Autumn Exhibition* (388); 1886 Grosvenor Gallery, *Works by Sir John Everett Millais, Bt.* (58); 1898 R.A., *Works by the late Sir J. E. Millais, Bt., PRA* (148); 1977 Brighton *Royal Children* (d13); 1979 Jersey *Sir John Everett Millais Commemorative Exhibition* (59); 1981 Agnew's (30).

LIT: *Mag. of Art* 1880 p. 276; *Academy* 26 February 1881 p. 160; *A.J.* 1881 p. 126; *Graphic* 26 February 1881 p. 211; *I.L.N.* 26 February 1881 p. 211; *Mag. of Art* 1881 p. xxi; *Portfolio* 1881 p. 70; *Saturday Review* 5 March 1881 p. 307; Spielmann, 1898 pp. 133, 174 and listed no. 200; Baldry, 1899 pp. 59, 65, 66 and repr. p. 58; Millais, 1899, Vol. II, pp. 117, 122–4, 401, 479 and repr. p. 125; Roy Strong, *And when did you last see your father?*, 1978, p. 119.

ENGR: T. L. Atkinson, mezzotint, 16 × 26 in (40.6 × 66 cm), Fine Art Society, 1887.
Repr. Millais, 1899, Vol. II, p. 125.

STUDIES: Two studies, one pencil, one pen and ink, on the same sheet, 14 × 10 in (35.5 × 25.4 cm).
Prov. Presented by Lady Millais, 1945, to the Royal Academy.
A rough figure study on verso of a design for an illustration to Thackeray's *Barry Lyndon* in pencil, 9¾ × 7¾ in (24.7 × 19.6 cm).
Prov. Artist's sale Christie's 2 July 1898 (17) bt Agnew; J. E. Reiss; his sale Christie's 6 February 1914 (47) bt Agnew for J. R. Holliday; his bequest 1927 to Fitzwilliam Museum.

Holloway purchased this picture from the Fine Art Society in June 1881, a month after buying its companion *The Princes in the Tower* at Christie's. Both paintings had been bought from Millais by the Directors of the Fine Art Society. *Princess Elizabeth* was one of the few works Holloway did not buy from Christie's.

Variously titled as *Princess Elizabeth in the Tower* and *Princess Elizabeth in prison at St. James's*, the painting shows the second daughter of King Charles I and Queen Henrietta Maria, much of whose life was spent in captivity, imprisoned in St. James's Palace. Andrew Lang's notes for the Fine Art Society exhibition in 1881 mention the Agnes Strickland's history of *The Lives of the last four Princesses of the Royal House of Stuart*, written in 1872, from which it is presumed Millais took the description of Princess Elizabeth writing a letter to the Parliamentary Commissioners from St. James's Palace, asking that her 'faithful governess' should be re-instated to her post. The princess had been denied her servants since she was first imprisoned. According to Agnes Strickland, her letter was read out to the House of Lords but had no effect. She was transferred to Carisbrooke Castle, Isle of Wight, in 1650; there she died alone, eight days later, aged 15.

A reproduction of the engraving in the biography of Millais written by his son in 1899 distinctly shows a portrait of Charles I, on the wall in the upper left-hand corner of the painting.[1] This, however, is no longer visible in the painting itself, nor is the crouching figure on the tapestry hanging to the left of the cabinet. The cabinet itself was owned by Millais and from 1878, when he moved from Cromwell Place, until his death in 1896, was in his studio in his house at 2 Palace Gate, Kensington.[2] Millais also owned a set of Beauvais tapestries and a Brussels tapestry panel which he often used for backgrounds for his pictures.[3] His model for the figure of Princess Elizabeth was his daughter Sophie, who was 12.[4]

The subject of Princess Elizabeth in captivity had been seen at R.A. exhibitions since the 1850s. Charles Lucy (1814–73) exhibited *The Royal Captives of Carisbrooke, A.D. 1650* (untraced) in the 1851 R.A. exhibition (720) with a quotation from an earlier book by Agnes Strickland on royal children. This was followed by *Royal Pensioners at Carisbrooke* (ex. R.A. 1855 [161], Carisbrooke Castle Museum) by C. W. Cope (1811–90), who was best known for his decorative history paintings at the Palace of Westminster.

It was reported early in 1880 that Millais finished *Princess Elizabeth* too late in 1879 to be able to submit it for exhibition that year, which is why it was shown in the following February exhibition at the Fine Art Society, devoted exclusively to 19 works by Millais.[5] The exhibition was noticed by most of the art journals, who generally commended *Princess Elizabeth*.[6] Cosmo Monkhouse in *The Academy* called it 'perhaps the most beautiful picture of a little girl which has been painted since Sir Joshua Reynolds; and the tender beauty of expression in *Princess Elizabeth*, shows that his later work may yet rival his earlier in sentiment.' The *Saturday Review* described it as 'a canvas just fresh from the artist's studio, [it] may be regarded as a fortunate example of this later style . . . the pensive and pathetic expression has been very skilfully rendered, and in the enjoyment of the technical merits of the picture, we are ready to concede that enough has been done to justify, if not exactly to explain, the title which it bears.'

'Pathetic' was the word with which most of the reviewers expressed their reaction to the work. The *Magazine of Art* claimed: 'The only absolute novelty of this most interesting exhibition is the lovely "Princess Elizabeth", a single figure of the little royal maiden composing the pathetic letter to the Parliamentary Commissioners.' And added that the letter she had written 'may yet be read at Oxford'.

John Everett Millais was born in Southampton but spent most of his early childhood in Jersey. Brought by his parents to London, he became, at 11, the youngest student ever admitted to the Royal Academy Schools. He made a successful debut at the R.A. exhibition in 1846 with *Pizarro Seizing the Inca of Peru* (594, Victoria and Albert Museum). In 1848, with six other young artists, most notably Dante Gabriel Rossetti (1828–82) and William Holman Hunt (1827–1910), he formed the Pre-Raphaelite Brotherhood. Millais's work of the later 1840s and the early 1850s (e.g. *Christ in the Carpenter's Shop*, 1849–50, Tate Gallery) is characterised by particular attention to detail.

In the later 1850s Millais' style became less meticulous as his interest shifted from the painstaking realisation of a scene to the capturing of a general mood. This development, seen in works such as *Autumn Leaves* of 1855–56 (Manchester City Art Gallery) and

The Eve of St. Agnes of 1862–63 (H.M. Queen Elizabeth the Queen Mother), went hand in hand with a growing reverence for artists of the past. He was much influenced by Velasquez, Hals and even Reynolds, whom he had previously held in the deepest contempt.

By the 1870s Millais was an immensely popular and successful artist. He was a prolific portraitist, numbering both *Gladstone* (1879, National Portrait Gallery) and *Disraeli* (1881, National Portrait Gallery) among his many distinguished sitters; he also painted a number of large-scale landscapes, showing generally rather bleak Scottish scenery (*Chill October*, 1870, Private Collection, currently on loan to Perth Art Gallery). In 1885 he became the first British painter to be created a baronet, and in 1896, the year of his death, was elected President of the Royal Academy.

[1] John Guille Millais, *The Life and Letters of Sir John Everett Millais*, 1899, Vol. II, p. 125.
[2] The cabinet is illustrated in the *Survey of London*, The Museums Area of South Kensington and Westminster, 1975, Vol. XXXVIII, pl. 94c. For further discussion of the cabinet, see Jeannie Chapel and John Hardy, 'The Millais Cabinet', *Burlington Magazine*, Vol. CXXII, 1980, pp. 424–7.
[3] See lots 8 and 9 in Millais' sale catalogue.
[4] John Guille Millais, 1899, Vol. II, p. 123.
[5] Reported in *Magazine of Art*, 1880, p. 276.
[6] The exhibition catalogue contained advertisements for engravings of *The Princes in the Tower* and *Princess Elizabeth* which were both listed as the property of Thomas Holloway Esq.

BIBLIOGRAPHY
Walter Armstrong, 'Sir J. E. Millais', *Art Annual*, 1885.
Marion H. Spielmann, *Millais and His Works*, Edinburgh and London, 1898.
Works of the later Sir John Everett Millais, Bart., President of the Royal Academy, Winter Exhibition, 1898, Royal Academy.
Alfred Lys Baldry, *Sir John Everett Millais, his Art and Influence*, 1899.
John Guille Millais, *The Life and Letters of Sir John Everett Millais*, 2 Vols., 1899 and 1905.
J. Eadie Reid, *Sir J. E. Millais, P.R.A.*, 1909.
Sir John Everett Millais, catalogue Walker Art Gallery, Liverpool and Royal Academy, 1967.

48. George Morland
1763–1804
The Cottage Door 1790 (*pl. 37*)
panel, 14 × 18 in (35.5 × 45.7 cm)
INSCR: G. Morland 1790
PROV: Henry Hare Townsend of Busbridge, nr Godalming by 1807; George Tierney of 61 Pall Mall; his sale Christie's 19 May 1883 (345) bt Martin together with *The Pressgang* £399.
EXH: 1934 R.A. *British Art* (459); 1972 Paris *La Peinture Romantique Anglaise et les Pre-Raphaelites* (193); 1975 Reading and Southampton (12).
LIT: Hassell, 1806 pp. 70–1; Richardson, 1897 p. 29; Williamson, 1904 pp. 105–6, 116–17; Dawe, 1904 p. 140; Gilbey and Cuming, 1907 p. 250; Wilson, 1907 pp. 87–8, listed pp. 184, 188, 191, 195 and repr. opp. p. 88; Henderson, 1923 p. 113; Sacheverell Sitwell, *Narrative Pictures*, 1937 pp. 46, 105 and repr. pl. 53.
ENGR: William Ward ARA, mezzotint, 1790 and 1806; R. Clamp, 1797; Arthur L. Cox, 1919.

This is a companion picture to *The Pressgang*. Painted in the same year, they have always been kept together as a pair. *The Cottage Door* was originally entitled *The Contented Waterman* and was also referred to as *My Poll and My Partner Joe*. Its first recorded owner, Henry Hare Townsend, owned many other Morlands with similar titles.

The Cottage Door was a favourite subject of Morland's (there are at least three other known pictures with this title) and was described in 1806 as: 'A representation of domestic comfort in low life is here depicted in all its simplicty; the wife busy with her needle, the infant playing with its doll, and the waterman and his partner Joe enjoying their pipe, with a repose in the landscape. The scene, evening, at a cottage-door, is in strict correspondence, and denotes the day's labor past.'[1]

This picture has been seen as the first part of the story continued by *The Pressgang*.[2] The prow of the boat seen on the left is similar to that in *The Pressgang*, and other details, such as the dog and the figure of the central characters in both paintings, are indications that the pipe-smoking man has been led into a trap. The loose treatment of the brushwork is common to both pictures, and has been compared to the French 18th-century style of painting.[3]

The calm and inactivity of this picture contrast dramatically with the violence of *The Pressgang*.

[1] John Hassell, *Memoirs of the Life of George Morland*, 1806, pp. 70–1.
[2] David Henry Wilson, *George Morland*, 1907, pp. 87–8.
[3] See Sacheverell Sitwell, *Narrative Pictures*, 1937, pp. 46, 105 and the exhibition catalogue *La Peinture Romantique Anglaise*, Paris, 1972, no. 193, in which Michael Kitson compares the right-hand figure to Greuze.

49. George Morland
1763–1804

The Pressgang 1790 (*pl. 35*)

panel, 14 × 18 in (35.5 × 45.7 cm)

INSCR: (on oar) G. Morland 1790

PROV: Henry Hare Townsend of Busbridge, nr Godalming by 1807; George Tierney of 61 Pall Mall; his sale Christie's 19 May 1883 (120) bt Martin together with *The Cottage Door*.

EXH: 1975 Reading and Southampton (13).

LIT: Hassell, 1806 p. 71; Richardson, 1897 p. 29; Williamson, 1904 pp. 105–6, 116–17; Gilbey and Cuming, 1907 p. 250; Wilson, 1907 pp. 87, 88, listed pp. 184, 188, 191, 195 and repr. opp. p. 96; Henderson, 1923 p. 113.

ENGR: William Ward ARA, 1790; R. Clamp, 1797.

Painted as a companion picture to *The Cottage Door*, it also formerly had a different title, *Jack in the Bilboes*. A bilboe was a long iron bar with a sliding shackle to confine the ankle of a prisoner, and a lock to fasten one end of the bar to the floor or deck.

This kind of subject, a narrative with figures and a scene beside the sea, was common in Morland's work. Smugglers and wreckers were interesting and topical subjects, as was the pressgang. As Hassell wrote: 'All the horrors of an agitated mind are expressed in the countenance of the once happy waterman, while the most ferocious passion and barbarism are exhibited in the press-gang. The female figure in the boat, we believe, is a portrait of a branch of Mr. Morland's family; the male, that of an acquaintance. The background, a row of warehouses by the waterside.'[1] The victim, his hands clasped in fear, is placed so that he makes a clear dividing line between the alarmed couple on the right, and in contrast to their smart appearance, the three rough assailants on the left. Both *The Pressgang* and *The Cottage Door* were engraved in 1790 by Morland's brother-in-law, the well-known mezzotint engraver William Ward (1766–1826).

[1] John Hassell, *Memoirs of the Life of George Morland*, 1806, p. 71.

50. George Morland
1763–1804

The Carrier preparing to set out 1793 (*pl. 38*)

oil on canvas, 34 × 46 in (86.3 × 116.7 cm)

INSCR: (on side of the wagon) G. Morland Gom[n]. Stage Cart N°. 1793.

PROV: G. H. Morland: his sale Christie's 9 May 1863 (182) bt Cox £257 5s.; Earl of Dunmore; purchased from him 29 October 1881 £400 by Thomas Holloway.

EXH: 1975 Reading and Southampton (22).

LIT: Richardson, 1897 p. 29; Williamson, 1904 pp. 105–6, 116–17; Wilson, 1907 listed pp. 185, 188, 194, 195; Henderson, 1923 p. 113.

ENGR: Arthur L. Cox, mezzotint, 1920.

This picture was painted when Morland was between the peak of his success, in the late 1780s, and the years of his financial and personal decline, when he was forced to make repeated visits to the country to escape from the bailiffs. This painting shows the arrangements for the departure of a cart which is being loaded with hampers, a rabbit cage and a large wooden box. A reluctant horse is being coaxed into being harnessed to the cart.

Morland produced a large amount of work ranging over a wide variety of subject matter. Dawe, in the Introduction to his biography of Morland, suggested that the painter's subject matter fell into seven categories: portraits of his family and himself and views of localities associated with him; single figures; children; didactic and social compositions; rural scenes with animals and rustic figures; interiors; coastal scenes.[1]

Born in London in 1763, the eldest son of a painter, engraver, picture dealer and cleaner, whose wife was also a painter and exhibited at the R.A., George Morland was first apprenticed to his father. In 1786 Morland married Anne, the sister of James Ward, the painter (1769–1859), and of William Ward, who made many mezzotint engravings of his work. Morland's paintings and engravings of animals and children were especially popular. He exhibited at the R.A. from the age of 10, mostly picturesque landscape paintings and animal pictures but also illustrations for *The Vicar of Wakefield* and *The Adventures of a Hackney Coach*.

Morland made frequent visits to Enderby in Leicestershire where he gathered material for his rural subjects. He specialised in a certain type of picturesque poverty, in farm labourers and farmyard animals, especially horses and pigs. His fondness for drinking and keeping disreputable company led him into debt and he was finally made to serve two years of a special prison sentence enabling him to live near the prison, not in it, and to carry on painting and drawing. Morland died in 1804.

[1] George Dawe, *The Life of George Morland*, 1807, ed. J. J. Foster, 1904.

BIBLIOGRAPHY
John Raphael Smith, *A Descriptive Catalogue of Thirty-Six Pictures painted by George Morland*, c. 1793.
John Hassell, *Memoirs of the Life of George Morland*, 1806.
George Dawe, *The Life of George Morland*, 1807, ed. J. J. Foster, 1904.
James Ward, 'Some Notes on George Morland', *Portfolio*, 1886, pp. 98–102.
Ralph Richardson, *George Morland*, 1895.
John T. Nettleship, *George Morland*, 1898.
H. M. Cundall, 'George Morland', *Art Journal*, 1904, pp. 315–20.
George Charles Williamson, *George Morland. His Life and Works*, 1904.

J. T. Herbert Baily, *George Morland*, 1906.

Sir Walter Gilbey and Edward William D. Cuming, *George Morland, His Life and Works*, 1907.

David Henry Wilson, *George Morland*, 1907.

Bernard L. K. Henderson, *Morland and Ibbetson*, 1923.

Selwyn Image, *Some Reflections on the Art of Thomas Rowlandson and George Morland*, 1929.

Francis Buckley, *George Morland's Sketch Books and their Publishers*, Uppermill, 1931.

51. William James Muller

1812–45

Interior of a Cottage in Wales with a Woman at a spinning wheel and a Child feeding chickens 1841 (*pl. 39*)

panel, 10 × 14 in (25.3 × 35.5 cm)

INSCR: W. Müller 1841

PROV: Samuel Mayou of Edgbaston, Birmingham by ? 1873 (with the title of *Interior of Welsh Cottage of Roe, Woman, Girl and Poultry*); his sale Christie's 21 April 1883 (33) bt Martin £210.

LIT: ? Solly, 1875, p. 153, Appendix II p. 334, Appendix IV p. 346.

This small panel is most probably a sketch for a larger painting entitled *Interior of a Cottage, North Wales* (33 × 28 in, 83.8 × 71.1 cm), which Muller exhibited at the B.I. (33) in 1843. The *Art Union* review pointed out how the exhibited picture differed radically from Muller's usual style and his subjects taken from his Near Eastern journeys.[1] From the description given, the two works have obvious similarities.

Muller began to paint interiors of Welsh cottages in 1833 on the first of his many sketching trips to North Wales. It was his custom to paint larger oil paintings from small sketches during the winter months in London, and exhibit them the following year. This type of genre painting was apparently due to his admiration for interiors by Rembrandt and Ostade, especially their use of exterior light casting shadows internally.

Solly, in his biography of Muller, refers to a painting in the collection of Samuel Mayou, the previous owner of the picture here, but lists it as painted in 1842, not 1841.[2] From his description it seems to have been the same painting as this. Entitling it *Interior of Welsh Cottage at Roe, Woman, Girl and Poultry*, Solly wrote: 'It is carefully painted, and represents a Welsh woman seated in a picturesque kitchen near an open door, through which a peep of country appears. Close to the door a girl is feeding poultry, and on the right are some jugs, pans and rural implements. The colour is rich and mellow and the arrangement of light and shade skilful.'

The majority of Muller's Welsh subjects were painted between 1840 and 1843, the year in which he left for his Lycian expedition, and were an assorted collection of landscapes and interior views. The interior paintings, like this, have basically the same format and ingredients and show some kind of rural activity.

[1] *Art Union*, 1843, p. 65.
[2] Nathanael Neal Solly, *Memoir of W. J. Müller*, 1875, p. 153.

52. William James Muller

1812–45

Opium Stall 1841 (*pl. 23*)

panel, 16 × 11 in (40.6 × 27.9 cm)

INSCR: W. Muller 1841

EXH: 1981 Agnew's (31)

PROV: Samuel Mayou of Edgbaston, Birmingham by 1873 (with the title of *Opium Seller, Manfalout*); his sale Christie's 21 April 1883 (34) bt Martin £336.

LIT: Solly, 1875 Appendix IV p. 346.

STUDY: *Opium Seller, Assiout*
watercolour, 10 × 7½ in (25.3 × 19 cm)
Inscr. W. M. Egypt
Prov. Bequeathed to the British Museum by John Henderson, 1878.
Lit. Binyon, 1898–1908 Vol. III p. 121, no. 28.

VERSIONS:
1. *Exh.* 1841 Society of British Artists (43) *Sketch of The Opium Seller at Manafalout* bt Bell 12 gns.
Lit. Art Union 1841 p. 66.
2. *The Opium Seller*
13½ × 10½ in (34.2 × 26.6 cm)
Prov. Mr Peel; W. Smith of Wisbech 1875.
Lit. Solly, 1875 p. 98.
3. *The Opium Seller*
panel, 13¾ × 10 in (34.2 × 25.3 cm)
Prov. Thomas Barratt (Chairman of Pears Soap) of Bell Moor, Hampstead 1898; his sale Christie's 11 May 1916 (85) bt Sir J. Beacham £50 8s.
Lit. Mag. of Art 1898 pp. 195–6 and repr. p. 192, possibly the same as no. 2.

In 1838–39 Muller visited Naples, Greece, Malta and Egypt, where, as was his practice, he made many small studies in watercolour and in oil.

His Egyptian paintings, dating from 1839 to 1841, sometimes numbered up to five or six versions of the same subject, such was the demand for his work. This painting of *The Opium Seller* was listed by Solly as in the Mayou collection with the title of *Opium Seller, Manfalout* and he mentions four or five copies of it.[1] Manfalout is on the Nile. Muller wrote about 'an Opium Shop at Monfaloot' (sic) in a letter printed by the *A.J.* in 1864 (it had been in their possession since 1843), in which he had described his travels. 'My rambles have been through a great part of Europe, and portions of Asia and Africa. Travel to me affords two pleasures: my love of botany and natural history in general.' About this painting, he said: 'I shall never forget with what pleasure I first made acquaintance with an Eastern Bazaar; and as scene after scene presented itself to me, there was but one thought working in my mind. "What would not Rembrandt have done with such subjects?". They remind one strongly of that fine painter. The sun streams through a little opening in the wall and falls on the figures, lighting them up with all but a supernatural brilliancy; reflection acts its part, and bit by bit the whole is revealed, and as figure after figure passes by, some in the richest dresses and superb stuffs, while others, such as the pipe-cleaners, walk on shouting their avocations, and literally clothed in rags, you have a constantly changing picture before you.'[2]

Muller kept detailed diaries of his journeys and his numerous sketches show coffee houses, mosques, slave markets and bazaars.

Samuel Mayou, from whose sale Holloway purchased this painting and the *Interior of a Cottage in Wales*, also owned *The Slave Market at Cairo* of the same date as *The Opium Stall*, 1841. He possessed another painting by Muller entitled *Opium Stall* which was later bought by Thomas J. Barratt, the Chairman of Pears Soap, who owned Landseer's *Monarch of the Glen* and *Bubbles* by Millais, which he used for advertising purposes.[3]

Muller's paintings were greatly admired for their fine colour and yet, as was pointed out in one of the articles about the Barratt collection, 'his pictures frequently sold for the modest equivalent of ten pounds; and, with the advanced request for his splendid productions, destined ultimately to bring their lucky possessors as many hundreds. For instance, "The Slave Market, Egypt" (1841), 15 in by 25 in, from the collection of Charles Birch, brought at the Gillott sale, in 1872, £1,510, when "The Chess Players, Egypt", from the same collection, reached nearly £4,000.'[4]

The Opium Stall in this collection differs in detail from the one illustrated in the *Magazine of Art* and also from the watercolour in the British Museum, *Opium Seller, Assiout*, which, despite the difference of locality, is a preliminary study for *The Opium Stall* in the College collection. The points of difference amount, in both cases, to changes in the central group of figures and the woman in the bottom right-hand corner varies in dress and is without a child in the Barratt picture and also in the British Museum watercolour. However, in all three known representations of this scene, Muller has used the same setting with the rounded arch and balcony on the left, and the strong diagonal shaft of light originating from the top right opening in the wall to highlight the opium seller cross-legged on his mat.

[1] Nathanael Neal Solly, *Memoir of W. J. Müller*, 1875, pp. 333, 346. Some references for the copies are listed above.
[2] *Art Journal*, 1864, pp. 293–5.
[3] For the Barratt collection, see four articles in *Magazine of Art*, 1898, pp. 132–8, 189–96, 261–8, 289–94.
[4] *Magazine of Art*, 1898, pp. 195–6; Muller's *Opium Stall* is illustrated on p. 192.

53. William James Muller
1812–45

Tomb in the Water, Telmessus, Lycia 1845 (*pl. 10*)

oil on canvas, 30 × 54 in (76.1 × 137.1 cm)

INSCR: W Müller 45

PROV: William Sharp of Endwood Court, Handsworth, nr Birmingham 1865; his sale Christie's 9 July 1881 (79) bt Mason £2,362 10 s.

LIT: Solly, 1875 p. 281 and repr. no. XVII, opp. p. 276, Appendix II p. 334, Appendix IV p. 346; *The Times* 12 July 1881 p. 4; Bunt, 1948 p. 48 and listed p. 108.

STUDY: *Water Tomb, Telmessus*
watercolour, 14⅛ × 21 in (36.3 × 53.3 cm)
Prov. Bequeathed to the British Museum by John Henderson, 1878.
Lit. Binyon, 1898–1907 Vol. III p. 125, no. 72.
Repr. S. Haynes, *Land of the Chimaera*, 1974 p. 52.

After his journey of 1838–39 to Egypt and the Mediterranean, Muller left England in 1843 with the Lycian expedition led by the traveller and archaeologist, Sir Charles Fellows (1799–1860). Its purpose was to recover the ancient marble sculptures which Fellows had previously discovered at Tlos and Xanthus, the old capital of Lycia, in south west Anatolia, in 1838. Muller went at his own expense, not as a topographical artist but to make 'general and pictorial' representations of the ancient monuments.

Muller had a special fascination for tombs. He drew and painted many different types, some carved out of the earth surface and some, like the *Tomb in the Water*, which were surrounded by water. His letters convey the intensity of his interest in the shapes, colours and condition of the tombs: 'There is much that is exceedingly poetic in these resting-places of the dead.'[1]

The tomb in the painting is in the bay of Fethiye, Turkey, (known until recently as Macry or Makri) the site of ancient Telmessus, formerly a trading port. It was mentioned by Sir Charles Fellows as being 'more interesting, on examination, than I fancied it could be from my hasty survey two years ago; but its strongest feature of interest is its tombs'.[2]

Muller's tomb is an accurate representation: Fellows emphasised that this type of upright sepulchre was peculiar to Lycia and that the tomb painted by Muller seemed to be low-standing in the water because winds on the sea had created a false tide-mark on it. This type of tomb, which Fellows called a 'Gothic-formed Horse Tomb', was built in imitation of wooden buildings.[3] The ends of it are left projecting and relief sculpture would have originally decorated it.[4]

It seems that this tomb was formerly on dry land but became surrounded by water as ground levels changed. Since the earthquake in 1958, following which land was reclaimed to build a new harbour, the area where the tomb stands is once again dry land and this sarcophagus is now to be seen 'rising somewhat incongruously from a gap in the modern paving'.[5]

The *Tomb in the Water*, possibly like *Interior of a Cottage*, is a smaller version of a picture of the same title, though sometimes referred to as *Tomb in the Mountains*. This larger painting (44 × 69 in, 111.7 × 175.2 cm) was exhibited at the B.I. in 1845 (498), that is, the same year as the painting here was finished, but unfortunately it has not been traced. The description in the *Art Union* review of 1845 suggests that they were similar pictures. 'The view suits well with the ancient reputation of the place, which lies at the foot of the abrupt ridge of hills by which the view is closed. The foreground is a plain, partially covered with water, amid which is the tomb, an object well fitted to be a prominent memento in such a locality. The water is endued with the limpidity and lustre of the element itself; and the admirable feeling with which it is treated contrasts powerfully with the substantial handling of the other subjects.'

This is borne out by Solly's account of the same picture: 'It is freshly painted, and in a light key. A broad quiet expanse of water reflects the mountains, which were honeycombed with tombs, and above these rises a bold crest capped with snow. A curious antique sculptured tomb is standing out of the water, in which it is reflected, and several storks are grouped about in the water and on the banks. The sky is of a pearly grey, and, the general effect calm and quiet, and also full of mystery.'[6]

A watercolour study entitled *Water Tomb, Telmessus* was bequeathed by John Henderson to the British Museum in 1878, together with the watercolour for *The Opium Stall*. John Henderson (1797–1878) was an archaeologist and collector of works of art, an artist and a Fellow of the Society of Antiquaries. His father, also John Henderson, had been an early patron of Turner and Girtin. The younger John Henderson left his large and valuable collection of works of art to various museums. His watercolours were bequeathed to the British Museum and included works by Canaletto, Turner, Girtin, Cozens, Cox and Muller.

William James Muller (who is referred to sometimes as Müller, and signed his name so) was the son of a refugee from Napoleon's invasion of Prussia in 1806, who became Curator of the Museum in Bristol. In 1827 Muller was apprenticed to J. B. Pyne for two years. Until his journey in 1834–35 to Switzerland and Italy, he mostly painted landscapes in the Bristol area and in Wales. He moved to London in 1839 and in 1840 became a member of the Clipstone Street Academy (founded in about 1823 or 1824 by John Prescott Knight [1803–81]; its members concentrated on painting realistic urban scenes).

In 1840 Muller went to France and in 1841 published *Sketches of the age of Francis I*, a volume of folio lithographs illustrating historical monuments from the Renaissance and other periods of the French monarchy.

Muller died of heart disease at the age of 33, but in his brief career he displayed a wide technical range and a variety of styles and subjects exemplified by the three paintings in this collection. He achieved great fame in a short space of time and as early as 1848, three years after his death, the *Art Union* warned against the 'immense number of forgeries of Muller now on the market'.[7]

[1] *Art Union*, 1844, pp. 41–2.
[2] Sir Charles Fellows, *An Account of Discoveries in Lycia*, 1841, p. 106.
[3] For a comparison, see the Tomb of Payava removed from Xanthus by Fellows in 1842 and now in the British Museum.
[4] Sir Charles Fellows, 1841, pp. 112–13, with a sketch.
[5] For a fuller explanation of this, see Sybille Haynes, *Land of the Chimaera*, 1974, pp. 52–3. I am most grateful for the assistance of Dr Margaret Lyttelton with this matter.

[6] This extract was partially quoted by Carey but mistakenly refers this to the College painting.
[7] *Art Union*, 1848, p. 33.

BIBLIOGRAPHY
'An Artist's Tour in Egypt', *Art Union*, 1839, pp. 131–2.
'Letter from Xanthus', *Art Union*, 1844, pp. 41–2.
'The Artist in Xanthus', *Art Union*, 1844 pp. 209–11.
Art Union, 1845, pp. 54, 318–19 (Obit.).
James Dafforne, 'British Artists: Their Style and Character, No. LXXVI, William John Müller', *Art Journal*, 1864, pp. 293–5.
Nathanael Neal Solly, *Memoir of W. J. Müller*, 1875.
J. B. Atkinson, 'William Müller'. *Portfolio*, 1875, pp. 164–8, 185–92.
Frederick Wedmore, 'William Müller and His Sketches', *Portfolio*, 1882, pp. 7–10.
James Orrock, 'William Müller', *Art Journal*, 1895, pp. 154–8.
Exhibition catalogue, 1896, Birmingham Art Gallery.
'A Letter from W. J. Müller', *Journal of Old Water-Colour Society*, Vol. XXV, 1947, p. 35.
Cyril G. E. Bunt, *The Life and Work of William James Müller of Bristol*, Leigh-on-Sea, 1948.
Exhibition catalogue, 1962, Bristol Art Gallery.
Martin Hardie, *Water-Colour Painting in Britain*, Vol. III, 1968, pp. 55–63.

54. Ludwig Munthe

1841–96

Snow scene 1873 (*pl. 9*)

oil on canvas, 50 × 81 in (126.9 × 205.6 cm)

INSCR: L Munthe 73

PROV: William Lee; his sale Christie's 26 May 1883 (88) bt Martin £451 10s as *A Grand Landscape: winter sunset, with figures*.

Ludwig Munthe was a Norwegian landscape painter whose work was very popular amongst Victorian collectors in Britain. The majority of his paintings were winter scenes of snow and ice, usually, as here, a view across a wide plain. This painting, according to a letter written by Munthe on 29 January 1892 from Dusseldorf to Carey, shows Norwegian winter fishing on a frozen fjord.[1]

The author of the series of 1882 articles in *The Magazine of Art* wrote of one of Munthe's winter landscapes as one of his invariable but always welcome snow-studies: '. . . Invariable in subject and in effect they certainly are, but they always differ from each other by some variety of natural incident, or the special development of some particular excellence in *technique*. All this artist does is marked by the best characteristic of a school of painting which is thoroughly well trained and solidly skilful, without any great personality or special charm . . . He has the sentiment of cold and snow and angry sunsets at his brushes.' The writer went on to say 'it would profit him – and us, too – now and then to vary his theme; but it must be admitted that, within these limits, he is an able and attractive painter, and is therefore justified in doing exactly as he will.'[2] Munthe's subjects indeed tended to be rather bleak and repetitive and there was little variety in the titles he gave his paintings.

Munthe was born in 1841 in Aaro, Sundal, in Norway, and from 1858 was a pupil of Franz Wilhelm Schiertz (1813–87) in Bergen. In about 1862 Munthe went to live in Dusseldorf, where he died in 1896.

He visited Holland and France and, in England, exhibited his landscapes on four occasions at the R.A. between 1877 and 1881.

[1] Letter to Carey, dated 29 January 1892, Royal Holloway College Archives.
[2] *Magazine of Art*, 1882, p. 116.

55. Patrick Nasmyth

1787–1831, RBA

Landscape with Trees and Figures in the foreground, a Church in the distance 1830 (*pl. 72*)

panel, 12 × 16 in (30.4 × 40.6 cm)

INSCR: Patk Nasmyth 1830

PROV: William Lee; his sale Christie's 26 May 1883 (28) bt Martin £483.

LIT: *The Times* 28 May 1883 p. 10.

At the time Holloway bought this painting at William Lee's sale at Christie's in 1883, *The Times*, reporting the sale, described it as 'a remarkable little picture in the feeling of Ruysdael'. Indeed, Nasmyth was well-known for a manner of painting very close to Dutch 17th-century landscapes. His contemporaries called him 'the English Hobbema'.

Patrick Nasmyth was one of a Scottish family of famous landscape painters. His father, Alexander Nasmyth (1758–1840), had lived many years in Rome. Patrick, who was christened Peter but called himself Patrick, was deaf from the age of 17. He studied in Edinburgh under his father whose Italianate influence can be seen in Patrick's work up to about 1812, when he changed his allegiance to Dutch landscape painters. Patrick was able to study them easily at first-hand when he moved to London before 1811, the year he began to exhibit his landscapes at the R.A. He made detailed studies of Hobbema, Ruysdael and Wynants. According to the autobiography of his brother James, the famous engineer whose many inventions included the Nasmyth Steam Hammer in 1839, Patrick 'acquired great skill in sketching trees, clouds, plants, and foregrounds . . . his graphic memoranda . . . show the care and industry with which he educated his eye and hand in rendering with truth and fidelity the intimate details of his art . . . The wild plants which he introduced into the foregrounds of his pictures were his favourite objects of study . . . In his landscapes he introduced picturesque farm-houses and cottages, with their rural surroundings . . . decayed pollard trees and old moss-grown orchards, combined with cottages and farm-houses in the most *paintable* state of decay, with tangled hedges and neglected fences, overrun with vegetation clinging to them with all "the careless grace of nature".'[1]

Nasmyth's work, mostly scenes drawn in the country around Windsor, in the New Forest and on the Isle of Wight, was very successful with dealers and collectors. His method was to make sketches on the spot and paint them in oil later in his studio.

His work, popular and easy to sell, became subject to forgery during his own lifetime and according to Frederick Peter Sequier, writing in 1870, his paintings did not cease in their appeal: 'Within the last few years Patrick Nasmyth's works have increased very much in value; even our collectors of modern pictures are very anxious that he should be represented in their collec-

tions . . . no one knew better where to pitch a tent and how to sketch a village or a rustic cottage, or how to make notes for a pretty picture than Patrick Nasmyth . . . Certainly, when we look at his large foreground plants, trunks of trees lying on the ground, and the details of his foregrounds generally, we think of Wynants and other painters of that time; and doubtless Nasmyth was acquainted with the works of the Dutch landscape-painters of the seventeenth century, and loved to study them; but beyond this we must not call him an imitator of the old Dutch landscape painters, for Nasmyth was a very original artist.'[2]

Nasmyth died at 44 in Lambeth. Such was the strength of the Scottish painting community then living in London, that 12 of them subscribed to erect a memorial tomb for him in the churchyard of the Lambeth Parish Church, St. Mary's.

[1] James Nasmyth, *An Autobiography*, ed. Samuel Smiles, London and Edinburgh, 1883, pp. 58–60.
[2] Frederick Peter Sequier, *A Critical and Commercial Dictionary of the Works of Painters*, 1870, p. 137.

BIBLIOGRAPHY
James Nasmyth, *An Autobiography*, Ed. Samuel Smiles, London and Edinburgh, 1883.
Sir James L. Caw, *Scottish Painting Past and Present, 1620–1908*, Edinburgh, 1908, pp. 157–9.
David and Francina Irwin, *Scottish Painters at Home and Abroad, 1700–1900*, 1975, pp. 238–40.

56. Erskine Nicol
1825–1904, ARSA 1855, RSA 1859, ARA 1866 ret. 1885

The Missing Boat 1876 (*pl. 19*)

oil on canvas, 34 × 46 in (86.3 × 116.7)

INSCR: E Nicol 1876

PROV: Thomas Frederick Walker of Birmingham 1877; his sale Christie's 21 April 1883 (128) bt Martin £703 10s.

EXH: 1877 R.S.A. (102) as *A Lee Shore*; 1878 R.A. (534); 1981 Agnew's (32).

LIT: *A.J.* 1878 p. 177; *Athenaeum* 11 May 1878 p. 610; Blackburn, *R.A. Notes* 1878 p. 51; *I.L.N.* 25 May 1878 p. 483; *The Times* 11 May 1878 p. 6; *Mag. of Art* 1879

p. 183, reprinted in Meynell, 1883 p. 152; *Portfolio* 1879 p. 62; Irwins, 1975 p. 305 and repr. pl. 145.

VERSION: *The Missing Boat*
oil on canvas, 30 × 20 in (76.1 × 50.7 cm)
dated 1877; Walsall Art Gallery.

Exhibited as *A Lee Shore* at the R.S.A. exhibition in 1877, this picture was re-entitled *The Missing Boat* by the following year when it was exhibited at the R.A. It was listed in 1879 as one of Nicol's 'best-known pictures'.[1] It followed an earlier painting by him entitled *A Storm at Sea* (ex. R.A. 1876 [152], not traced), described as '[a group] not themselves storm-tossed, but watchers of the waves. An old salt scans the horizon eagerly with the glass; his comrade looks out with a thoughtful action of the hand. Behind them stands an old woman, whose heart is more ominously pre-occupied.'[2] The untraced painting of *A Storm at Sea* was described by another writer as approaching 'as nearly to the pathetic as he could command'.[3] There was also *A Storm at Sea* exhibited by Nicol at the R.S.A. in 1881 (30), lent by Ed Priestman of Bradford.

The grouping of the untraced *A Storm at Sea* sounds similar to *The Missing Boat*. In both, the other half of the story, what has happened to the boat being searched for, is not shown. David and Francina Irwin, complimenting the picture, wrote that it 'effectively conveys the anxiety of the watchers on the quayside calculating the chances of the return of a fishing vessel caught in high seas, but unlike his contemporary Thomas Faed, he totally avoids any note of the sentimental.'[4]

The fashion for painting 'lost at sea' subjects began when Frank Holl's *No Tidings from the Sea* (Royal Collection) was exhibited at the R.A. in 1870. William Small exhibited *The Wreck* (untraced) at the R.A. in 1876 (13) which Henry Blackburn recommended should be 'purchased and presented to the National Life-Boat Association . . . as an engraving on the walls of English homes, it would add to the funds of that institution'.[5] Blackburn commented on the 'dismay depicted on the faces of brave men and women *for want of a life-boat* . . . it will touch the hearts of many of us islanders, whose shores are strewn with wreck'.

The subject of shipwrecks generally was popular

throughout the 19th century. The theme of disaster at sea was perpetuated by the Newlyn School in Cornwall, founded in 1884 by Stanhope Forbes (1857–1947), during the next two decades.[6]

The Times mentioned the frequency of this subject in their review of *The Missing Boat* in the R.A. exhibition of 1878, and expressed reservations over Nicol's approach: 'A subject how often painted! yet, thanks to the human interest, always paintable, but which would be much more forcible in Mr. Nicol's hands if there were less emphasis and more expression in his faces – two things not to be confounded, but which he often confounds.'

This was contradicted to some extent by the reviewer in the *Athenaeum* who, following an evocative description of the painting itself, commented: 'The interest and, indeed, the merit of the work centre principally in the face of the old fisherman, which is a fine example of sound solid painting and remarkable study of individual character.'

Such 'problem' subjects were characteristic of Nicol's oeuvre. *Notice to Quit* (ex. R.A. 1862), *Renewal of the Lease Refused* (ex. R.A. 1863) and *A Flaw in the Lease*, suggest the hazards of rural life under the landowner. Other types of contemporary problem were also painted by him, as may be seen in *Emigrants* (1864, Tate Gallery) and *An Irish Emigrant landing at Liverpool* (1871, National Gallery of Scotland).

Nicol was known for his Irish subjects, although he was born in Leith, Scotland. In 1838 he began at the Trustees' Academy as a pupil of Sir William Allan (1782–1850) and Thomas Duncan (1807–45). From 1846 he lived in Dublin but returned in 1851 to Edinburgh and sent paintings to the R.A. exhibitions. In 1863 Nicol settled in London and annually visited Ireland, where he found much of his pictorial material. In London he was a member of the Auld Lang Syne Club (see Thomas Faed).

As pointed out by the Irwins, many of Nicol's paintings are akin to those of David Wilkie (1785–1841) especially such works as *Renewal of the Lease Refused*.[7] They show scenes between rural workers and their employers, intended not as works of humour but sober documents of rural life. In 1885 Nicol retired from painting because of ill-health, and returned to live in Scotland.

[1] *Portfolio*, 1879, p. 62.
[2] ed. Wilfrid Meynell, *The Modern School of Art*, 1886–88, p. 26.
[3] A. G. Temple, *The Art of Painting in the Queen's Reign*, 1897, p. 300.
[4] David and Francina Irwin, *Scottish Painters at Home and Abroad, 1700–1900*, 1975, p. 305.
[5] Henry Blackburn, *Academy Notes*, 1876, pp. 6–7.
[6] See *Artists of the Newlyn School 1880–1900*, exhibition catalogue, Newlyn Art Gallery, etc., 1979.
[7] Irwin, op. cit.

BIBLIOGRAPHY
James Dafforne, 'British Artists: Their Style and Character, No. XCI, Erskine Nicol, R.S.A., A.R.A.', *Art Journal*, 1870, pp. 65–7.
W. W. Fenn, 'Erskine Nicol', *Magazine of Art*, 1879, pp. 180–4; reprinted in: ed. Wilfrid Meynell, *Some Modern Artists and their Work*, 1883, pp. 148–52.
'Etchings from Pictures by Contemporary Artists', *Portfolio*, 1879, pp. 61–2.
Walter Armstrong, 'Scottish Painters X', *Portfolio*, 1887, pp. 227–34.
Sir James L. Caw, *Scottish Painting Past and Present, 1620–1908*, Edinburgh, 1908, pp. 163–4.
David and Francina Irwin, *Scottish Painters at Home and Abroad, 1700–1900*, 1975, pp. 364–5.

57. Jules Achille Noël
1815–81

Abbeville, with Peasants and Horses in the foreground 1857 (*pl. 15*)

panel, 21 × 18 in (53.3 × 45.7 cm)

INSCR: Jules Noel 1857

PROV: William Lee; his sale Christie's 26 May 1883 (89) bt Martin £52 10s together with *The Quay, Hennebont*.

58. Jules Achille Noël
1815–81

The Quay, Hennebont, with Boats and Figures 1857 (*pl. 14*)

panel, 21 × 18 in (53.3 × 45.7 cm)

INSCR: Jules Noel 1857

PROV: William Lee; his sale Christie's 26 May 1883 (90) bt Martin £52 10s together with *Abbeville*.

These two paintings were purchased by Holloway as companion pictures. They were painted in the same year and have the same dimensions. Both are on panel. There is no trace of either having been exhibited at the Salon of 1857.

The paintings contain many of the same elements and those characteristic of Noël's work. A painter of marine pictures and landscapes, his dual interests are evident here: both scenes include water and landscape. In the painting of *Abbeville*, Noël has depicted the gothic church which overlooks the Somme in the North of France. Abbeville is a Normandy port and was particularly interesting for its picturesque old houses, most of which were destroyed in the Second World War. *The Quay, Hennebont*, on the other hand, is more a marine painting than a landscape. Hennebont is situated on the West coast of Brittany, inland from Lorient on the river Blavet.

Jules Achille Noël was born in Quimper, Brittany, and was a pupil of the painter Charioux of Brest. He began to exhibit at the Salon in Paris in 1840 (mostly marine subjects). In 1846 he was appointed Professor at the Lycée Henri IV, where he taught for about 30 years. He travelled widely over the Continent and in the East.

Noël also produced watercolours and lithographs. He won a third-class medal at the Salon in 1853, and in 1859 painted a large marine picture, *The Visit of Queen Victoria and the Prince Consort to Cherbourg, 1858* (National Maritime Museum) which is considered as one of his most successful works.[1] Noël continued to exhibit at the Salon until 1879, and died two years later in Algiers.

The obituary in the *Magazine of Art* recorded that 'although he has left a great number of paintings and watercolours, and obtained several medals, he cannot be said to have achieved great things, but he was, nevertheless, a very good professor and a conscientious artist.'[2]

[1] This was exhibited in *This Brilliant Year*, Royal Academy, 1977 (22).
[2] *Magazine of Art*, 1881, p. xxxi.

59. John Pettie

1839–93, ARA 1866, HRSA 1871, RA 1873

A State Secret 1874 (*pl. 57*)

oil on canvas, 48 × 64 in (121.8 × 162.4 cm)

INSCR: J Pettie 1874

PROV: Edward Hermon M.P. of Wyfold Court, Henley-on-Thames 1875; his sale Christie's 13 May 1882 (77) bt Martin £1,150.

EXH: 1874 R.A. (223); 1875 R.S.A. (290) as *State Secrets*; 1981 Agnew's (33).

LIT: *Academy* 16 May 1874 p. 555; *Athenaeum* 2 May 1874 p. 600 and 30 May 1874 p. 738; *Graphic* 23 May 1874 p. 502; *I.L.N.* 2 May 1874 p. 411; *Saturday Review* 16 May 1874 p. 621; *Spectator* 30 May 1874 p. 693; *The Times* 2 May 1874 p. 12; *Portfolio* 1878 p. 129; *Mag. of Art* 1881 p. 14; Meynell, 1883, p. 200; Stephens, 1884, p. 40; *A.J.* 1893 p. 209; *A.J.* 1907 pp. 107, 110 and repr. p. 110; Hardie, 1908 pp. 97–8, 109, 175, 227 and repr. opp. p. 98; Hardie, 1910 p. 5; Gaunt, 1972 p. 343 and repr. pl. 156; Hardie, 1976 p. 51; Arts Council, *Great Victorian Pictures*, 1978 p. 67.

SKETCH: 30 × 20 in (76.1 × 50.7 cm)
Formerly owned by William McTaggart RSA
Lit. Hardie, 1908 p. 227.

?VERSION: *Getting rid of State Secrets*
Prov. Henry Rougier 1879; his sale Christie's 19 June 1880 (92) bt Agnew £183 15s; sold by them 22 June 1881 to T. J. Dugdale.
Exh. 1879 Yorkshire Fine Art and Industrial Ex. York, Fine Art Department (70).

To a letter from Carey in 1887, requesting information about this picture, Pettie replied that he had not painted any particular scene from history although it could represent 'a *possible* typical incident'. He had in mind an episode of the type which might well have happened 'in the lives of Richelieu or Mazarin or other Princes of the Roman Church, indeed the two last mentioned who had each his "familiar" in the person of a simple monk, may have suggested to me the idea . . . In any case the title "A State Secret" is the only one I could give it.'[1]

Pettie has painted a Cardinal, his face set and intent on the destruction of a 'secret' document, holding it in his fingers while it blazes in flames. He is being watched by a terrified monk in the shadowy background, whose horror is expressed through his frightened face and wringing hands. Other documents are strewn about in disorder, some on the floor and some on the heavily carved table. On the table stands a bronze statuette, apparently of Hercules crushing Antaeus.[2] This scattering of objects across the foreground of the painting is characteristic of many of Pettie's works. The scene is set against a tapestry hanging of undefined subject which acts as a backdrop to give a stage-like effect and heighten the drama of the scene.

According to Pettie's biographer, Martin Hardie, there was a sketch (30 × 20 in 76.1 × 50.7 cm; untraced) for *A State Secret*, which was owned by Pettie's friend and fellow Scottish painter, William McTaggart (1835–1910). 'In this [sketch], the horrified monk on the right was painted out by Pettie, but still shows through the paint'.[3]

Hardie wrote of the painting itself that to help Pettie paint the paper in flames, Mrs Andrew Ker, a cousin of Pettie's, 'tells me she burned nearly a packet of notepaper, sheet by sheet, in Pettie's studio, that the right effect might be secured, – the suggestiveness of the gloomy background, the careful treatment of all the accessories.'[4] The burning document and the colour of the Cardinal's robes do, indeed, concentrate attention on the central action of the picture and serve to balance the composition.

Pettie had introduced a red-robed Cardinal, and papers scattered on the floor, in another painting of a slightly earlier date: *Treason* (ex. R.A. 1867 [322], Sheffield City Art Galleries). This type of historical subject, which conveys drama and suspense, was much favoured by Pettie. His *A Drum-head Court Martial* (ex. R.A. 1865 [192], Sheffield City Art Galleries), a civil war subject, was his first great success at the R.A. It was followed by such paintings as *An Arrest for Witchcraft* (ex. R.A. 1866 [179], National Gallery of Victoria, Melbourne, Australia) and *The Flag of Truce* (ex. R.A. 1873 [401] Sheffield City Art Galleries).[5]

A State Secret was ridiculed in the magazine *Fun*, which reproduced the picture re-named *Burning his Fingers or The Red-Hot Cardinal*, and showed a fireman with a fire extinguisher drenching the Cardinal. On the same page were ridiculed two other of that year's exhibits at the R.A. which are both now in the College collection, Fildes's *Applicants for Admission to a Casual Ward* and MacWhirter's *Night*.[6]

The painting had a mixed reception by the critics at the R.A. exhibition of 1874. They mostly concentrated on Pettie's handling of the light effects, which were considered to be the most successful element of the picture. The *Graphic* wrote: 'The Cardinal hastily burning treasonable documents is a thoroughly dramatic conception; the story is ably told, and the technical merits of the work are of a remarkable kind. Note the clever management of the Cardinal's red robes, the felicitous rendering of the flaming paper, the suggestive background and carefully treated accessories.'

The *Athenaeum* commented on the work twice (2 May and 30 May) and expressed a considerable change of heart. They began their first report by stating that Pettie 'will secure abundance of popular applause with *A State Secret*'; but their second notice was less enthusiastic: 'It is certainly unworthy of an artist who has sometimes shown a dashing kind of ability . . . We fear that notwithstanding the undoubted "cleverness" of some parts of the painting here e.g. the red dress, and certain minor accessories, the design is hardly equal to what educated people expect to find in Burlington House.'

The *I.L.N.* attempted to analyse *A State Secret* in more depth. They started with praise: 'Mr. Pettie justifies his recent election to Academic full membership'. They then continued to comment more closely on the details of the picture, beginning with the bronze on the table, which they found 'not without suggestiveness. The mass of red (rather artificially lighted, as we think, and with reflexes too strong) cannot fail to catch the visitor's eye; the energy both of the conception and execution will almost as certainly strike his imagination, and he is not likely to readily forget the vengeful look of the Cardinal . . . The effect of the flame against the scarlet robe is an exceedingly clever bit of

Catalogue

imitation . . . [it] just escapes the melodramatic exaggeration chargeable to some previous efforts. We can only object that the artist's skill of hand is only too palpable, and, therefore, apt to intrude between the subject and spectator.'

John Pettie was one of the many leading Scottish 19th-century painters who left his native country to live and work in London. He was born in 1839 in Edinburgh, the son of a storekeeper. In 1855, he attended the Trustees' Academy as a pupil of Robert Scott Lauder and John Ballantyne. He moved to London in 1862 to continue to work as an illustrator for the journal *Good Words*, which had been transferred there in that year from Edinburgh.

In London Pettie shared a studio with his fellow Scottish painters, Tom Graham (1840–1906) and William Quiller Orchardson (1832–1910). Together they had re-instated the Edinburgh Sketching Club, formerly The Smashers, in Fitzroy Square, which had been formed in Edinburgh about 1856.[7] Pettie exhibited regularly at the R.A. until the year of his death, 1893. The majority of his pictures had historical costume subjects, taken from amusing or spectacular episodes especially of the Elizabethan or Cavalier and Roundhead periods. Caw described 'his best pictures' as those 'amongst the happiest efforts in historical genre in our time'.[8] Pettie would mostly seize a moment of theatrical drama from either his imagination, as in *A State Secret*, or literature, in particular from Shakespeare or Scott.[9] His ability to dramatise a situation was summed up by Robert Walker in an article in *Good Words*: 'At his best, it is his force that impresses you, his mastery over dramatic composition, his delight in broad, strong, manly colour. He was never subtle; we must not look in the canvases for delicate suggestion or tender sentiment. Each of his pictures tells a story, and tells it well.'[10]

Pettie's style remained more or less consistent throughout his career. He paid special attention not only to the richness of colour in his paintings, but also to the texture of the costumes. Both characteristics are particularly noticeable in his portraits, which he had begun to exhibit at the R.A. in 1871 with a portrait of his friend John MacWhirter (q.v.), now in the Aberdeen Art Gallery. The most distinct influences on his portrait painting were the early Venetian painters and Rembrandt.

Pettie died suddenly in Hastings in 1893 and was buried in Paddington Cemetery.

[1] Letter to Carey, dated 10 Semptember 1887, Royal Holloway College Archives, and published by him.
[2] Identified by the reviewer in *Illustrated London News*, 2 May 1874, p. 411.
[3] Martin Hardie, *John Pettie R.A., H.R.S.A.*, 1908, p. 227.
[4] Op. cit. pp. 97–8.
[5] Sheffield has one of the best collections of works by Pettie, deriving from the bequest of John Newton Mappin in the 1880s; see Elijah Howarth, 'The Art Treasures of Sheffield: The Mappin Gallery', *Windsor Magazine*, September 1895, pp. 257–67.
[6] *Fun*, 9 May 1874, p. 190.
[7] See entry for John MacWhirter.
[8] Sir James L. Caw, *Scottish Painting Past and Present 1620–1908*, Edinburgh, 1908, pp. 240–43.
[9] See the exhibition catalogue, *The Lamp of Memory – Scott and the Artist* by Catherine Gordon, Buxton Museum and Art Gallery, 1979.
[10] Robert Walker, 'John Pettie R.A.,' *Good Words*, 1893, p. 756.

BIBLIOGRAPHY
James Dafforne, 'British Artists: Their Style and Character, No. LXXXVI, John Pettie, A.R.A.', *Art Journal*, 1869, pp. 265–7.
Wilfrid Meynell, 'Our Living Artists – John Pettie R.A.', *Magazine of Art*, 1881, pp. 11–16.
ed. Wilfrid Meynell, *Some Modern Artists and Their Work*, 1883, pp. 196–202.
F. G. Stephens, *Artists at Home*, 1884, pp. 39–41.
Walter Armstrong, 'Scottish Painters X', *Portfolio*, 1887, pp. 230–1.
Robert Walker, 'John Pettie R.A.', *Good Words*, 1893, pp. 750–7.
W. Matthews Gilbert, 'The late John Pettie, R.A., H.R.S.A.', *Art Journal*, 1893, pp. 206–10.
Stothard, Blake and Pettie, Winter Exhibition, 1894, Royal Academy.
Martin Hardie, 'John Pettie, R.A., H.R.S.A.', *Art Journal*, 1907, pp. 97–116.
Sir James L. Caw, *Scottish Painting Past and Present, 1620–1908*, Edinburgh, 1908, pp. 240–3.
Martin Hardie, *John Pettie, R.A., H.R.S.A.*, 1908.
Introduction by Martin Hardie, *John Pettie, Sixteen Examples in Colour of the Artist's Work*, 1910.
David and Francina Irwin, *Scottish Painters at Home and Abroad, 1700–1900*, 1975, pp. 342–4.

60. Paul Falconer Poole

1807–79, ARA 1846, RA 1861, ret. 1879, RI 1878

Crossing the Stream 1844 (*pl. 42*)

panel, 19½ × 15 in (49.5 × 38 cm)

INSCR: P F Poole 44

PROV: Samuel Mayou of Edgbaston, Birmingham; his sale Christie's 21 April 1883 (42) bt Martin £220 10s.

EXH: 1961 Agnew's *Victorian Painting 1837–1887* (11); 1981 Agnew's (34).

VERSIONS:
1. *Crossing the Stream*
oil on canvas, 19 × 14½ in (48.2 × 36.8 cm)
Prov. Anon. sale Sotheby's Belgravia 30 March 1976 (214) bt Mrs M. Slater.
Repr. Collectors Guide October 1973 p. 39.
2. *The Mountaineer*
Prov. William Sharp of The Larches, Birmingham 1848
Lit. Art Union 1848 p. 352 with engraving by T. Garner.

Crossing the Stream is similar in type to its companion *The Gleaner*, and the title, like *The Gleaner*, is one which re-appears for other paintings by Poole. *Crossing the Brook* of 1845 (Bury Art Gallery) is a larger painting, differing quite considerably from the work here, in that it depicts a woman clutching a child to her and about to cross a stream with a happy swinging movement. This was engraved by the *A.J.*, as was a version of *Crossing the Stream*.[1] Entitled *The Mountaineer* in the *A.J.* of 1848, this version differs only very slightly from the painting here;[2] at the time it was engraved it was in the collection of William Sharp of Birmingham, but has not been traced. The *A.J.* description of the engraved *The Mountaineer* remarked first on the 'individuality of character in each' of his works. It continued to comment somewhat lyrically on the engraving as having 'evidently been sketched from rustic life as the traveller often meets with it among some of the waste places in Wales or Ireland. A young female, with a chubby-faced child at her back, is in the act of crossing a brook, formed by the torrent which flows tortuously from the hills through the rugged country . . . the picture is one of great interest – an interest excited by the characteristic expression in the faces of the two figures – the one full of glee, the other marked by weariness, yet unmixed with pain. The drawing of these figures is very good, and their attitudes unconstrained and natural.'

[1] *Art Journal*, 1859, p. 42.
[2] *Art Journal*, 1848, p. 352.

61. Paul Falconer Poole

1807–79, ARA 1846, RA 1861, ret. 1879, RI 1878

The Gleaner 1845 (*pl. 41*)

oil on canvas, 19 × 15 in (48.2 × 38 cm)

INSCR: P F Poole 45

EXH: 1981 Agnew's (35).

PROV: Samuel Mayou of Edgbaston, Birmingham; his sale Christie's 21 April 1883 (43) bt Martin £204 15s.

This is a companion picture to *Crossing the Stream*. They were purchased together by Holloway from the collection of Samuel Mayou of Edgbaston.

Further paintings of the same title by Poole followed in the next decade.[1] These, however, were not necessarily of the same composition as the picture here. The next decade, indeed, produced considerably more famous gleaner subjects, such as Millet's *Gleaners* of 1857. Lesser-known English painters also used gleaners for rural subject matter.[2]

This picture by Poole is a favourite combination of a woman and child against a landscape background. Richard Garnett described Poole as having 'found his themes in village lasses, or groups of children, or gypsies, straying over heaths or gathered around roadside springs, or lingering at stiles in expectation of truant lovers.' The landscapes, he continued, were 'always an important element in the picture, linked to the figures by some subtle bond of spiritual affinity'.[3]

These two pictures were painted at the same time as Poole's most famous work, *Solomon Eagle exhorting the people to repentance, during the plague of the year 1665* (ex. R.A 1843 [423], Sheffield City Art Galleries), which provides an enormous contrast with the works here.[4] *Solomon Eagle* was a highly successful, fairly large-scale history painting crowded with figures set in a stage-like composition. It was followed by further attempts at large-scale subject pictures but his smaller-scale, single genre figure, rustic works were much more popular.

Poole was born in Bristol, the son of a grocer who later became a coal merchant, and taught himself to paint. He began to exhibit at the R.A. in 1830 and his exhibits there, until 1879, alternated between subject pictures with grand titles and paintings entitled simply (e.g. *The Parting Moment* or *Rest by the Wayside*). In 1847 Poole entered the Palace of Westminster decoration competition in which he won a second-class prize of £300, with *Edward III's Generosity to the People of Calais*.

The *Portfolio* of 1884 summed up Poole's capabilities when they wrote that he 'produced slowly and deliberately . . . he strove for intellectual or emotional expression rather than the imitation of the appearance of things; subject was a motive and incentive to his artistic energy, an important factor in his art, which leant to the dramatic and romantic. It is true that he began with rustic themes, and the influence of Mulready is apparent in the specimens of this class of work now shown . . . By degrees Poole passed from semi-historic to the romantic, or purely imaginative. Spenser, Shakespeare, Boccacio [sic], inspired him . . . both in landscape and figure he attained sentiment at the expense of perspective truth or correct drawing . . . It was a pity that a certain raggedness and want of decision in his touch marred a style which must be acknowledged as always mannered but imbued through and through with a poetic individuality.'[5]

[1] For example, one appeared in the W. Llewellyn sale at Foster's, 4 April 1855 (18), sold for £21. A second *The Young Gleaner* was exhibited in 1856 at the Royal Scottish Academy (426) and measured 5¾ × 8 inches. Another *The Gleaner* was engraved in the *Art Journal*, 1864, p. 320 from the collection of J. Bickerstaff, of Preston.

[2] These are discussed by Howard David Rodee, *Scenes of Rural and Urban Poverty in Victorian Painting and their Development 1850–1890*, Columbia University Ph.D Thesis, 1975.
[3] Richard Garnett, 'A Hampstead Painter: The late Paul Falconer Poole, R.A.', *Hampstead Annual*, 1900, p. 12.
[4] See Arts Council, *Great Victorian Pictures*, 1978, pp. 68–9.
[5] *Portfolio*, 1884, p. 43.

BIBLIOGRAPHY
'British Artists: Their Style and Character, No. XLIII, Paul Falconer Poole A.R.A.', *Art Journal*, 1859, pp. 41–3.
Portfolio, 1879, p. 189 (Obit.).
Old Masters and Poole, Winter Exhibition 1884, Royal Academy.
Richard Garnett, 'A Hampstead Painter: The late Paul Falconer Poole, R.A.', *Hampstead Annual*, 1900, pp. 9–24.

62. James Barker Pyne

1800–70

Haweswater from Waller Gill Force 1850 (*pl. 7*)

oil on canvas, 33 × 44 in (83.7 × 111.7 cm)

INSCR: J B PYNE 1850 N°. 321

PROV: Commissioned by Mr Agnew of Manchester 1848; William Sharp of Endwood Court, Handsworth, nr Birmingham; his sale Christie's 9 July 1881 (58) bt Mason £273.

EXH: 1851 Messrs Graves & Co., Pall Mall; 1981 Agnew's (36).

ENGR: 1. W. Gauci, lithograph, published by Thos. Agnew & Sons, Manchester 1853 in *The English Lake District*
    Lit. Agnew's *1817–1967*, Intro. Sir Geoffrey Agnew, 1967 pp. 63–4.
2. T. Picken, chromolithograph, published by Day & Son 1859 in *Lake Scenery of England*.

It was announced in the *Art Union* of 1848 that '*MR. AGNEW*, of Manchester, has given a commission to Mr. Pyne, for twenty-four views of scenery in the vicinity of the English Lakes. The enterprising provincial publisher intends hereafter to issue copies of them in lithography, of a size and style corresponding with the "Holy Land" of David Roberts.'[1]

Haweswater from Waller Gill Force, painted in 1850, was one of these views commissioned by either Thomas Agnew (1794–1871), the founder of the firm of art-dealers, or his son Sir William Agnew (1825–1910).

Pyne listed the work in his *Picture Memoranda* which included a total of 729 pictures between the years 1839 and 1868.[2] *Haweswater* was numbered 321 (hence the number inscribed on the lower left hand corner of the painting) and there is a note that it was painted in June 1850 as 'One of Mr. Agnews [sic] series'. It was not exhibited at the R.A. nor at the B.I.

The *A.J.* of 1851 reported that Pyne 'during three years, [has] been engaged in the work ... The series is nearly completed in oil, and will be exhibited early in the season ... As a series we have never seen anything more interesting or more beautiful.'[3] Finally, 25 were exhibited at Graves's Gallery in Pall Mall before they were executed in lithograph, in 1853, as *The British Lake District*, and later in chromolithograph for the *Lake Scenery of England* published by Day and Son in 1859.

Pyne painted the view of Haweswater from the west side of the lake with Mardale Head and the hills beyond. A few fishermen occupy the foreground and a boat is to be seen on its journey half way across the lake. The other views depicted by Pyne for this series were mostly of the lakes themselves, with one or two showing the mountains and valleys. His obituary in the *A.J.* summed up his achievement with this sort of landscape painting by stating that he 'aimed at representation of open expansive landscape, where distance demands light and atmosphere; and he more especially selected lake-scenery as that the best suited for the expression of his views ... As a rule, the paintings of this artist were not popular: like Turner's they were not generally intelligible ... the prevalence of white and of delicate blues and reds in Pyne's paintings are not sufficiently understood and appreciated.'[4]

Pyne was as adept with watercolour as with oil paint. He much admired Turner's work (an admiration which was mutual) and was influenced by him. Like Turner, Pyne spent much time abroad in the search for pictorial material. He visited the Continent in 1846 and 1851, when he remained in Germany and Italy for three years.

Pyne, born in 1800 in Bristol, was self-taught. He firstly painted landscapes in that area and also gave lessons in painting to W. J. Muller (q.v.). He moved to London in 1835 and exhibited his first picture at the Academy the following year. He exhibited only seven paintings there between 1836 and 1855, mostly because the bulk of his work was exhibited at the Society of British Artists, the B.I. and the N.W.S. He became a member of the Society of British Artists in 1841 and later its Vice-President and he was also a member of the Graphic Society.

[1] *Art Union*, 1848, p. 315. These views were the only major project in the field of coloured lithographs published by Agnew's.
[2] Pyne's *Picture Memoranda* in two volumes are in the Victoria and Albert Museum Library.
[3] *Art Journal*, 1851, p. 132.
[4] *Art Journal*, 1870, p. 276.

BIBLIOGRAPHY

'British Artists: Their Style and Character, No. XVI, James Baker Pyne', *Art Journal*, 1856, pp. 205–8.
Art Journal, 1870, p. 276 (Obit.).

63. Briton Riviere

1840–1920, ARA 1878, RA 1881, Hon. DCL (Oxf) 1891

Sympathy 1877 *(pl. 51)*

oil on canvas, 48 × 40 in (121.8 × 101.5 cm)

INSCR: Briton Riviere 1877

PROV: Purchased from the artist by Thomas Taylor of Aston Rowant, Oxfordshire; his sale Christie's 28 April 1883 (70) bt Martin £2,625 (the copyright being retained by Agnew's).

EXH: 1878 R.A. (496); 1922 R.A. Winter Ex. (70); 1981 Agnew's (37).

LIT: *The Academy* 25 May 1878 p. 470; *Annual Register* 1878 p. 422; *A.J.* 1878 p. 148; *Athenaeum* 11 May 1878 p. 610; *Graphic* 18 May 1878 p. 498; *I.L.N.* 4 May 1878 p. 410 and 11 May 1878 p. 435; *Mag. of Art* 1878 pp. 70, 138 and repr. p. 136; *Spectator* 1 June 1878 p. 698; *The Times* 4 May 1878 p. 12; *Mag. of Art* 1879 p. 255 reprinted in Meynell, 1883, p. 147 and repr. same page;

Mag. of Art 1882 p. 313; Stephens, 1884, pp. 71, 72; Armstrong, 1891, pp. 17, 25; Cooke & Wedderburn, 1903–12 Vol. XXXIII, pp. 309–10 and Vol. XXXIV, p. 259; John Ernest Phythian, *Fifty Years of Modern Painting* 1908 p. 337; *Proceedings*, 1968 pp. 229, 238; Peter Conrad, *The Victorian Treasure-House* 1973 p. 36; Forbes, *R.A. Revisited*, 1975 p. 126; Arts Council, *Great Victorian Pictures* 1978 p. 72.

REPR: Blackburn, *R.A. Notes* 1878 p. 49; Gaunt, 1972 pl. 147.

STUDIES: 1. *Sympathy c.* 1878
oil on canvas, 17¾ × 14¾ in (45 × 37.4 cm)
Prov. John Hargreaves of Maiden Erlegh, Berkshire; his sale Christie's 2 May 1896 (105) bt Agnew 260 gns; sold by them 4 May 1896 to Henry Tate, by whom presented to Tate Gallery 1897.
Repr. M. Clive, *The Day of Reckoning*, 1964, opp. p. 7.
2. *Exh.* 1902 Fine Art Society *Studies and Designs by Briton Riviere*, charcoal *Design for "Sympathy"* (24), charcoal *Studies for "Sympathy"* (127).

ENGR: Frederick Stackpoole A.R.A., mezzotint, 19¾ × 24 in (50.1 × 60.9 cm) published by Thos. Agnew & Sons.
Exh. 1887 Manchester Royal Jubilee Ex. (1040).

In 1891 Walter Armstrong wrote that 'none of Riviere's pictures have been more popular than this ... [she] has found her way into hundreds of homes, both humble and luxurious'.[1]

Indeed the image of the small girl sitting on the stairs is so strong that, although receiving great acclaim from some most unlikely sources, such as Ruskin, the painting also became an object of derision in its own time. *Punch* took the motif of the girl and the dog for the central part of a cartoon ridiculing the R.A. exhibits of that year, which were drawn piled up on a pedestal with the inscription '.ARS.BRITANNICA.MDCCCLXXVIII.'.[2] In the magazine *Fun* the painting, easily recognisable, was re-entitled 'Gastralgia, The Terror of Childhood'.[3]

Riviere explained the painting and the motivation for it in a letter in which he wrote that 'the arrangement and pose of the little girl in "Sympathy" was first suggested to me by a wood drawing which I did for an

American publication long before I painted the picture . . . The little girl was painted from my daughter Miss Millicent A. Riviere. The dog with some slight alterations (as my animals are never portraits) was done from a bull terrier belonging to a man who has supplied me with dogs for some considerable time.'[4]

The fact that the sitter was Riviere's daughter is supported by a manuscript letter in the Victoria and Albert Museum Library from Riviere to J. H. E. Gill, dated 26 May 1878. It states: 'My picture of Sympathy was sold last July directly and was painted [sic] or I should have been happy to sell it to you. It is strange the fact of its likeness to your little girl as it was painted from and is almost a likeness of my own.'

Ruskin mentioned *Sympathy* on two occasions. In 1880 he wrote: 'It is long since I have been so pleased in the Royal Academy as I was by Mr. Briton Riviere's "Sympathy". The dog is uncaricatured doggedness, divine as Anubis, or the Dog-star; the child entirely childish and lovely, the carpet might have been laid by Veronese. A most precious picture in itself, yet not one for a museum. Everyone would think only of the story in it; everbody be wondering [sic] what the little girl had done, and how she would be forgiven, and if she wasn't, how soon she would stop crying, and give the doggie a kiss, and comfort his heart. All which they might study at home among their own children and dogs just as well; and should not come to the museum to plague the real students there, since there is not anything of especial notableness or unrivalled quality in the actual painting.'[5]

The *I.L.N.* reviewer of the 1878 Academy exhibition called Riviere 'the Prince of dog-painters at the Academy' and *Sympathy* 'an exquisite composition' and 'about the most touching picture that Mr. Briton Riviere has ever painted'. The following week the writer marvelled again at the picture: 'the gem of Mr. Briton Riviere's quartet of beautiful contributions'. In the expression of the dog were 'the exquisite perception of the artist and the subtle refinement of his thought . . . This "Sympathy" as a "dog" picture we place in the very front rank of Mr. Briton Riviere's productions.'

The *Magazine of Art* agreed that 'the painting and anatomy of the dog are excellent, and his expression

most touching . . . wonderfully painted, wonderfully drawn and modelled dog'. This was echoed by the *Graphic*, who wrote that *Sympathy* 'is one of the most perfect linkings of human and animal in the bond of common feeling that was ever put on canvas'. *The Times* and the *Academy* too found the painting outstanding. The *Athenaeum*, however, pointed out that Riviere 'has proved himself gifted with somewhat opposite faculties' (i.e. sentiment and humour), and considered *Sympathy* 'rather slight in execution, the colouring – child's blue dress, yellow stair-carpeting, and chocolate-brown of the banisters and lighter tint of the door – is effective, and the suggestion of childish troubles and animal sympathy, to say the least, amusing.'

It was, however, the *Spectator* who mentioned Riviere's most important predecessor, Landseer, who had died in 1873. They named Riviere as 'the only animal painter in England who has taken the place which was vacated by the death of Landseer . . . Riviere has surpassed Landseer in his own way, for he has given feeling to his animals, and yet kept them strictly within their own nature . . . Never attempting to render in his works human expression in a dog's face, he has nevertheless mastered the points where canine and human nature touch, and painted them with an insight and comprehension with which no other artist of whom we know can at all compare.'

Riviere enjoyed great success during his lifetime. His paintings seem always to have attracted notice and surprisingly high prices were paid for some of his work. For instance, Holloway paid £2,625 for *Sympathy*, excluding the copyright. His popularity may well have been due to the public's interest in animal painting generally, which had become, through Landseer, an established part of English painting.

[1] Walter Armstrong, 'Briton Riviere, R.A.', *Art Annual*, 1891, pp. 17, 25.
[2] *Punch*, 1 June 1878, p. 251.
[3] *Fun*, 20 June 1878, p. 254.
[4] Letter to Carey, dated 1 September 1887, Royal Holloway College Archives, and published in part by him.
[5] John Ruskin, *The Works of John Ruskin*, ed. E. T. Cook and Alexander Wedderburn, (Library Edition), 1903–12, vol.

XXXIV, p. 259. Ruskin was writing on *A Museum or Picture Gallery, Its Functions and Its Formation*, in a section entitled *On the Old Road*. See also Vol. XXXIII, p. 309–10 for further comment.

64. Briton Riviere

1840–1920, ARA 1878, RA 1881, Hon. DCL (Oxf) 1891

An Anxious Moment 1878 (*pl. 79*)

oil on canvas, 26 × 40 in (66 × 101.5 cm)

INSCR: B. Riviere 1878

PROV: William Lee; his sale Christie's 26 May 1883 (76) by Martin £1,732 10s (the copyright being retained by Agnew's).

EXH: 1878 R.A. (392); 1887 Manchester Royal Jubilee Ex. (377) (the owner's name was given as William Agnew); 1922 R.A. Winter Ex. (203); 1981 South London Art Gallery *Dulwich College – A School and its Art* (18).

LIT: *The Academy* 8 June 1878 p. 517; *A.J.* 1878 p. 148; *Athenaeum* 11 May 1878 p. 610; Blackburn, *R.A. Notes* 1878 p. 40 and repr. same page; *Graphic* 18 May 1878 p. 498; *I.L.N.* 4 May 1878 p. 410 and 11 May 1878 p. 435; *Mag. of Art* 1878 p. 70; *Saturday Review* 1 June 1878 p. 692; *Spectator* 1 June 1878 p. 698; *The Times* 4 May 1878 p. 12; *Mag. of Art* 1879 p. 255 reprinted in Meynell, 1883, p. 147; *Portfolio* 1880 p. 141; Stephens, 1884 p. 71; Hodgson, 1887 p. 81; Walter Armstrong, *Celebrated Pictures exhibited at the Manchester Royal Jubilee Exhibition, Fine Art Section*, 1888 p. 39; Armstrong, 1891 p. 17 and repr. p. 18; Cook & Wedderburn, 1903–12, Vol. XXXIII, p. 529; Henry Currie Marillier, *"Christie's", 1766 to 1925*, 1926 p. 60; *Proceedings* 1968 pp. 229, 238.

At the William Lee sale at Christie's in 1883, when Holloway purchased this painting for the College, *An Anxious Moment* 'was received with rounds of applause when it appeared on the easel'.[1] Such was the appreciation with which Riviere's pictures were greeted, regardless of the seriousness of their content. For, as Walter Armstrong stated, when this picture was shown at the Royal Jubilee Exhibition at Manchester in 1887, the motive was 'absurdly trivial'.[2]

An Anxious Moment depicts a flock of geese in a farmyard showing alarm at the presence of a black hat lying in their path. The subject, as was pointed out by the *Portfolio* in 1880, is related to a painting by Riviere of the same year entitled *So Full of Shapes is Fancy* (Aberdeen Art Gallery) which illustrates a dog frightened by a hat and a gardener's coat hanging against a wall and described as 'a good example of Mr. Riviere's minor works'.[3]

Riviere himself wrote: 'When and how the subjects [of both pictures in the College collection] occurred to me I do not recollect but I know that they – like all the subjects I have painted – were thought of and noted down some years before they were painted.'[4] The painting was noticed by a great many of the critics when it was shown at the 1878 Academy exhibition.

Many of the reviews linked *An Anxious Moment* and *Sympathy* together when they wrote about them. The *Graphic* described *An Anxious Moment* as 'the picture of the year for humour', as opposed to *Sympathy*, 'the picture of the year for sentiment'. *An Anxious Moment* was considered by the *I.L.N.* as an 'intensely droll picture . . . in every eye and every bill there is an irresistibly comic expression of bewildered anxiety. The birds are superbly painted.' Indeed, most of the reviews saw the painting as genuinely funny. *The Magazine of Art* wrote: 'In "An Anxious Moment", the versatile artist takes a humorous subject, and treats it with a great sense of fun . . . the action of the birds as they crowd against the wall to avoid the portentous hat is exceedingly good.'

The Academy also rated the painting highly, calling it 'pre-eminently good in execution . . . managed with an amount of dexterity and variety well worthy of deliberate inspection'. This was re-emphasised by *The Times*. They entitled the picture *Geese in Alarm* and wrote that it was 'destined to be one of the few great successes of the year . . . The satire is unmistakable – not too subtle, but full of genuine humour, and true to the life'. It was the *Athenaeum*, however, who summed up the general feeling of the difference between *Sympathy* and *An Anxious Moment*: 'There is but one step, it is said, from the sublime [*Sympathy*] to the

ridiculous [*An Anxious Moment*] and in the next work by the same hand [i.e. *An Anxious Moment*] we encounter an example of the aphorism: it shows a flock of geese making their way through a gate in a country lane . . . The mass of white in the breasts of the geese is pleasantly matched with the reddish-yellow colour of their bills, and a bright strip of green meadow or orchard in the background.' In many respects Riviere was considered to be one of Landseer's closest rivals and this painting was, perhaps, an attempt by Riviere to give character to the birds, as Landseer might have done.

Briton Riviere was born in London of a family of French origin. He studied painting at Cheltenham under his father, showed an early ability to draw and paint, and made frequent visits to London Zoo to study animals and birds at first-hand. In 1858 Riviere exhibited his first works at the Academy, where he was to go on to exhibit not only paintings but also etchings and sculpture. Riviere took the degree of B.A. at Oxford in 1867 and M.A. there six years later.

Most of Riviere's works include animals or birds, all based on a thorough anatomical study. Many of his paintings were engraved by Frederick Stackpoole (1813–1907) between 1870 and 1890, which helped to widen his fame. Riviere was a good draughtsman and was employed by *Punch* from 1868 to 1871 for illustrations and also carried out commissions for *Good Words*.

Not all his paintings were humorous or sentimental. He produced some highly dramatic works based on literary or biblical subjects, many of which were exhibited with quotations. His paintings showing lions are some of his most powerful images, like *Daniel in the Lions' Den* (ex. R.A. 1872 [539], Walker Art Gallery, Liverpool), *The King Drinks* (ex. R.A. 1882 [468], Diploma work, R.A. collection) and *Phoebus Apollo* (ex. R.A. 1895 [161], Birmingham City Art Gallery).[5]

[1] H. C. Marillier, *"Christie's", 1766 to 1925*, 1926, p. 60.
[2] Walter Armstrong, *Celebrated Pictures exhibited at the Manchester Royal Jubilee Exhibition, Fine Arts Section*, 1888, p. 39. It is assumed that it was the same painting which was exhibited at this exhibition, although the name of the owner was given as William Agnew. This may well be explained by

Agnew's possible retention of the copyright when the picture was sold in 1883.
[3] *Portfolio*, 1880, p. 141.
[4] Letter to Carey, dated 1 September 1887, Royal Holloway College Archives and published by him.
[5] For *Daniel in the Lions' Den*, see Arts Council, *Great Victorian Pictures*, 1978, p. 72.

BIBLIOGRAPHY
James Dafforne, 'The Works of Briton Riviere', *Art Journal*, 1878, pp. 5–8.
W. W. Fenn, 'Briton Riviere, A.R.A.', *Magazine of Art*, 1879, pp. 252–5; reprinted in: ed. Wilfrid Meynell, *Some Modern Artists and Their Work*, 1883, pp. 141–7.
F. G. Stephens, *Artists at Home*, New York, 1884, pp. 69–72.
Walter Armstrong, 'Briton Riviere, R.A.', *Art Annual*, 1891, pp. 1–32.
F. G. Stephens, 'Briton Riviere, R.A., D.C.L.', *Portfolio*, 1892, pp. 61–6, 77–83.
M. V. B. Riviere, 'The Family of Riviere in England', *Proceedings of the Huguenot Society of London*, 1968 for 1967, Vol. XXI, No. 3, pp. 219–40.

65. David Roberts

1796–1864, ARA 1838, RA 1841

Pilgrims approaching Jerusalem 1841 (*pl. 24*)

oil on canvas, 47 × 83 in (119.3 × 210.7 cm)

INSCR: David Roberts 1841

PROV: Painted for Lord Monson of Gatton Park, nr Reigate, Surrey for £330; by descent; the Earl of Warwick; his sale Christie's 9 May 1870 (117) bt Hall £420; Baron Albert Grant of the Kensington House Gallery; his sale Christie's 27–8 April 1877 (64) bt Gilbert £351 15s; W. H. Duignan; his sale Christie's 7 June 1879 (145) bt in 235 gns; J. W. Adamson; his sale Christie's 5 May 1883 (117) bt Martin £388 10s.

EXH: 1841 R.A. (399); 1981–82 Scottish Arts Council Touring Exhibition *David Roberts* (19).

LIT: *Annual Register* 1841 p. 46; *Art Union* 1841 p. 79; *Literary Gazette* 1841 p. 315; *Spectator* 1841 p. 451; *The Times* 4 May 1841 p. 5; Ballantine, 1866 pp. 145, 249, no. 111 and sketch opp. p. 144.

STUDIES: 1. *Jerusalem from the Mount of Olives* watercolour and pencil, 13½ × 21 in (34.2 × 53.3 cm)

Inscr. Jerusalem from the Mount of Olives April 8th 1839.

Prov. The artist's studio sale Christie's 18 May 1865 (852) bt Campbell 41 gns; John Gordon of Cluny; anon. sale Christie's 2 March 1976 (162) bt Brook Street Gallery for a Private Collection in Israel.

2. *Jerusalem from the Road leading to Bethany*
drawing

Prov. 1st Earl of Ellesmere; his sale Christie's 2 April 1870 (5) bt Hopgood £43 1s.

3. *Jerusalem from the Mount of Olives*
drawing

Prov. 1st Earl of Ellesmere; his sale Christie's 2 April 1870 (17) bt Vokins £74 11s.

ENGR: 1. unpublished, begun in mezzotint by David Lucas, $36 \times 20\frac{1}{2}$ in (91.4×52 cm).

Lit. Ballantine, 1866 p. 255.

2. coloured lithograph by Louis Haghe for *The Holy Land, Syria, Idumea, Arabia, Egypt and Nubia*, Vol. I 1842 and Vol. I 1855.

VERSIONS: 1. *Jerusalem from Mount Olivet* 1842
oil on canvas, $32\frac{1}{2} \times 59\frac{3}{4}$ in (82.5×151.7 cm)

Inscr. David Roberts RA 1842; on verso, David Roberts No. 2 DURHAM (crossed out)

Prov. ? Painted for Rev. B. Hurnard; presented by subscribers to the Castle Museum, Norwich to commemorate the part taken by Norfolk units in the capture of Jerusalem by Troops under General Allenby.

Repr: Connoisseur Vol. LI, 1918 p. 51.

2. *Jerusalem from the South East* 1845
$47\frac{1}{2} \times 83$ in (120.6×210.7 cm)

Prov. Painted for Lord Francis Egerton (later 1st Earl of Ellesmere) of Worsley Hall, Lancashire for 300 gns (including frame); by descent; Earl of Ellesmere; his sale Christie's 18 October 1946 (27) bt in 5 gns; and his sale Christie's 7 February 1947 (108) bt Smith 5 gns.

Exh. 1845 R.A. (405)

? *Study. Jerusalem from the South*
drawing

Prov. 1st Earl of Ellesmere; his sale Christie's 2 April 1870 (9) bt Vokins £64 1s.

Lit. Athenaeum 1845 p. 496; Ballantine, 1866 p. 162 and list of works no. 131.

3. *The View of Jerusalem from the Mount of Olives* ? 1855 or 1859
oil on canvas, $21\frac{1}{2} \times 36\frac{1}{2}$ in (54.5×93 cm)

Inscr. David Roberts RA 1855 or 1859

Prov. Anon. sale Christie's 13 July 1956 (238) bt R. G. Walker, Ministry of Works for the Government Art Collection (no. 3555) £71 8s currently at British Embassy at Tel Aviv.

Exh. 1888 Melbourne; 1898 West Ham.

4. *Jerusalem looking South* 1860
$47\frac{1}{2} \times 71\frac{1}{2}$ in (120.6×181.5 cm)

Prov. Bought by Ernest Gambart for £400 (excluding frame); ? Llewellyn; ? his sale Christie's 9 March 1861 (97) bt Jones £380; R. C. Naylor of Hooton Hall, Chester; his sale Christie's 7 August 1875 (848) bt Lane 850 gns; the Countess of Dudley; her sale Christie's 15 June 1889 (94) bt in 250 gns; the Earl of Dudley; his sale Christie's 25 June 1892 (33) bt Agnew 140 gns; sold by them to C. Morland Agnew 27 June 1892; his widow's sale Christie's 24 March 1933 (44) bt Boot 10 gns.

Exh. ? Brussels.

? *Study. Jerusalem from the North*
drawing

Prov. 1st Earl of Ellesmere; his sale Christie's 2 April 1870 (21) by Vokins £152 5s.

Lit. Ballantine, 1866 p. 203 and list of works no. 246.

5. *Jerusalem from the Mount of Olives* 1860
painted over the unfinished engraving of the subject which is stuck on canvas, $20\frac{1}{2} \times 35\frac{1}{4}$ in (52×89.5 cm)

Inscr. David Roberts RA 1860

Prov. Painted for the dealer, Louis Victor Flatow for £105 or £262 10s (Ballantine gives both figures); his sale Christie's 29 March 1862 (132) bt Morby £210; T. M. Whitehouse of Graiseley Old Hall, Wolverhampton; his sale Christie's 29 March 1890 (39) bt Vicars £73 10s entitled *Jerusalem from the Valley of Jehosaphat* for Leicester Art Gallery.

Lit. Ballantine, 1866 pp. 252, 255 and list of works no. 242.

Exhibited at the R.A. in 1841 as *Jerusalem from the Mount of Olives*, this painting was subsequently also entitled *Jerusalem, from the Road leading to Bethany* (sale catalogue 1870), *A Grand View of Jerusalem* (sale catalogue 1877) and *Pilgrims in Sight of Jerusalem. View from the Mount of Olives* (sale catalogue 1879).

The painting was commissioned by Lord Monson (of Gatton Park, near Reigate, Surrey); the son of the Earl of Warwick, in about 1840 he had started collecting British paintings, but was cut short by his early death.[1] Roberts noted this in his handwriting under a sketch of the painting reproduced in James Ballantine's biography of him and also that it 'being the first and last of a collection of the British School commissioned by His Lordship for his new house at Gatton, which had he lived, from his judgement & love of art, of which he was no indifferent practitioner himself – would have most probably formed a princely collection. I recd from his Lordship for this Picture £330.'[2] An addition, not published by Ballantine but in his *Record Book* of 1829 to 1864, was also in Roberts's handwriting: 'Frame included. The Picture I believe when he found himself dying was presented by him to his mother the Countess of Warwick.' Above this entry, again in Roberts's hand, is further information: 'A Duplicate of this Picture I painted for the Rev. Mr. B. Hurnard for which he paid me £100. Frame included.'[3]

Monson himself had visited the Holy Land and according to Ballantine, had 'died as a result of illness' following that visit.[4] In a letter from Monson to Roberts on the death of Wilkie in 1841, Monson wrote of this painting: 'Your picture of Jerusalem is rendered now even more valuable to me from its having been painted at his [Wilkie's] suggestion' and followed this with a request for Roberts's help in building up a gallery of British paintings.[5]

As noted by the *Athenaeum* in 1845, Jerusalem 'seems his most popular landscape, possibly owing to the subject, which will never cease to be sought for with eager and reverential curiosity.'[6] Roberts set out in August 1838 for the Middle East, going firstly to Alexandria.[7] By way of Cairo, Mount Sinai and Petra, Roberts travelled on to Jerusalem. He and his party arrived on Good Friday, 1839, to find the city packed with pilgrims for the Easter celebrations. The R.A.

catalogue describes Easter time in Jerusalem and continues: 'During Easter, Christian pilgrims from all parts of the East assemble at Jerusalem, from whence, accompanied by the Governor, and escorted by a strong guard, they proceed in a body to bathe in the river Jordan . . . The scene represents them coming in sight of the holy city on their return. "How doth the city sit solitary that *was* full of people! How is she become as a widow! She that *was* great among the nations, and princes among the provinces, how is she become tributary! Her gates are desolate; all her beauty is departed". – Lamentations of Jeremiah.'

Roberts intended to embody the work done on his travels in a large volume of lithographs; but he had also provided himself with enough material to last him over a long period of time. The subject of Jerusalem seen from a distance was certainly a favourite one with Roberts and the many versions of it probably all spring from an initial watercolour and pencil sketch, presumably done on the spot, dated 8 April 1839, though it differs in detail from the final lithograph and the oil painting which followed. None of these oil painting versions are exactly similar. Ballantine remarked that Roberts 'repeated many of his subjects . . . [although] he always varied his figures and the effect of light and shade, so that, though many of his pictures are called replicas, no two are like'.[8]

Five versions in oil of *Pilgrims approaching Jerusalem* have been recorded. In chronological order the first is *Jerusalem from Mount Olivet* (Norwich Castle Museum) of 1842, smaller and not listed by Ballantine. The second, *Jerusalem from the South East* of 1845 (number 131 in Ballantine) has not been traced, is of the same size as *Pilgrims approaching Jerusalem* and was exhibited at the R.A. of 1845.

It was commissioned by Lord Francis Egerton of Worsley Hall, Lancashire, who became the first Earl of Ellesmere in 1846 and built Bridgewater House in London. Lord Francis Egerton also owned 25 drawings for the Holy Land lithographic series, which he had bought for a total of £500.[9] Egerton's interest in Roberts's Holy Land subjects was due to the fact that he himself had travelled there and had produced a volume in 1841, with views in lithograph done from his

drawings, entitled *Journal of a Tour in the Holy Land in May and June 1840*. A third version of the painting appeared at Christie's in 1956 and was bought by the Government Art Collection. This is now at the British Embassy at Tel Aviv. There is no reference to it in Ballantine.

The fourth version, also untraced, *Jerusalem looking South*, 1860 (Ballantine number 246), was, according to Roberts's *Record Book*, painted for the famous London-based dealer Ernest Gambart for £400, excluding the frame.[10] In the same year Roberts painted a fifth version for another dealer in London, Louis Victor Flatow. *Jerusalem from the Mount of Olives* (Leicestershire Museums and Art Gallery, Ballantine number 242), is a much smaller painting than *Pilgrims approaching Jerusalem*. Roberts painted it on a proof from an unpublished plate and pasted it on to a canvas. According to Ballantine, David Lucas (1802–81), a mezzotint engraver, who was best known for his work with Constable, had begun an engraving in mezzotint but by 1866, the date of publication of Ballantine, it was still unfinished.[11]

On his return from the Holy Land in 1839, Roberts at once set to work on the lithographs from his work done there, or, as was explained a few years later in the *A.J.*: 'On the artist's return, he submitted his drawings to that "most enterprising and prince of all publishers", Alderman Sir F. G. Moon, who arranged with him to bring out a work illustrative of Scripture history, and to give him the sum of £3,000 for the copyright of the sketches, and for superintending their reproduction in lithography.'[12] Three years before Messrs Moon and Graves had produced the first volume of *The Holy Land, Syria, Idumea, Arabia, Egypt and Nubia* of which 20 parts had been published spasmodically by 1849. Louis Haghe (1806–85), a Belgian lithographer and a friend of Roberts's, was responsible for the drawings on the stone which he did from Roberts's original watercolours. There were three views of Jerusalem in Volume I. The closest to the *Pilgrims approaching Jerusalem* painting was entitled *Jerusalem, from the Road leading to Bethany* (no number), and dated, like the watercolour and pencil sketch mentioned above, 8 April 1839. This lithograph was republished 13 years

later by Messrs Day and Son as number 6 in Volume I of their *Holy Land* edition.

Pilgrims approaching Jerusalem was exhibited at the R.A. with two other pictures: *Portico of the Temple of Dendera, in Upper Egypt* (223, Bristol City Art Gallery) and *Ruins of Baalbec, Mount Lebanon in the distance* (994, untraced).

Pilgrims approaching Jerusalem was extremely well received at the Academy. While *The Times* simply described it as 'a grand Oriental Picture', the *Art Union*'s opinion was that the picture was 'A chef-d'oeuvre of the Artist; realising a scene linked with so many gloomy and glorious associations – the city that "sits solitary"; that *was* great "among the nations" . . . The painter has judiciously thrown the city into the background, from which rise its square and ungainly towers; while in the foreground he has introduced a procession of pilgrims, on their way to bathe in the river Jordan. The picture is one of the highest class; deeply interesting in subject, and of surpassing excellence as a work of art.'

The *Literary Gazette* also praised it, remarking on its 'yet grander [than his other R.A. pictures that year] aspect and deeper interest. The multitude of Christian pilgrims, assembled to perform the religious rite of bathing in the river Jordan, animate the canvas in a singularly effective manner, and impart to it a picturesqueness of infinite variety and beauty'. The *Spectator*, however, had reservations about the oil painting over the drawings by stating that his three pictures 'do not embody the imaginative suggestions of his sketches'.

Surprisingly Ruskin criticised Roberts's Holy Land drawings generally in *Modern Painters*.[13] He expressed his dislike of them at length, declaring that they were not honest drawings to study in depth. At the same time, he did acknowledge the influence which Roberts's work had on his own.[14]

1 See *Early Victorian England, 1830–1865*, ed. G. M. Young, 1934, p. 114.
2 James Ballantine, *The Life of David Roberts, R.A.*, Edinburgh, 1866, opp. p. 144, and also quoted by Carey.
3 *Record Book* 1829–64, no. 98, in the possession of Mr Frank Bicknell, a descendant of Roberts. Roberts had entitled the painting *Jerusalem from the Mount of Olives with pilgrims*

entering the River Jordan. This was possibly the painting which was duplicated for Rev. B. Hurnard, for in a letter to his daughter Christine of 9 August 1842 (also in the possession of the family), Roberts wrote: 'The Jerusalem has made a very fine subject, which for Hurnards sake I am glad of. I send it off to him in Norfolk in the course of a day or two.'

[4] James Ballantine, 1866, p. 145.

[5] Ibid. This letter, dated 12 June 1841, was published in the *Literary Gazette* of 1841 (p. 675). This was pointed out by Miss Helen Guiterman whose assistance with the two Roberts paintings has been invaluable.

[6] *Athenaeum*, 17 May 1845, p. 496 in reference to the Royal Academy exhibit of Version 2, *Jerusalem from the South East.*

[7] For a full account of his journey, see Helen Guiterman, *David Roberts R.A. 1796–1864*, 1978, pp. 6–19.

[8] James Ballantine, 1866, p. 254.

[9] Op. cit. p. 146.

[10] See Jeremy Maas, *Gambart, Prince of the Victorian Art World*, 1975, pp. 113, 156.

[11] James Ballantine, 1866, p. 255. The engraving was possibly after the Royal Holloway College painting. In Roberts's *Record Book* is a note in Henry Bicknell's writing which starts: 'A plate in mezzotint from this picture was commenced by David Lucas in [blank]'.

[12] *Art Journal*, 1858, p. 202.

[13] John Ruskin, *The Works of John Ruskin*, ed. E. T. Cook and Alexander Wedderburn (Library Edition), Vol. III, p. 224.

[14] See Kenneth Clark, *Ruskin Today*, 1962, p. 351.

66. David Roberts
1796–1864, ARA 1838, RA 1841

A Street in Cairo 1846 (*pl. 22*)

oil on canvas, 30 × 25 in (76.1 × 63.4 cm)

INSCR: David Roberts RA 1846

PROV: Painted for Elhanan Bicknell for £52 10s; his sale Christie's 25 April 1863 (75) bt Agnew £530 5s; sold by them 6 May 1863 to Duncan Fletcher for £556 15s; his sale Christie's 20 May 1865 (31) bt Flatow; F. T. Turner; his sale Christie's 4 May 1878 (47) bt Thomas Taylor of Aston Rowant Gallery, Oxfordshire, £640 10s; his sale Christie's 28 April 1883 (64) bt Martin £745 10s.

EXH: 1846 R.A. (91) as *Street in Grand Cairo*; 1951–52 R.A. *The First Hundred Years of the Royal Academy* 1769–1868 (335); 1981–82 Scottish Arts Council Touring Exhibition *David Roberts* (22).

LIT: *Art Union* 1846 p. 174; *Critic* 23 May 1846 pp. 589, 590; *Literary Gazette* 1846 p. 433; *The Times* 11 May 1846 p. 5; Gustav Friedrich Waagen, *Treasures of Art in Great Britain*, 1854, Vol. 11, p. 349; Ballantine, 1866 pp. 163, 250, no. 141; *Mag. of Art* 1882 p. 312.

STUDY: *Cairo*

watercolour, 13½ × 9¼ in (34.2 × 23.4 cm)

Inscr. Mosque of El Rhamree Cairo Janr. 1st 1839 David Roberts

Prov. ? Painted for Elhanan Bicknell (as *A Street in Cairo*); his sale Christie's 29 April 1863 (121) bt Wells £80 17s; presented to Castle Museum, Nottingham by A. E. Anderson in 1932.

Exh. 1981–82 Scottish Arts Council Touring Exhibition *David Roberts* (29).

VERSIONS: 1. 1841 B.I. Ex. (108) *Street in Cairo* 75 × 62 in (190.4 × 157.4 cm)

2. *A Street in Grand Cairo* 1842 55 × 43 in (139.6 × 109.1 cm)

Prov. Painted for George Knott for £210 including frame, entitled *Bazaar of the Coppersmiths* and re-touched for Joseph Arden of Rickmansworth in whose collection it was by 1857; his sale Christie's 26 April 1879 (71) bt J. W. Birch £945.

Lit. A.J. 1857 p. 311, Ballantine, 1866 p. 249 no. 105.

ENGR: Coloured lithograph by Louis Haghe for *The Holy Land, Syria, Idumea, Arabia, Egypt and Nubia*, Vol. III, 1849.

This painting shows the view towards the Mosque of El Rhamree in Cairo. Like *Pilgrims approaching Jerusalem* it was painted as a result of Roberts's visit to Eygpt in 1838–39. He went through Cairo in October 1838 and returned that December, when he rented a house there in order to have time to draw.[1] He complained: 'It has been a most arduous undertaking in these narrow Stinking crowded Streets and mostly in my European dress.'[2]

Roberts was fascinated by mosques and drew many of them for his volume of lithographs of *Egypt and Nubia*. In his diary for 1 January 1839, he wrote of his drawings done in the streets that they 'will add to the knowledge in Europe of various styles of architecture existing in different countries and ages'.[3] Earlier, on 19 December, the day before his return to Cairo, he had written generally about his Egyptian drawings that they 'are possessed of great interest, independent of their merits as pictures. I am the first English artist who has been here, and there is much in the French work that conveys no idea of these splendid remains. We shall see what impression they make in England. Subjects of another class and equal interest remain at Cairo, and the ground is equally untrodden.'[4] His claim to breaking new ground is interesting, especially as it shows his ignorance of Muller's (q.v.) Egyptian visit of the same date, 1838–39. J. F. Lewis (1805–76), a dedicated painter of Middle-Eastern subjects, lived in Cairo from 1842 to 1851.[5]

A Street in Cairo, painted seven years after Roberts's return, was bought by Elhanan Bicknell, a well-known collector, friend and patron of many painters,[6] whose son Henry had married Roberts's daughter Christine.[7]

According to Dr Waagen, who visited the Bicknell collection and published his account of English private collections in 1854, the painting hung in the dining room at Elhanan Bicknell's house at Herne Hill, Camberwell. Waagen described it as 'of masterly execution, in the finest silvery tone'.[8] Roberts noted in his *Record Book* that *Street in Grand Cairo* (giving it its exhibited title) had been purchased by E. Bicknell for 50 guineas.[9] Bicknell also owned a watercolour drawing of the same title, painted for him, according to the sale catalogue, and included in his sale after his death.[10] It may have been the preliminary watercolour sketch for this painting. It is now in the Castle Museum, Nottingham.

The lithograph which was made by Louis Haghe (like the one for *Pilgrims approaching Jerusalem*) from the watercolour done on the spot was also published in *The Holy Land* series, in the part containing the illustrations of *Egypt and Nubia* of 1849.[11] This volume includes a historical description for each plate, written by William Brockenden FRS. The plate *Minaret of the Mosque El Rhamree* (later to become *Street in Cairo* when painted as an oil) is described: 'This mosque is situated in the main line of the street leading to the Bab el Nasr. There are great symmetry and beauty in its minaret . . . It is surmounted by a bronze crescent, and the props, often decayed and unsafe, from which lamps are suspended during the feast of Rhamadan. A flight of steps, seen on the right, leads up to the porch of the principal entrance, above which lamps are placed . . . those objects of beauty, the minarets of the mosques, frequently burst upon the eye of the observer as they rise above the buildings, and strikingly characterise the architecture of Cairo.'

Exhibited as *Street in Grand Cairo* at the R.A. exhibition of 1846, the picture was well-received. The *Literary Gazette* called the painting 'a good example of the picturesque' and *The Times* considered that Roberts 'displays his talent for indicating that eastern architecture which rises up so fantastically against the clear sky, and gives his tone by his favourite introduction of the rich glow of evening.'

The *Art Union*'s contibution was simply to describe its content and mention the 'gleam of light which has great value in the composition'. The *Critic* considered that in all Roberts's exhibited works that year 'his genius shines out in all its strength. The associations connected with the scenes which this artist paints go far in producing the strong interest and lasting impression which his pictures excite.' Of *A Street in Cairo* in particular, they wrote: 'This is chiefly useful as conveying a notion to us of Egyptian street architecture. The narrow roadway, with houses having projecting stories supported by carved beam-ends and sloping props, the curious tower, the galleries crossing from side to side of the street; the Ethiopians, Turks, and Copts, all clad in flowing costumes, render this an interesting picture.' Nevertheless, they had reservations: 'It has, however, few artistic merits to boast of. The detail is often obscure and inexact, and the handling more slovenly than we remember in any of this artist's work.' Certainly the loss of immediacy is noticeable when compared with the original watercolour but Roberts utilised his store of raw material from his journey of 1838–39 for some years to come.

David Roberts was born in Stockbridge, Edinburgh, the son of a shoemaker. He started as an apprentice to a house painter, and from 1815 onwards he worked as a decorator in theatres all over Britain; during this time met Clarkson Stanfield (q.v.) who was to become a life-long friend. In 1822 Roberts was in London, again working as a scene painter, and he was responsible in 1826 for the sets of the first London production of Mozart's *Il Seraglio*. Also in 1826 Roberts first exhibited at the R.A. with *View of Rouen Cathedral* (221). This marked the beginning of his career as an easel painter: four years later he left theatre work to concentrate on his own painting.

In 1832 Roberts went to Spain, which he considered to have been overlooked by painters. From Spain he continued to Tangiers, returning to England through Spain 12 months later. He published *Picturesque Sketches in Spain* in 1837 as well as providing Spanish subjects for landscape annuals. His second important journey, to the Near East, began in 1838, and resulted in a vast output of work, including the two paintings in this collection.[11]

In 1851 Roberts first visited Italy, which likewise provided him with new subject matter for most of that decade. He continued to travel widely over the Continent, his interest remaining in architectural subjects of all ages, exteriors and interiors. He began painting a series of Thames subjects in about 1860.

After Roberts's death in 1864 there was a six-day studio sale at Christie's of his remaining works in May 1865, preceded by an exhibition of his sketches and watercolours at the Architectural Society's Rooms in Conduit Street, London, from February to May of that year.

[1] For a full account, see Helen Guiterman, *David Roberts R.A. 1796–1864*, 1978.

[2] Op. cit. p. 11.

[3] Quoted by James Ballantine, *The Life of David Roberts, R.A.*, Edinburgh, 1866, p. 107.

[4] Op. cit. p. 102.

[5] For Eastern subject painting, see the exhibition catalogue, *Eastern Encounters, Orientalist Painters of the Nineteenth Century*, 1978, Fine Art Society.

[6] For the collection of Elhanan Bicknell, see *Art Journal*, 1857, pp. 8–10.

[7] For the collection of Henry Bicknell at Cavendish House, Clapham Common, see *Art Journal*, 1872, pp. 90–92.

[8] Gustav Friedrich Waagen, *Treasures of Art in Great Britain*, 1854, Vol. II, p. 349.

[9] Record Book 1829–1864, no. 129.

[10] Sale at Christie's, 29 April 1863 (121) *A Street in Cairo* was bought by Wells for £80 17s.

[11] David Roberts, *The Holy Land, Syria, Idumea, Arabia, Egypt and Nubia*, 1849, Vol. II, no. 13.

[12] For further information concerning his Holy Land visit, see the exhibition catalogue, *David Roberts: Sketches in The Holy Land, 1839*, 1976, Agnew's.

BIBLIOGRAPHY

F. W. Fairholt, 'British Artists: Their Style and Character, No. XXXVI. David Roberts R.A.', *Art Journal*, 1858, pp. 201–3.

Art Journal, 1865, p. 43 (Obit.).

James Ballantine, *The Life of David Roberts, R.A.*, Edinburgh, 1866.

Allan Cunningham, *Lives of the Most Eminent British Painters*, revised ed. by Mrs Charles Heaton, 1880, Vol. III, pp. 363–76.

Walter Armstrong, 'Scottish Painters V', *Portfolio*, 1887, pp. 136–8.

Sir James L. Caw, *Scottish Painting Past and Present, 1620–1908*, Edinburgh, 1908, pp. 153–5.

Jane Quigley, 'David Roberts', *Walker's Quarterly*, Vol. X, 1923, pp. 3–32.

David Roberts and Clarkson Stanfield, exhibition catalogue, Guildhall Art Gallery, 1967.

David and Francina Irwin, *Scottish Painters at Home and Abroad, 1700–1900*, 1975, pp. 331–4.

Helen Guiterman, *David Roberts R.A. 1796–1864*, 1978.

67 and 68. William Scott
1811–90

Thomas Holloway 1845 (*pl. 2*)
oil on canvas, 45½ × 33 in (115.6 × 83.7 cm)
Jane Holloway 1845 (*pl. 3*)
oil on canvas, 44½ × 34 in (112.9 × 86.3 cm)

PROV: Presumed to have been presented to the College from the estate of Miss Mary Ann Driver (sister of Jane Holloway) in 1900.

Very little indeed is known about this painter. A portrait by him of the Scottish missionary Robert Moffat, dated 1842, is in the National Portrait Gallery; further examples of his work have been difficult to trace. It was not unusual for collectors such as Holloway to choose unknown painters for family portraits.

69. Abraham Solomon
1823–62, ARA 1862

Departure of the Diligence, Biarritz 1862 (*pl. 20*)

oil on canvas, 35 × 50 in (88.8 × 126.9 cm)

INSCR: (on the trunk on the right) ⚒

PROV: Included in the sale Christie's of the Remaining Works of Abraham Solomon, Deceased 14 March 1863 (74) bt George Earl £91 7s; Mr. Fitzpatrick; his sale Christie's 8 June 1864 (100) bt in 180 gns; W. S. Johnson; his sale Christie's 5 May 1883 (99) bt Martin £451 10s.

EXH: 1981 Agnew's (38).

LIT: Lambourne, 1968 p. 277.

REPR: Gaunt, 1972, pl. 101.

? STUDY: *The Departure of the Diligence, Biarritz* 16 × 23 in (40.6 × 58.3 cm)

Prov. Included in the sale Christie's of the Remaining Works of Abraham Solomon, Deceased 14 March 1863 (81a) bt George Earl £15 4s 6d; anon. sale Christie's 20 December 1909 (83), bt in 6 gns.

This painting was Solomon's last work before he died in Biarritz. It was catalogued by Christie's in their 1863 sale of his remaining works as 'An important work left unfinished', although there seems no reason to suppose that it is not finished. In any event, it was not exhibited at the R.A. in 1863.

Solomon had gone to Biarritz in the autumn of 1861 for a rest cure for a heart condition he suffered from and *Departure of the Diligence, Biarritz* was painted there in 1862 before he died in December of that year. It contains much in the way of incidental detail and careful grouping of the figures, who weave an intricate pattern across the picture surface, for which Solomon was so admired.

Abraham Solomon, born in London, was the son of Michael Solomon, the first Jew to be granted the freedom of the City of London.[1] Abraham was the fourth child of eight. His younger brother, Simeon (1840–1905) became a well-known painter and his sister Rebecca (1832–86), who studied with Abraham, also exhibited history paintings and portraits frequently at the R.A. from 1852 to 1869.

At 13 Solomon began to study at Sass's Academy in Bloomsbury and two years later won the Isis silver medal for drawing at the Society of Arts. In 1839 he joined the R.A. Schools. He soon gained popularity with his genre and literary subject paintings, many of which were engraved and so helped to promote him further.

His paintings were admired for their brilliance of colour and for his interest in costume. Solomon's greatest success at the Academy came in 1854 with *First class. – the meeting.* 'And at first meeting loved' (314, Ottawa) and *Second class – the parting.* 'Thus part we rich in sorrow, Parting poor' (361, Private Collection). These are a pair of scenes in a railway carriage; the first one was repainted owing to objections that a young lady should not be talking to a young man whilst her father was asleep and therefore not a chaperon. Solomon then painted the father awake and attentive to the young man and sitting opposite him instead of in the diagonal corner.

Until 1854 Solomon had exhibited either portraits or subjects taken from historical or literary sources; these two paintings were his first contemporary genre scenes, and their success probably inspired him to paint the pair which followed a few years later and were even more successful. *Waiting for the Verdict* was exhibited at the R.A. of 1857 (562) and *Not Guilty* in 1859 (557, both in a Private Collection).[2] They depict two separate scenes of a family outside a court-room and so great was their appeal that a large number of engravings of them was published.

[1] D.N.B.
[2] See Arts Council, *Great Victorian Pictures*, 1978, pp. 74–5.

BIBLIOGRAPHY
James Dafforne, 'British Artists: Their Style and Character, No. LIX, Abraham Solomon', *Art Journal*, 1862, pp. 73–5. *Art Journal*, 1863, p. 29 (Obit.).

David Fincham, 'Three Painters of the Victorian Scene', *Apollo*, Vol. XXIII, 1936, pp. 241–5.
Lionel Lambourne, 'Abraham Solomon, Painter of Fashion, and Simeon Solomon, Decadent Artist', *The Jewish Historical Society of England*, Vol. XXI, 1968, pp. 274–86.

70. Clarkson Stanfield
1793–1867, ARA 1832, RA 1835

After a Storm (*pl. 29*)

millboard, 8½ × 13 in (21.5 × 33 cm)

INSCR: C. Stanfield RA

PROV: Samuel Mayou of Edgbaston, Birmingham; his sale Christie's 21 April 1883 (47) bt Martin £162 15s.

EXH: 1981 Agnew's (39).

Little is known about this small-scale marine painting by Stanfield. The painting is signed but not dated. It contains certain similar features, although on a much smaller scale, to those in one of his most famous paintings *The Day after the Wreck. A Dutch East Indiaman on shore in the Ooster Schelde: Zierikzee in the distance* which was exhibited at the R.A. in 1844 (187, Sheffield City Art Galleries).[1]

The composition is similar, with the wrecked ship in a rough sea on the horizon and the smaller sailing boat placed in front of it; but *The Day after the Wreck* has much more detail in the left foreground and a closer and more substantial view of the coast to the right of the picture.

Ruskin, in *Modern Painters*, had high praise for Stanfield's sea pictures and his handling of water. He wrote that Stanfield had a 'thorough knowledge of his subject, and thorough acquaintance with all the means and principles of art.' However, he had reservations: 'We wish that he were less powerful, and more interesting . . . we should like him to be less clever, and more affecting, less wonderful, and more terrible; and, as the very first step towards such an end, to learn how to conceal . . . one work of Stanfield's alone presents us with as much concentrated knowledge of sea and sky, as, diluted, would have lasted any one of the old masters his life.'[2]

[1] See Arts Council, *Great Victorian Pictures*, 1978, no. 53.
[2] John Ruskin, *The Works of John Ruskin*, ed. E. T. Cook and Alexander Wedderburn (Library Edition), 1903–12, Vol. III, pp. 534–5.

71. Clarkson Stanfield
1793–1867, ARA 1832, RA 1835

The Battle of Roveredo 1796 1851 (*pl. 13*)

oil on canvas, 72 × 108 in (182.8 × 274.2 cm)

INSCR: Clarkson Stanfield RA 1846

PROV: painted for F. D. P. Astley; Sam Mendel of Manley Hall, Manchester 1870; bt from him by Agnew 22 September 1873; sold by them 8 December 1873 to Baron Albert Grant of the Kensington House Gallery for £3,850; his sale Christie's 27 April 1877 (92) bt Agnew £2,520; sold by them 15 May 1877 to Edward John Coleman of Stoke Park, Buckinghamshire; his sale Christie's 28 May 1881 (52) bt Thomas £3,465.

EXH: 1851 R.A. (196); 1855 Paris, Expo. Univ. (937); 1857 Manchester Art Treasures Exhibition (483); 1870 R.A. Winter Exhibition (163); 1979 Bonn, Rheinisches Museum and Sunderland Art Gallery (302); 1981 Agnew's (40).

LIT: *A.J.* 1851 p. 156; *Athenaeum* 10 May 1851 p. 504; *Critic* 14 June 1851 p. 8; *Examiner* 10 May 1851 p. 294; *I.L.N.* 24 May 1851 p. 464; *Literary Gazette* 1851 p. 349; *Spectator* 28 June 1851 p. 619; *The Times* 3 May 1851 p. 8; *A.J.* 1857 p. 138; *A.J.* 1867 p. 171; *Athenaeum* 1867 p. 694; *A.J.* 1870 p. 155 reprinted in Dafforne, 1873 pp. 32–3; *Portfolio* 1879 p. 139; Cunningham, 1880 p. 335; *The Times* 30 May 1881 p. 8.

REPR: Gaunt, 1972, pl. 79.

STUDIES: 1. *In the Alps* 1851
panel, 15½ × 23½ in (39.3 × 59.6 cm)
  Inscr. C. Stanfield RA 1851
  Prov. Thomas Williams of St. John's Wood 1870; T. O. Reilly; his sale Sotheby's 5 November 1974 (92) and repr. bt Apollo Galleries, Croydon.
  Exh. 1870 R.A. Winter Ex. (162) as *Roveredo*.
2. *Castle and Town of Roveredo*
24 × 16 in (60.9 × 40.6 cm)

Prov. S. Hammond; his sale Christie's 17 June 1854 (68) bt Lloyd £162 15s.
3. *Battle of Roveredo*
original sketch, 14 × 9 in (35.5 × 22.8 cm)
  Prov. Ernest Gambart; his sale Christie's 3 May 1861 (110) bt Grundy £80 17s.
4. *French Troops crossing the Tyrol*
  Exh. 1862 London Int. Ex. (362, lent by Messrs Graves).
5. *The small finished picture*
19 × 13 in (48.2 × 33 cm)
  Prov. Messrs. Hayward & Leggatt; their sale Christie's 8 December 1864 (290) bt Gibbs.
6. The following untraced studies appeared in Clarkson Stanfield's Studio Sale, Christie's 8–14 May 1868:
  i. (40) *Study of Roveredo*
    framed drawing, bt Ellis £6 6s.
  ii. (177) *Study of Soldiers for the Roveredo picture*
    drawing, bt Hayward 5s.
  iii. (189) *Large Study of French Soldiers*
    bt Hogarth £11 11s.
  iv. (190) *Large Study of French Soldiers*
    bt Hayward £2 10s.
  v. (499) *Study of a Monk for Roveredo*
    drawing, bt Repton 14s.
  vi. (502) *Study for the Picture of Roveredo*
    drawing, bt Hogarth 11s.
  vii. (621) *Roveredo*
    pencil, bt Agnew £14 14s; sold by them 26 May 1868 to Sam Mendel.
7. *Roveredo*
panel, 12 × 24 in (30.4 × 60.8 cm)
  Prov. Hubert Martineau; his sale Christie's 2 March 1901 (135) bt Agnew £178 10s; sold by them 4 March 1901 to Percy Marsden of 45 Hanover Gate Mansions, London NW1; his sale Christie's 18 June 1926 (118) bt Sampson £22 1s.
8. *Roveredo and The Ortler*
13½ × 20 in (34.2 × 50.7 cm)
  Prov. Private Collection, Denmark 1974.
This painting was exhibited in 1851 at the Academy, with an anonymous quotation which read:
'See the blood the Alpine valley stained, the cloister-garth profaned:

Nothing calm is left, or holy, where man's angry step had trod.
See the snow-wreaths, softly sparkling, over crags serenely darkening,
All is ever pure and peaceful, where none has a path but God'.

The scene is the battle on 4 September 1796 when the French defeated the Austrians, having used the castle as their barracks. Roveredo is in the Italian Tyrol between Trento and Verona on the river Adige and is now called Rovereto. The *A.J.* review of the 1851 exhibition contained a good description of the battle fought by 'Masséna and Augereau, against Davidowich who was guarding the Tyrol with 40,000 men. This large picture shows rather the advance of the French as crossing the Adige, than the battle. On the right of the composition appears the fortress, the fire from which has almost ceased. In the foreground the French infantry are fording the river, and at some distance they are again seen passing the bridge, under fire from distant batteries . . . On the left the inhabitants are seen flying from their houses, and the whole of the lower composition is crowned by the snow-clad Alps.'

The idea for this painting could have been in Stanfield's mind as early as 1832. An engraving entitled *Roveredo* was published in that year in *Heath's Picturesque Annual*, from drawings by Stanfield, as *Travelling Sketches in the North of Italy, The Tyrol, and on the Rhine* by Leitch Ritchie.[1] The engraving was accompanied by a short description of the town and depicts the same view of the castle as the painting but from a slightly different angle. The scene is one of peace, with trees in the left foreground before the buildings and a troop of soldiers on the right marching in an orderly fashion into the distance along the valley road.

The only preparatory work recorded recently for *The Battle of Roveredo* is a small oil sketch on panel, signed, and dated 1851: *In the Alps*.[2] This shows again a slightly different viewpoint from either the engraving mentioned above or the finished painting: there are no soldiers and again it is a landscape view with no action involved in it. The foreground is left comfortably void except for a large boulder on the left. This sketch marks another step in the preparation for the eventual battle scene and is one of a number of sketches for the picture.

The reviews of the painting at the Academy exhibition for 1851 were, without exception, full of praise. The *A.J.* called the composition 'more full of material than any that the artist has before painted. The shades are deep and pure, the lights lustrous and sunny, and nothing can exceed some of the textures which give such characteristic identity to the surface imitations . . . It is a production of great power, and its colour is one of its best qualities.' The *Literary Gazette* claimed it to be 'a splendid picture of its kind . . . the view painted on the spot; the figures are cleverly put in, and the scene is as well described by the picture as if we had an old Peninsular hero at our elbow'. The *Athenaeum* was even more laudatory and said it was 'another subject well adapted to exhibit this painter's *forte* . . . The details of the picture are made out with a perspicuity of language unusual with this artist. The natural circumstances of the site were well adapted for the expression of the painter's art . . . This is Mr. Stanfield's crowning effort.'

Likewise the *I.L.N.* called it 'a wonderful picture', the *Critic* 'his great work this year', the *Examiner* 'one of the masterpieces of the fine painter' and *The Times* stated that Stanfield was 'among the landscape painters . . . without a rival'.

The painting passed through some interesting collections. When it was shown at the first winter exhibition of deceased masters' paintings at the R.A. in 1870 it was owned by Sam Mendel of Manley Hall, Manchester, the cotton king who went bankrupt in 1875.[3] This painting, however (like Mendel's two other paintings which also found their way into the College collection, Creswick's *First Glimpse of the Sea* and Elmore's *Emperor Charles V at the Convent of Yuste*) was not included in his sale of paintings at Christie's of 23 and 24 April 1875. Agnew's in turn sold them to the 'company promoter' Baron Albert Grant, of the Kensington House Gallery, in whose bankruptcy sale they were in 1877. *The Battle of Roveredo* finally came to Holloway from the collection of Edward John Coleman of Stoke Park, near Stoke Poges. It was sold with the *View of the Pic du Midi d'Ossau* and Landseer's *Man proposes, God disposes* and these three paintings

were amongst the first purchases that Holloway made, attracting attention for the high prices he paid for them. In the catalogue for the Coleman sale the painting was wrongly listed as having been painted in 1854, as it was also in Carey's catalogue.

[1] *Heath's Picturesque Annual, Travelling Sketches in the North of Italy, The Tyrol, and on the Rhine* by Leitch Ritchie, 1832–45, opp. p. 185.
[2] Sold at Sotheby's, 5 November 1974 (92).
[3] See George Redford, *Art Sales*, 1888, Vol. I, pp. 200–01.

72. Clarkson Stanfield

1793–1867, ARA 1832, RA 1835

View of the Pic du Midi d'Ossau in the Pyrenees, with Brigands 1854 (*pl. 12*).

oil on canvas, arched top, 84 × 60 in (213.2 × 152.3 cm)

PROV: Painted for Elhanan Bicknell of Herne Hill for £735; his sale Christie's 25 April 1863 (121) bt Vokins £2,667; Edward John Coleman of Stoke Park, Buckinghamshire 1870; his sale Christie's 28 May 1881 (53) bt Thomas £2,677 10s.

EXH: 1854 R.A. (315); 1870 R.A. Winter Ex. (228); 1979 Bonn, Rheinisches Museum and Sunderland Art Gallery (305); 1981 Agnew's (41).

LIT: *A.J.* 1854 p. 164; *Athenaeum* 13 May 1854 p. 594; *Examiner* 29 April 1854 p. 261; *Literary Gazette* 6 May 1854 p. 425; *A.J.* 1857 pp. 10, 139; Dafforne, 1873 pp. 33–4; *The Times* 30 May 1881 p. 8; David Robertson, *Sir Charles Eastlake and the Victorian Art World*, Princeton, 1978, pp. 207, 375–7.

STUDIES: 1. *Pic du Midi* finished sketch
Prov. Benjamin Godfrey Windus of Tottenham; his sale Christie's 26 March 1859 (42) bt Gambart £87 3s.
2. *The Pic du Midi* oil sketch, 6 × 9½ in (17.1 × 24.1 cm)
Prov. David Price, his sale Christie's 4 April 1892 (229) bt Crisp £341 3s.
3. The following untraced studies appeared in Clarkson Stanfield's Studio Sale, Christie's 8–14 May 1868:
i. (148) *the Val d'Ossau and Pic du Midi*
drawing, bt in 70 gns.

ii. (150) *Pic du Midi*
drawing, bt Agnew £199 10s; sold by them 11 May 1868 to Leech.
iii. (181) *A Spanish Contrabandista*
study for the picture, bt Vokins £11 0s 6d.
iv. (182) ditto, bt Hayward £5 15s.
v. (183) ditto, bt Vokins £16 5s 6d.
4. *Le Pic du Midi*
Prov. Anon. sale Christie's 26 March 1892 (109) bt Anderson £262 10s.
5. Pencil sketch in letter from Stanfield to Elhanan Bicknell, 15 September 1852, at Yale Center for British Art; 3¼ × 2 in (8.3 × 6.7 cm). AC. no. B1978.43.364.

? VERSION: *Pic du Midi d'Ossau, in the Pyrenees*
Exh. 1866 R.A. (78); 1870 R.A. Winter Ex. (194).
Lit. *A.J.* 1867 p. 171; *Portfolio* 1879 p. 139; Cunningham, 1880, p. 336.

It seems that Stanfield's intention here was, as with *The Battle of Roveredo*, to incorporate small scale figures into his overpowering landscape in order to create an imposing sense of contrast.

This painting was commissioned by Elhanan Bicknell of Herne Hill, the father-in-law of David Roberts (q.v.) and a well-known patron and friend to painters. Letters from Stanfield to Bicknell trace the history of the commissioning of the painting. The first is dated 29 June 1852: 'I shall be most happy to paint a Picture for you of the kind of subject and shape you suggest, and I happen to have a very fine subject by me 'one of my last years sketches' "The Pic du Midi d'Ossau" in the Pyrenees . . .'. On 15 September of the same year Stanfield drew a small pencil sketch with the dimensions marked and stated: 'The size of the canvas as I have got it is "Six feet Eight inches" in height by "Five ft. Seven inch[s]." in width but should you wish any alteration to meet the proportions of your chimney piece it is not too late and can be made either larger or smaller . . .'. By 24 February 1853 Stanfield wrote explaining he had been ill and that 'It is therefore "I am sorry to say" out of the question to have the Picture ready for next Exhibition but I send you the size as you desire.' The size was now to measure seven by five feet without the frame.

More than a year later, on 29 May 1854, Stanfield wrote: 'the price of the picture I have painted for you' I beg to say seven hundred guineas is the price I put on it' and which if you don't think too much' I should be glad to have the half of that sum paid to my Bankers . . . *for I am very poor.'* Stanfield acknowledged full payment for the painting later in the year.[1] In a further lettter to Bicknell, dated 7 August 1854, Stanfield wrote that the picture was to be sent to Bicknell the following day. He added: 'I hope you will find it improved and that it will look better in your new room than it did in the Academy.'[2]

The subject is a band of brigands on a mountain in the Pyrenees, over 9,000 feet high. The painting was entitled *Pic du Midi – Smugglers* in the Coleman sale catalogue in 1881 and there were sketches for the painting sold in Stanfield's studio sale in 1868, some of which were described as studies of Spanish contrabandisti. In the 1857 *A.J.* description of the Bicknell collection, it was stated that 'this is a class of subject to which Mr. Stanfield seldom turns, a circumstance which we think gives additional value to the picture. No painter could resist making a study of this scene, but few could verify the sublime simplicity of that aspiring *Pic'*.[3]

The reviews were not quite so uniformly enthusiastic as they had been about Stanfield's *The Battle of Roveredo*. The *A.J.* remarked that 'the work is by no means so interesting as the marine pictures of the artist, although it is an imposing subject, carried out with appropriate feeling'. It was considered a remarkable achievement, but the general impression was somewhat hesitant: the critic in the *Athenaeum* wrote: 'Mr. Stanfield has a grand panoramic picture, not very tender or etherial in its middle tones; but grand and full of the artist's usual matured facility. It represents one of the grandest peaks of the Pyrenees; and is the result of Mr. Stanfield's visit to Spain [and Southern France which he made with his wife and daughters in 1851] . . . We do not mean to say that the artist has given us all that the scene contains for a master of more time and less facility; but still we feel exalted by a view so vast presented to us with such evident ease.'

Ruskin, in *Modern Painters*, although he named

Stanfield as 'the leader of the English Realists' and commented on 'the look of common sense and rationality which his compositions will always bear', felt that Stanfield should study mountainous structures more closely: 'He is at present apt to be too rugged, and in consequence, to lose size.'[4] He had much more praise for Stanfield's cloud forms, thought him second only to Turner and called his cloud drawing 'very grand and very tasteful, beautifully developed in the space of its solid parts and full of action'.[5]

Clarkson Stanfield was born in Sunderland, the son of James Field Stanfield (1749–1824) an ex-seaman, actor and miscellaneous author.

In 1808 he was apprenticed as a seaman in the East coast trade but was pressed into the Royal Navy in 1812, serving in the Sheerness guard-ship. In 1815 he made a voyage to China as a seaman in the East India Company, returning in 1816. He then became a theatre scene painter, mainly in London, and by the time he resigned as head of the Drury Lane scene-room in 1834 he had risen to be the most famous and important theatre painter of the day. In this field his name was often linked with that of his friend David Roberts (q.v.), whom he met in 1820. On various occasions after 1834 Stanfield painted scenes for Macready the actor and for the amateur productions of Charles Dickens, both men being his close friends.

He exhibited his first picture at the R.A. in 1820 and continued to show there regularly until his death, mostly marine paintings of British or Continental subjects. He made the first of several visits to Italy in 1824 and subsequently toured France, Germany, Spain and Holland. He was an original member of the Society of British Artists, its President in 1829 and the first of the few painters to be patronised by William IV.

During the 1830s Stanfield executed three major commissions. The first was a series of 10 pictures, principally Venetian, for the dining room at Bowood, Wiltshire for Lord Landsowne. This was followed by five similar works for the Duchess of Sutherland at Trentham Hall in Staffordshire, completed in 1837; and finally the painting of *The Battle of Trafalgar* (ex. R.A. 1836 [290]) for the United Services Club.

His marine masterpiece, *The Abandoned* (ex. R.A.

1856 [94]), has been lost since 1930.[6] The two inland scenes in this collection are among the most important works of Stanfield's later years which are not of marine subjects.

[1] These letters are in the Bicknell Volume of Artists Correspondence, Yale Center for British Art, Paul Mellon Collection. This volume was very kindly brought to my attention by Dr Pieter van der Merwe.
[2] Autograph letter to Bicknell, dated 7 August 1854, published with permission from the Pierpont Morgan Library, New York.
[3] *Art Journal*, 1857, p. 138.
[4] John Ruskin, *The Works of John Ruskin*, ed. E. T. Cook and Alexander Wedderburn (Library Edition), 1903–12, Vol. iii, p. 226.
[5] Op. cit. p. 390.
[6] See Arts Council, *Great Victorian Pictures*, 1978, p. 93.

BIBLIOGRAPHY
'British Artists, Their Style and Character, No. XXIV, Clarkson Stanfield', *Art Journal*, 1857, pp. 137–9.
Art Journal, 1867, p. 171 (Obit.).
Athenaeum, 25 May 1867, pp. 692–4 (Obit.).
The Gentleman's Magazine, 4 July 1867, pp. 108–11 (Obit.).
Winter Exhibition, 1870, Royal Academy.
James Dafforne, *Pictures by Clarkson Stanfield R.A.*, 1873.
M. M. Heaton, 'Clarkson Stanfield', *Portfolio*, 1879, pp. 124–5, 135–9.
Allan Cunningham, *Lives of the Most Eminent British Painters*, revised ed. by Mrs Charles Heaton, 1880, Vol. III, pp. 325–37.
David Roberts and Clarkson Stanfield, exhibition catalogue, Guildhall Art Gallery, 1967.
F. S. Richardson, 'Clarkson Stanfield and Some of His Watercolours', *Old Water Colour Society's Club*, 1974, Vol. XLIX, pp. 30–44.
Pieter van der Merwe, *The Life and Theatrical Career of Clarkson Stanfield*, University of Bristol unpublished Ph.D. Thesis, 1979.
The Spectacular Career of Clarkson Stanfield 1793–1867, exhibition catalogue, Tyne and Wear County Council Museums, 1979.

73. John Syer
1815–85, RI

The Windmill 1878 (*pl. 71*)

oil on canvas, 21½ × 32 in (54.5 × 81.2 cm)

INSCR: J Syer 78

PROV: Horace Woodward of Birmingham; his sale Christie's 15 May 1880 (104) bt in 72 gns; his sale Christie's 29 April 1882 (65) bt Martin £66 3s.

Bought with *Welsh Drovers* of the same year, *The Windmill* also came from the collection of Horace Woodward of Birmingham, and combines small-scale figures in a landscape. The main focus of attention is the windmill, silhouetted against the sky on the brow of the hill.

John Syer was born in 1815 in Atherstone, Warwickshire, and studied painting with a miniaturist, J. Fisher, in Bristol. He regularly visited Devon, where his work was apparently very popular with collectors. He began to exhibit at the R.A. in 1846: landscapes and coastal scenes, the majority being Welsh or Devon views. He was greatly influenced by the landscape painter David Cox (1783–1859) and by William James Muller (q.v.).

From 1856 to 1875 Syer was a member of the Society of British Artists, from which he resigned on being elected to the Royal Institute of Painters in Watercolours. He died in Exeter in 1885, while on a sketching tour.

74. John Syer
1815 85, RI

Welsh Drovers 1878 (*pl. 69*)

oil on canvas, 32 × 48 in (81.2 × 121.8 cm)

INSCR: J. Syer / 78

PROV: Painted for Horace Woodward of Birmingham; his sale Christie's 15 May 1880 (103) bt in 185 gns; his sale Christie's 29 April 1882 (75) bt Martin £157 10s.

? STUDY: *Moel Siabod*
watercolour, 25¼ × 35⅜ in (64.1 × 89.6 cm)
 Inscr. J. Syer 77
 Prov. Bequeathed to Birmingham City Art Gallery by Mrs F. E. Wills 1918.

This painting and the other picture by Syer in this collection, *The Windmill*, were both painted for Horace

Woodward of Birmingham, one of a number of patrons who tended to buy their pictures direct from the artist themselves.

A watercolour at the Birmingham City Art Gallery, entitled *Moel Siabod*, was possibly a study for this painting. Moel Siabod is near Capel Curig in North Wales and the watercolour was executed in 1877, the year before the painting of the *Welsh Drovers*. It may have been a preliminary idea for the oil painting, for both are essentially the same composition with the same group of figures and animals. The major difference is that in the watercolour the rough road winds directly round to the left rather than continuing in a diagonal as it does in the oil painting. Evident in both works is Syer's interest in the close detail of the vegetation and the view to the distant mountains. The cattle drovers are distinctly supplementary to the general effect of landscape.

75. Constant Troyon
1810–65

Evening, driving Cattle 1859 (*pl. 73*)

oil on canvas, 26 × 32 in (66 × 88.2 cm)

INSCR: C TROYON 1859

PROV: William Lee; his sale Christie's 26 May 1883 (100) bt Martin £1,995.

EXH: 1974 R.A. *Impressionism* (51).

LIT: *The Times* 28 May 1883 p. 10.

Troyon exhibited many paintings of similar titles at the Salon exhibitions in Paris during the 1850s; so it is difficult to discover if this particular work was exhibited there. Titles such as *The Departure for Market* and *Return to the Farm*, or just *Sheep* and *Cows* recur throughout his oeuvre. The combination of landscape, farm animals and figures is characteristic of much of his work. *The Times* report of the William Lee sale at Christie's in 1883, when Holloway purchased this painting, stated: 'It is admitted that to obtain any example of Troyon, the French Cuyp, is now very difficult, and we believe the late owner of the picture

now sold paid £1,400 for it some years back.'[1] Holloway paid £1,995.

This shows Troyon's popularity among 19th-century English collectors. Mantz pointed out in the *Gazette des Beaux-Arts* that Troyon's success in England was not particularly astonishing in a country which had produced Constable and where so many of the most beautiful Cuyps were owned by Englishmen. The obituary of Troyon in the *A.J.* in 1865 described him as 'one of the best landscape cattle painters of the modern French school . . . his works are well composed, show careful study of nature, and truth of drawing'.[2]

Constant Troyon was born at Sèvres, where his father worked in a porcelain factory. Troyon began to paint landscapes from nature in that district and at St. Cloud: his first exhibits at the Salon in 1833 were three local views. He then began to paint landscapes further afield and was rewarded by winning medals from 1838 onwards. His contact with the Barbizon painters, Dupré, Rousseau and Diaz in the early 1840s helped him to develop his style. However, much more decisive was his visit in 1847 to Belgium and Holland and his discovery of 17th-century Dutch painters, especially Potter and Cuyp. He was deeply impressed by Rembrandt and made copies of his pictures. The Dutch countryside also affected him, which explains why many of his landscapes had relatively flat territory as backgrounds. Troyon not only set his animals against a low horizon but also, as here, tended to paint them proceeding towards the spectator. They were described in 1889 as 'grand, solid, slow, heavy, patient'.[3]

After his visit to Holland, Troyon changed his style and began to lighten his palette and turn his attention seriously towards landscapes with animals, especially sheep and grazing cattle. He became famous as a painter of cattle. His works proved very popular in France and England, and were particularly praised for their handling of the effects of light at different times of the day, although his subjects were limited in range.

Troyon received the Legion d'Honneur decoration awarded by Louis Napoleon in 1849 – for him the seal of success. He acquired his own collection of paintings, which included Delacroix's *Christ on the Sea of Galilee* of 1854 (Walters Art Gallery, Baltimore,

USA) and works by Corot, Millet, Rousseau, Diaz, Dupré and Boudin.

[1] *The Times*, 28 May 1883, p. 10.
[2] *Art Journal*, 1865, p. 207.
[3] C. H. Stranahan, *A History of French Painting from Its Earliest to Its Latest Practice*, 1889, p. 260.
[4] See Arts Council, *Delacroix*, 1964, pp. 37–8.

BIBLIOGRAPHY
M. du Camp, *Les Beaux-Arts à l'Exposition Universelle de 1855*, 1855, pp. 242–4.
Art Journal, 1865, p. 207 (Obit.).
Paul Mantz, 'Artistes Contemporains: Troyon', *Gazette des Beaux-Arts*, Vol. XVIII, 1865, pp. 393–407.
Charles Blanc, *Les Artistes de mon temps*, Paris 1876.
Henri Dumesnil, *Troyon*, Paris, 1888.
Arthur Hustin, 'Troyon', *L'Art*, Vol. XLVI, 1889, pp. 77–90, Vol. XLVII, 1889, pp. 85–96.
C. H. Stranahan, *A History of French Painting from Its Earliest to Its Latest Practice*, 1889, pp. 258–61.
'Constant Troyon', *Art Journal*, 1893, pp. 22–4.
Arthur Hustin, *Constant Troyon*, Paris, 1893.
Louis Souille, *Constant Troyon*, Paris, 1900.

76. Joseph Mallord William Turner

1775–1851, ARA 1799, RA 1802

Van Tromp going about to please his Masters, Ships at Sea, getting a good Wetting – Vide Lives of the Dutch Painters 1844 (*pl. 26*)

oil on canvas, 36 × 48 in (91.4 × 121.8 cm)

PROV: Possibly the *Van Tromp* sold to Charles Birch 12 March 1845 for £400 from George Pennell (from Joseph Gillott's account book); John Miller of Liverpool 1850; his sale Christie's 22 May 1858 (248) bt Gambart £567 5s as *Van Tromp*; with John Miller by 18 December 1858, sold by him 21 January 1867 to Agnew as *The Van Tromp*; sold by Agnew 2 March 1867 to Henry Woods MP of Warnford Park for £2,782 10s; his sale Christie's 5 May 1883 (147) bt Martin £3,675 (with the incorrect title of *Van Tromp's Shallop at the Entrance to the Scheldt*).

EXH: 1844 R.A. (253); 1850 Liverpool Academy (37); 1852 Royal Scottish Academy (21); 1857 Manchester Art Treasures (282); 1934 R.A. *British Art* (158);

1951–52 R.A. *First Hundred years of the R.A. 1769–1868* (158); 1966–67 Cologne, Rome, Zurich, Warsaw *English Painting from Hogarth to Turner (1730–1850)*; 1967 Agnew *Loan Exhibition of Turner Paintings and Watercolours* (33); 1970–71 The Hague, London Tate Gallery, *Shock of Recognition* (49) & (47); 1972 Berlin *J. M. W. Turner* (34); 1977 Tate Gallery *Turner: A Special loan Exhibition of 20 rarely seen Paintings* (22); 1981 Agnew's (42).

LIT: *Art Union* 1844 p. 158; *Athenaeum* 1844 p. 433; *Critic* 1844 p. 197; *I.L.N.* 11 May 1844 p. 306; *Literary Gazette* 1844 p. 306; *Spectator* 1844 p. 451; Burnet, 1852 p. 120 no. 229; *A Handbook to the Gallery of British Paintings*, Manchester Art Treasures Exhibition (reprinted from the *Manchester Guardian*), 1857 pp. 66–7; Thornbury, 1877 pp. 92 (with wrong title) 580, 606; Dafforne, 1877 p. 113 (incorrectly states painting as in the National Gallery); C. W. Carey, 'The "Van Tromp" Pictures of J. M. W. Turner R.A.', *Mag. of Art*, 1899 pp. 173–5 and repr. p. 174; Bell, 1901 p. 150, no. 245; Armstrong, 1902 pp. 161, 231; Finberg, 1939 pp. 400, 508, no. 559 and 1961 ed. p. 516, no. 593; C. C. Cunningham, 'Turner's Van Tromp Paintings', *Art Quarterley*, Vol, XV, 1952 pp. 323–9 and repr. p. 327; Rothenstein and Butlin, 1964 pp. 58, 68 and repr. pl. 123; Bachrach, 1974 p. 20; William Gaunt, *Marine Painting*, 1975 p. 121 and repr. p. 117, no. 105; Butlin and Joll, 1977 pp. 233–4, no. 410 and repr. pl. 396; ed. Gage, 1980, p. 196, n. 7.

REPR: Wedmore, 1900 Vol. I, opp. p. 132.

This picture bears one of Turner's characteristically lengthy descriptive titles. It depicts an episode in the life of the Dutch Admiral Martin Harpertzoon Tromp (1597–1653), who performed the famous feat in 1652 of bringing 300 Dutch merchant ships up the Channel, through the Straits of Dover and the North Sea into Dutch waters. He had 80 Dutch warships escorting the convoy and swept the British opposition aside, defeating Admiral Blake's fleet off Dungeness. He was said to have achieved all this with a broom tied to his flagship's masthead to sweep the British from the seas. 'His masters' came to congratulate Tromp and his captains. The 'masters' in 1652 are not William of Orange but the

interim government of the Burgher Regents under the leadership of the Grand Pensionary Jan De Witt. This Tromp is not to be confused with his son, Koornelis Van Tromp (1629–91) who adopted the 'Van' into his name as a result of his father's successes. It was he who was sacked by De Ruyter, reinstated by William III and had, also, a distinguished naval career. By the 18th century the British were calling them both Van Tromp. They had become legends by then and there was a popular song about Van Tromp's broom:

'Tie a broom to the mast,' said he,
'For a broom is the sign for me,
That wherever I go, the world may know,
I sweep the mighty sea'.

Tromp is indeed about to be soaked by the waves splashing up against the yacht's side.

Turner always had a passion for the sea, and was fascinated by the activities of the Dutch Admiral. This was the fourth and last of a series of paintings of 'Van Tromp' subjects ranging over 14 years. The first was *Admiral Van Tromp's Barge at the Entrance of the Texel, 1645* (ex. R.A. 1831 [288], Sir John Soane's Museum). This was followed the next year by *Van Tromp's Shallop, at the Entrance of the Scheldt* (ex. R.A. 1832 [206], Wadsworth Atheneum, Hartford, Conn., USA). The third was *Van Tromp returning after the Battle off the Dogger Bank* (ex. R.A. 1833 [146], Tate Gallery). After that, Turner did not return to a Van Tromp subject until 1844, with this, the fourth painting. Together with *Fishing Boats bringing a Disabled Ship into Port Ruysdael* (408), exhibited in the same year, it marks the end of Turner's R.A. exhibits inspired by the Dutch marine tradition. He was to exhibit in only five more R.A. shows until his death in 1851.

In 1898 the Curator of the College collection, C. W. Carey, began to investigate the possibility that the painting was mis-entitled.[1] Holloway had purchased it with the title *Van Tromp's Shallop at the entrance to the Scheldt* and the information that it had been in the 1832 R.A. exhibition. Previously, when the painting had changed hands, it had been simply referred to as *Van Tromp*, in 1858, and *The Van Tromp*, in 1867. It was Carey who established the correct title and date for the painting in the *Magazine of Art* in 1899, although he was still not fully aware of the whole Van Tromp series.[2] The matter was taken up again by Cunningham in his article 'Turner's Van Tromp's Paintings' in the *Art Quarterly* in 1952.[3] It is not clear why Turner added the reference '*Vide* Lives of the Dutch Painters' in the title of the painting.

Turner exhibited six further paintings at the R.A. in 1844, the most important being *Rain, steam and speed – The Great Western Railway* (62, National Gallery).[4] It was this picture, more than the others, which caught the attention of the critics at the R.A. Its subject, the controversial railway, and Turner's treatment of it caused most of the exhibition reviewers to single it out rather than *Van Tromp going about* or the other exhibits. The most outstanding comment came from Thackeray in *Fraser's Magazine*. He wrote, in amazement, following some severe remarks, 'the world has never seen any thing like this picture'.[5]

A remarkable fact concerning the R.A. exhibits of 1844, including both *Rain, Steam and Speed* and *Van Tromp going about*, was that Ruskin who was producing *Modern Painters* at that time, made no mention of any of them, which was especially surprising since he admired this period of Turner's work.[6]

Among the contemporary reviewers of the 1844 Academy to mention *Van Tromp* was the *Art Union*, who commented at length and took pains to quibble about the details and the 'scenery'. 'It often happens, in the pictures of this artist, that the professed subject constitutes the least remarkable feature on the canvas. We see here a boat carrying a full spread of canvas, going so many knots, and with certain indications of shipping a sea at her quarter, where we must suppose Van Tromp to be standing. We cannot admit Mr. Turner's accuracy here; he ought, for the sake of general probability, to have placed Van Tromp at the bow of his boat. Again we would ask, as this event must have taken place in the North Sea, why does not the artist make a difference between Dutch and Venetian scenery, or at least the seas and skies of these widely-apart countries?'

In contrast however the *Athenaeum* considered the painting the most successful and was quite lyrical about it: 'We must point to the best, according to our judgement, which he this year exhibits, (253) *Van Tromp* at sea. Here we are treated, with a vengeance, to all the – Jasper, and turkis, and almondine, which the poet has so daintily sung.'[7]

The *I.L.N.* called it 'A Sea View' and applied the same criticism of *Rain, Steam and Speed* to *Van Tromp going about*, which was 'a picture of singular power, and showing what the artist could do if he would confine his erratic genius within bounds'.

It was the writer in the *Spectator* who summed up the general feeling about Turner's works at that time: a view made up mainly of caution and hesitant praise which resulted from a basic misunderstanding of Turner's paintings. There was no particular mention of *Van Tromp going about* in the *Spectator's* review. Their comments were aimed at all his exhibits: 'Turner is preëminent for the daring originality of his efforts: slight and extravagant as his works are, there is truth as well as power of art in his representation of natural phaenomena, when viewed at a proper distance – say from the middle of the room. If not complete pictures, they are wonderfully fine studies of composition, colour, and atmospheric effect: his seas are boiling surges, his clouds are floating masses of vapour; space and light are depicted, though form and substance are vague and flimsy.'

Opinion had not changed much in the 13-year interval between 1844, when the painting was at the R.A., and its showing in 1857 at the Manchester Art Treasures Exhibition. A notice in the *Manchester Guardian* described the picture as 'the solitary example furnished by this Exhibition of the painter's third manner . . . There is a want of substance and precision about the figures which renders it impossible for us to interpret the story, and though there is motion in the sea, and breeziness and air and light in the sky, and all through the picture, we cannot but class it among the weaker works in the third manner of the painter.'[8] It was still not fashionable to admire Turner's later works.

Joseph Mallord William Turner was born in Covent Garden, the eldest son of a barber and wig-maker. In 1789 he was admitted at the R.A. Schools and his first exhibit there was a watercolour shown in the following year. In 1791 he made the first of many tours around the country to do drawings and engravings, many of which were later published.

Turner's first oil painting to be shown at the Academy in 1796 was *Fishermen at Sea* (R.A. [305], Tate Gallery), which was followed by a continuous flow of exhibits at the Academy throughout his life. He became Professor of Perspective in 1807, an appointment he held until 1837.

Turner's first visit abroad was in 1802 when he travelled to France and Switzerland. His first journey to Italy, in 1819, had a great impact on his work: he used 19 sketchbooks in four months, which served as a rich store for ideas to be taken up at a later date.

Turner wrote his own treatise, the *Liber Studiorum*, using examples from his landscape paintings. He also had many engravings published, both as illustrations for books, such as those for Roger's *Italy* in 1830, and as records of his own travels, such as *Turner's Annual Tour – Wanderings by the Loire* and *by the Seine* in 1834 and 1835.

Turner exhibited four works at the Academy in 1850, the year before he died. His range of subject matter was vast, and the techniques and media he used were many and unconventional. In 1836 he first met Ruskin, which inspired Ruskin's fierce allegiance to Turner and prompted him to publish his first volume of *Modern Painters* in 1843.

[1] See Report by him, Royal Holloway College Archives, in which he requested to change the title of the painting and his explanation of the current misunderstandings surrounding the picture.

[2] *Magazine of Art*, 1899, pp. 173–5.

[3] C. C. Cunningham, 'Turner's Van Tromp Paintings', *Art Quarterly*, Vol. XV, 1952, pp. 323–9.

[4] See John Gage, *Turner: Rain, Steam and Speed*, 1972.

[5] *Fraser's Magazine*, 1844, p. 713.

[6] See Martin Butlin and Evelyn Joll, *The Paintings of J. M. W. Turner*, 1977, no. 407, p. 232.

[7] Dr Christopher Worth has kindly informed me that this is a misquotation from Tennyson's *The Merman* (originally published in 1830 and reprinted in the *Poems* of 1842), which runs,
'They would pelt me with starry spangles and shells,
Laughing and clapping their hands between,
All night, merrily, merrily:
But I would throw to them back in mine

Turkis and agate and almondine.'

[8] *A Handbook to the Gallery of British Paintings*, 1857, pp. 66–7.

BIBLIOGRAPHY

John Burnet, *Turner and His Works*, 1852.

Walter Thornbury, *The Life of J. M. W. Turner R.A.*, 2 Vols., 1862, reprinted 1877.

James Dafforne, *The Works of J. M. W. Turner R.A.*, 1877.

Philip Gilbert Hamerton, *The Life of J. M. W. Turner, R.A.*, 1879, reprinted 1895.

W. Cosmo Monkhouse, *Turner*, 1879.

Frederick Wedmore, *Turner and Ruskin*, 2 Vols., 1900.

C. F. Bell, *A List of the Works Contributed to Public Exhibitions by J. M. W. Turner R.A.*, 1901.

Sir Walter Armstrong, *Turner*, 1902.

Bernard Falk, *Turner the Painter*, 1938.

A. J. Finberg, *The Life of J. M. W. Turner R.A.*, Oxford, 1939, reprinted 1961.

Charles Clare, *J. M. W. Turner, His Life and Work*, 1951.

John Rothenstein and Martin Butlin, *Turner*, 1964

Lawrence Gowing, *Turner: Imagination and Reality*, New York, 1966.

Jack Lindsay, *J. M. W. Turner, His Life and Work, A Critical Biography*, 1966.

John Cage, *Colour in Turner*, 1969.

Graham Reynolds, *Turner*, 1969.

John Cage, *Turner: Rain, Steam and Speed*, 1972.

A. G. H. Bachrach, *Turner and Rotterdam 1817, 1825, 1841*, Privately printed, 1974.

Exhibition Catalogue, *Turner*, 1974–75, Royal Academy.

Luke Herrmann, *Turner: Paintings, Watercolours, Prints and Drawings*, 1975.

Martin Butlin and Evelyn Joll, *The Paintings of J. M. W. Turner*, 2 Vols., Yale and London, 1977.

Eric Shanes, *Turner's Picturesque Views in England and Wales 1825–1838*, 1979.

Andrew Wilton, *The Life and Work of J. M. W. Turner*, 1979.

Andrew Wilton, *Turner and the Sublime*, 1980.

ed. John Gage, *Collected Correspondence of J. M. W. Turner*, 1980.

Eric Shanes, *Turner's rivers, harbours and coasts*, 1981.

77. James Webb

1825–95

Dordrecht (*pl. 34*)

oil on canvas, 9 × 14 in (22.8 × 35.5 cm)

INSCR: Dordrecht James Webb and James Webb sold to Ashe Esq. J.W. on reverse.

PROV: Ashe; Hon. Cecil Duncombe; his sale Christie's 20 March 1880 (23) bt Grindley £178 10s; Thomas Frederick Walker of Birmingham; his sale Christie's 21 April 1883 (132) bt Martin £23 2s.

EXH: 1865 B.I. (29) *Dordrecht, Holland* (£100); 1981 Agnew's (43).

? ENGR: L. Valmon, etching, 19½ × 13 in (49.5 × 33 cm) published Arthur Tooth & Sons, entitled *Dordrecht*.

Two paintings by Webb with this title are recorded: one in the College collection, the other in the Graves Art Gallery, Sheffield. The latter, however, is dated '1875/6' and is of larger dimensions (23¾ × 40¾ in, 60.3 × 103.5 cm) and does not resemble the painting in this collection. There are other paintings by Webb of Dordrecht, such as *Sailing boats, Dordrecht* (with the Leger Galleries in 1965). He exhibited a painting of *Dordrecht, Holland* at the B.I. in 1865 (29), priced at £100, but no size was given which makes it impossible to know whether it was the picture acquired by Holloway.

Webb painted a number of such marine subjects, which do not change greatly in content or style.

78. James Webb

1825–95

Carthagena, Spain 1874 (*pl. 18*)

oil on canvas, 30 × 50 in (76.1 × 126.9 cm)

INSCR: James Webb 1874 Carthagena; on verso: James Webb 1874 / Carthagena

PROV: Horace Woodward of Birmingham; his sale Christie's 15 May 1880 (106) bt in 120 gns; his sale Christie's 29 April 1882 (73) bt Martin £105.

EXH: 1874 R.A. (183).

Carthagena, on the south-east coast of Spain, was formerly a powerful, fortified town and important naval harbour. It is protected by two forts crowning the precipitous volcanic cliffs east and west of the harbour mouth: the Castillo de las Galeras and the Castillo de San Julian. The painter's view is from the foreshore in front of the Castillo de las Galeras across to the Castillo de San Julian. Webb has even included the detail of a small fraction of the imposing structure under scaffolding.

There is another painting, *Carthagena*, at the Shipley Art Gallery in Gateshead, of the same date but smaller dimensions (24 × 11 in, 60.9 × 27.9 cm); the same background with the fort is painted from a slightly different angle, and the foreground details are considerably changed.

James Webb's oeuvre consists of landscape and marine views, executed in many countries. He was particularly interested by buildings perched on a high site: examples are his *View of Namur, Belgium, Mont Orgueil, Castle Jersey, Mont Saint Michel, Lindisfarne, Bamborough* and many views of Constantinople.

He began to exhibit at the R.A. in 1853 (until 1888) and exhibited also at the B.I., the Society of British Artists, the New Watercolour Society and the Grosvenor Gallery.

79. Theodore Alexander Weber

1838–1907

Dover Pilot and Fishing Boats (*pl. 33*)

oil on canvas, 24 × 36 in (60.9 × 91.4 cm)

INSCR: Th. Weber

PROV: J. Ivimey; his sale Christie's 29 April 1882 (170) bt Martin £31 10s.

Weber was a painter of landscape and marine pictures. Born in Leipzig in 1838, in 1854 he became a pupil of Wilhelm Krause (1803–64) in Berlin. In 1856 he left Berlin to go to Paris and finish his studies with Eugène Isabey (1803–86). He exhibited at the Salon where he won some awards; he also exhibited five works at the R.A. between 1871 and 1873, some in Brussels at the same time, and others in Munich in 1891 and 1892.

In 1886 Weber was appointed official painter to the Marine and Colonial Ministry of France.

Appendix

Memorandum on the version of *The Railway Station* on view at Sotheby's Belgravia and offered for sale by auction on 9 April 1980.

It is my considered opinion that the version currently on view here was painted either, for the most part, by Marcus Stone RA or, more likely, entirely by him, even though it is clearly signed and dated (1862) by Frith.

The reasons for this assertion are as follows. In their descriptive notes Sotheby's refer to pp. 45–7 of my book entitled *Gambart* (1975). These pages refer only to Flatow the dealer, who bought the original of *The Railway Station*, by way of introduction. No mention is made here of *The Railway Station*. Pages 135–8, however, refer extensively to the commissioning, purchase, exhibition and making replicas of the picture. The fourth paragraph of p. 136 is a paraphrase of a diary entry in the *Journals of Walter White* (1898), together with a chapter note number referring the reader to this source. The paraphrase closely follows the wording of the original source which is quoted in full here:

'May 26 (1862)
Called on Marcus Stone, found him copying Frith's picture of Railway station – the picture for which the painter was paid 8,000 guineas. I had a good look at it, and came to the conclusion 'twas not worth the money. The very best portion comprises the three heads of the sailor kissing his child, and the weeping wife and mother; the expression is wonderfully lifelike. Saw the picture taken down, locked in a case, and carted off to its exhibition-room in the Haymarket. In the copy M.S. is making, all the figures were outlined by an engraver's outliner who can do nothing else, he had £40 for his job. Marcus will have £300 for his, and has to make besides a second copy. Told him of the favourable notice in

"The Times" of his picture, "Artist's First Work" now in the Exhibition.'

In 1862 White was Assistant Secretary to the Royal Society which was then housed at Somerset House. This diary shows that he kept a close eye on happenings at the R.A. Moreover, his brother William, who introduced the diary, wrote: 'He was accurate, painstaking, and receptive' and further below: 'The original handwriting of the diarist has been carefully copied and followed.' (p. IV)

The last sentence of the above diary refers to Stone's *Artist's First Work*, a picture 'now in the Exhibition'. This referred to *A Painter's First Work* then on view at the Royal Academy. The picture was exhibited with a singularly apt quotation from Butler's *Hudibras*:
'For genius, oft misunderstood
Resorts to rude means for food,
Disdains all warnings to be quiet
And prospers on its homely diet.'

Let us consider how Stone stood in relation to the world and, more particularly, to his profession in 1862. He was the son of Frank Stone RA, a successful genre painter and a friend of Frith. Marcus had painted from an early age. So quickly did he mature that in 1858, at the age of 18, he exhibited his first picture at the R.A. In that same year, however, his father died suddenly, leaving his son to fend for himself in a highly competitive world (*The Life and Work of Marcus Stone, RA*, by A. L. Baldry, 1896, pp. 8–9). He exhibited again in 1859, 1860 and 1861. By 1862 therefore he was a highly competent and fully professional painter, but still in need of earning a good living and willing to resort 'to rude means for food'. Frith, on the other hand, was at the height of his reputation, his most famous pictures already behind him and impatient to press on with other work, including the highly lucrative but onerous

commission to paint the three London Street Scenes commissioned from him by Gambart in 1862 for £16,000 (although the contract was not actually signed until 19 August).

White's diary entry is bald, clear and unembellished and, probably not knowing Frith (he is not in the index), he would have had no axe to grind. But in the absence of the relevant picture and with the certainty that the passage could not apply to other known versions, it has not been possible until now to test its validity against the version at Sotheby's. In the absence, too, of a picture painted by Stone at approximately the same date, comparative analysis would have been impossible. However, by an apparent and certainly extraordinary coincidence, Stone's *A Painter's First Work* of 1862 is being offered in the same sale and Sotheby's have, obligingly, hung the picture next to *The Railway Station*. Under excellent lighting, and with a magnifying glass, I have scrutinised both pictures minutely and repeatedly, paying particular attention to materials, faces, hair, eyes, shoes and glass. The handling of the paint in both cases seems, to me, identical. Moreover, it also seems to me that the paintwork in *The Railway Station* under review does not resemble that which is normal to Frith. Both these pictures are painted with an almost completely flat surface; nor does this version bear any of Frith's highly individual calligraphy, so evident in the original, which is also painted with far more impasto.

My belief that this version was painted by Stone is further strengthened by a process of elimination against other known versions, traced or untraced.
(a) It cannot be the original. That is at Royal Holloway College.
(b) It cannot be the 1863 version. That is at Leicester, and measures $20\frac{1}{2} \times 44$ in.

(c) It cannot be the later version. This is in the Royal Collection.

(d) It cannot be a preparatory oil sketch dated 1861, untraced.

(e) It cannot be a sketch measuring 17 × 35 in, untraced.

(f) It cannot be painted over an engraving, because the size of that version is 20 × 44 in. The version under review is 28 × 60 in.

Stone's copy, which White had seen him paint, must be the version last traced to W. Freeman and Son in 1945 and which has the same measurements and bears the same date.

How is it then that this version is clearly signed and dated 1862 by Frith? To understand this question properly one would need to understand the complexities of the mid-Victorian art market. I can only refer the reader to *Gambart* in which I have attempted to do this. I am confident that any reader of this work would soon realise that neither Frith nor Flatow were above deception and duplicity, particularly where they may be used as a means of making a lot of money in the quickest possible time. Even apart from this, it was not at all unusual for artists to employ other artists as studio assistants, particularly in the painting of replicas for engravers. The original picture had always, whenever possible, to be on public view, so as to obtain the maximum number of subscriptions to the engraving. Frith records his admiration of Flatow in this respect.

I believe that Stone was eminently capable of painting a version of *The Railway Station* and that Frith would consider that merely adding a signature and dating it were sufficient evidence that he had 'finished' the picture. Seen in the context of the period, such practice is not as sharp as it seems today.

Incidentally, Frith characteristically makes no mention of any such goings-on in his autobiography, and only publishes a very much shortened version of his contract with Flatow, with the excuse that it would weary the reader. Nor does he even mention Marcus Stone, a fellow RA, although he alludes to his father several times. To me, the real mystery is the fate of the second copy. To judge only from a small transparency, it seems that it could well be the version at Leicester.

25 March 1980

Jeremy Maas

The Collection

The Catalogue and College number is given first; the plate number follows in italics.